KU-672-427

Contents

Aidan Kelly in Rough Magic's production of Take Me
Away by Gerald Murphy, 2004 © Pat Redmond

editor's note

Compiling the 3rd edition of the Irish Theatre Handbook provides a snapshot of the island's current drama, dance and opera (we are delighted to include this last again in the guide). In the year that marks the centenary of the Abbey Theatre, drama continues to hold its own as companies young and established perform to acclaim on the international scene.

In dance, not one but two International Dance Festivals of Ireland have taken place since the publication of the second Irish Theatre Handbook (2001), bringing luminaries such as Akram Khan and Merce Cunningham (2002) as well as Mark Morris (2004) to these shores in strong programmes of contemporary international and Irish choreography. The Dublin Fringe Festival has expanded its dance programme in the last two years while other major Irish arts festivals have commissioned more, such as Kilkenny Arts Festival (*The Murder Ballads*, 2002), and the Dublin Theatre Festival which co-produced *Giselle*, the hit of the 2003 Festival and currently touring the US, with Fabulous Beast Dance Theatre.

And finally, since the publication of the 2nd edition in 2001, the Theatre Shop has expanded its own online information provision for the drama, dance and opera sectors with two brand-new websites. The Irish Theatre Handbook now has its own internet edition at www.irishtheatreonline.com. Updated quarterly, it contains up-to-the-minute listings of Irish companies, venues and festivals, plus details of Arts Officers, Awards and Competitions, Drama and Dance Training, Funding Bodies, Scholarships and Bursaries, Support Organisations, Youth Drama and Dance Groups. The Irish Playography database is also freely accessible at www.irishplayography.com. This online searchable catalogue has information on the writers, cast, crew, rights and script availability of 1,200 new Irish plays produced professionally since 1975.

Editorial guidelines for the 3rd Irish Theatre Handbook are as follows: Subsidised Companies are defined as those companies or production houses in receipt of €30,000 or more from The Arts Council/An Chomhairle Ealaíon or those in receipt of stg £20,000 or more from the Arts Council of Northern Ireland. Partially/Non-subsidised companies are all other producers of professional drama, dance and opera based in the Republic of Ireland and Northern Ireland, with the exception of the commercial producers as listed. Programming Venues and Festivals are those that are professionally managed and programming a significant amount of professional theatre each year. The international festivals listed are a selection of the world's leading festivals with an emphasis on those that programme English-language work and/or have a history of featuring Irish work. The drama and dance training section lists courses which are at least one year in duration and offer official accreditation from a recognised body. A number of exceptions were made for courses that are of major significance to the sector.

As in the 2nd edition, the information contained in the much expanded Suppliers and Services section was supplied by the subsidised companies, programming venues and Irish festivals listed in the Irish Theatre Handbook. This ensures that the individuals and companies listed have all worked within the professional drama, dance and opera sector. The Theatre Shop, however, cannot and does not endorse the standard of service provided by the individuals or companies listed.

Paula Shields

a note on telephone numbers: When listing Northern Ireland and Republic of Ireland numbers in the *Irish Theatre Handbook* local codes were used. To phone Northern Ireland from the Republic it is necessary to replace the local code 028 with the direct dialling code 048.

Frankie McCafferty and Michael FitzGerald in Druid's production of
Sharon's Grave by John B. Keane, 2003 Photographer: Keith Patterson

The Abbey Theatre

26 Lower Abbey Street
Dublin 1
Republic of Ireland
tel box office: + 353 (0)1 878 7222
tel admin: + 353 (0)1 887 2200
fax: + 353 (0)1 872 9177
email: marketing@abbeytheatre.ie
web: www.abbeytheatre.ie

artistic director: Ben Barnes
managing director: Brian Jackson
peacock director: Ali Curran

The Abbey Theatre, founded in 1904, comprises the world-famous Abbey and Peacock Theatres. The theatre's artistic policy centres on the promotion and development of new Irish writing, the revitalisation and presentation of plays from the Irish repertoire, as well as classics of the European and world stages.

The Abbey Theatre's Literary Department and Archive arrange pre-show talks and events and the Outreach/Education Department facilitates a wide range of programmes for children, young adults and community groups.

The Abbey celebrates its centenary, abbeyonehundred, in 2004 with a wide-ranging programme of Irish and European classics and an exciting portfolio of new writing.

As part of its commitment to promoting high quality theatre at home, touring is a vital element of the Abbey Theatre's programme. The theatre has also developed an outstanding international reputation, and plans to expand on this network in the future.

recent productions at the abbey:
The Playboy of the Western World by JM Synge (2004)
The Burial at Thebes by Seamus Heaney (2004)
The Cherry Orchard by Anton Chekhov, adapted by Tom Murphy (2004)
Aristocrats by Brian Friel (2003)
The Shape of Metal by Thomas Kilroy (2003)

recent productions at the peacock:
Savoy by Eugene O'Brien (2004)
Defender of the Faith by Stuart Carolan (2004)
Finders Keepers by Peter Sheridan (2004)
The Wolf of Winter by Paula Meehan (2004)
The Wild Duck by Henrik Ibsen, a new version by Frank McGuinness (2003)

photo: Kelly Campbell in The Burial at Thebes from Sophocles' Antigone, adapted by Seamus Heaney, 2004 © Tom Lawlor

Aisling Ghéar

Cultúrlann McAdam Ó Fiaich
216 Falls Road
Belfast BT12 6AV
Northern Ireland
tel/fax: + 44 (0)28 9020 8040
email: eolas@aislingghear.com

reachtaire drámaíochta: Bríd Ó Gallchóir
reachtaire forbartha: Gearóid Ó Cairealláin

Aisling Ghéar, a small, independent company which supports the Irish speaking community throughout the country, is based at the Cultúrlann in West Belfast. All their productions are in Irish and the majority of these are accompanied by simultaneous translation to English, making them accessible to a wide range of theatre-goers.

Founded in November 1996, Aisling Ghéar is now the only full-time, professional Irish language theatre company in Ireland and provides a wide range of top quality theatre. The company stages six or seven productions per year at the Cultúrlann and tours extensively throughout Ireland and Gaelic-speaking Scotland. Amongst its priorities are: support for new writing by producing one new play each year; support for students studying Irish language drama at A-Level and Ardteist; to produce at least one classic a year; translations of modern European theatre, from Machiavelli to Beckett.

recent productions:
Lá Fhéile Míchíl by Eoghan Ó Tuairisc (2004)
An Triail by Mairéad Ní Ghráda (2003)
Críoch-Chluiche, translation by Brighid Mhic Sheáin of Samuel Beckett's *Fin de Partie* (2003)
Madragola by Niccolò Machiavelli, translation by Dónall Mac Giolla Chóill (2003)
Aistriúcháin, translation by An tAth. Breandán Ó Doibhlin of Brian Friel's *Translations* (2002)

Photo: Donncha Crowley, Dearbhla Hannigan and Lesley Conroy in Lá Fhéile Míchíl by Eoghan Ó Tuairisc, 2004 Photograph courtesy of 'Lá'

The Ark

Eustace Street
Temple Bar
Dublin 2
Republic of Ireland
tel: + 353 (0)1 670 7788
fax: + 353 (0)1 670 7758
email: info@ark.ie
web: www.ark.ie

director (acting): Belinda Moller
theatre programmer: Ronan Tully
tour manager: Leo McKenna

The Ark is a cultural centre dedicated to producing high-quality innovative work across the arts for children aged 4-14 years. Six to eight programmes are presented annually including drama, dance, music, experimental performance work, the visual arts, and new media.

recent productions:
The Carolling Corcorans Christmas Telly Special by Eric Fraad and Liz Roche (2003)
The Day I Swapped My Dad For Two Goldfish by Jocelyn Clarke (2003)
Blowfish by Veronica Coburn (2002)
The Carolling Corcorans by Eric Fraad and Liz Roche (2002)
Rover Saves Christmas by Roddy Doyle (2002)

See also Venues

photo: Orla Fitzgerald and Matthew Dunphy in *The Day I Swapped My Dad for Two Goldfish* adapted by Jocelyn Clarke, 2003 © Tommy Clancy

Barabbas...the company

7 South Great George's Street
Dublin 2
Republic of Ireland
tel: + 353 (0)1 671 2013
fax: + 353 (0)1 670 4076
email: info@barabbas.ie
web: www.barabbas.ie

joint artistic directors: Veronica Coburn
Raymond Keane
general manager: Tríona Ní Dhuibhir
administrator: Siobhán Consenheim

Barabbas...the company is dedicated to developing its own unique style of theatre. A company of theatre makers, Barabbas' work extends from non-verbal, lyrically visual devised productions to commissioned work, new interpretations of extant texts and street spectacle. Theatre of Clown inspires the company's core theatrical essence. Barabbas aims to engage, delight and entertain the widest possible audience.

Barabbas offers training to professional practitioners and students of theatre each year. The company consistently refines and develops its own pedagogy and practice through exploratory and developmental workshops with like-minded professionals.

Barabbas tours both nationally and internationally. Since its foundation in 1993, the company has performed at venues and festivals throughout Ireland, in the USA, the UK, New Zealand, Denmark, Germany and France.

recent productions:
A Midsummer Night's Dream by Shakespeare (2004)
HURL by Charlie O'Neill (2003)
Blowfish by Veronica Coburn (2002)
Dog by Raymond Keane (2002)
Nightmare on Abbey Street by Gerard Stembridge (2002)

photo: Seán Kearns and Deirdre Molloy in A Midsummer Night's Dream by Shakespeare 2004 © Pat Redmond

Barnstorm Theatre Company

Church Lane
Kilkenny
Republic of Ireland
tel: + 353 (0)56 775 1266 / 777 0495
fax: + 353 (0)56 775 1266
email: barnstorm@eircom.net
web: www.barnstorm.ie

artistic director: Philip Hardy
general manager: Vincent Dempsey
company administrator: Maeve Butler

Established in 1991, Barnstorm seeks to develop new forms of theatre practice that will engage a wide range of audiences, including sections of the community not traditionally theatre-going, eg. children, young people and local communities.

These include theatre for young audiences, presenting high quality, professional theatre for children and young people (from under-6's to late teens); youth theatre projects (13 – 18 years); training workshops for adults; community theatre, working with a community to research, devise and present theatre; outreach, engaging with groups and/or individuals (young people and their leaders) in the practice and presentation of theatre/ drama; new writing, providing opportunities for the development of new writing and/or playwrights through a series of initiatives including the Playwriting Workshop, New Plays for Young Audiences projects and commissions.

Barnstorm is committed to providing access to theatre to all young people in Ireland by touring its children's theatre productions annually.

recent productions:
Digger, Doc and Dee-Dee by Volker Ludwig, adapted by Maeve Ingoldsby (2004)
The Elves and the Shoemakers by Mike Kenny (2003)
Little Victories by Shaun Prendergast (2003)
Whose Shoes by Mike Kenny (2002)
The Leaving by Brendan Griffin (2002)

photo: Alan Walsh in Digger, Doc and Dee-Dee by Volker Ludwig, adapted by Maeve Ingoldsby, 2004 © Dylan Vaughan

Bedrock Productions

68 Dame Street
Dublin 2
Republic of Ireland
tel: + 353 (0)1 671 0292
fax: + 353 (0)1 670 3890
email: info@bedrockproductions.com
web: www.bedrockproductions.com

artistic director: Jimmy Fay
company manager: Sarah Ling
literary manager: Alex Johnston

Established in 1993, Bedrock produces challenging, energetic and ambitious theatre. Its text-based drama has come from international playwrights such as Caryl Churchill, Sarah Kane, Heiner Muller, Bernard Marie Koltes, Bertolt Brecht and Stephen Berkoff.

Bedrock also works with new writing by some of Ireland's greatest talents, including Alex Johnston, Mark O'Rowe, Ken Harmon, Gavin Kostick, Des Bishop and Arthur Riordan. Their productions often fuse theatre with live music and film. The company tours both nationally and internationally.

In 1995 Bedrock initiated and administered the Dublin Fringe Festival.

recent productions:
Entertainment by Alex Johnston (2003)
Feint, devised (2003)
The Massacre at Paris by Christopher Marlowe, adapted by Alex Johnston (2002)
Blasted by Sarah Kane (2001)
Wideboy Gospel by Ken Harmon (2000)

photo: Fiona O'Shaughnessy and Lalor Roddy in Blasted by Sarah Kane, 2001 © Ros Kavanagh

Big Telly
Theatre Company

The Town Hall
The Crescent,
Portstewart BT55 7AB
Northern Ireland
tel: + 44 (0)28 7083 2588/6473
fax: + 44 (0)28 7083 2588
email: info@big-telly.com
web: www.big-telly.com

artistic director: Zoë Seaton
general manager: Louise Rossington

Big Telly concentrates on the visual potential
of theatre through fusion with other art
forms such as dance, music, circus, magic and
film to create a unique sense of spectacle.
The company places audiences firmly at the
centre of its work through innovative
creative processes, extensive educational and
outreach programmes and open rehearsals.

Big Telly's productions are designed to tour, and
are particularly suitable for small to middle
scale venues.

recent productions:
The Thief by Zoë Seaton, Paul McEneaney
and Paul Boyd (2004)
The Colleen Bawn by Dion Boucicault (2003)
The Playboy of the Western World
by J. M. Synge (2003)
McCool XXL by Paul Boyd (2002)
Fish by Zoë Seaton and Paul McEneaney (2000)

*photo: Michael Condron and Alan Mooney in The Colleen
Bawn by Dion Boucicault, 2003 © Peter Nash*

Blue Raincoat
Theatre Company

Lower Quay Street
Sligo
Republic of Ireland
tel: + 353 (0)71 917 0431
fax: + 353 (0)71 917 1100
email: bluerain@iol.ie
web: www.blueraincoat.com

artistic director: Niall Henry
company manager: Tara McGowan

Since foundation in 1991, Blue Raincoat
Theatre Company's artistic programme has
consisted of original work alongside
contemporary presentations of classic texts.
The company stages annual national and
international tours of their work.

In addition to theatrical performance, Blue
Raincoat operates an extensive programme of
outreach initiatives for various community
groups and theatrical training for professional
actors. Cairde, a summer community-based
performance festival with a diverse programme
of events, forms an additional element of Blue
Raincoat's annual programme.

The company maintains a full-time ensemble
who has trained with Corinne Soum and
Steve Wasson of the Ecole de Mime Corporeal
Dramatique in London. Ensemble members
continuously develop their skills, taking part
in regular voice and movement workshops.

Blue Raincoat also founded The Factory
Performance Space in Sligo town.

recent productions:
Birdie Birdie by Michael Harding (2004)
The Strange Voyage of Donald Crowhurst by
Malcolm Hamilton (2003)
Purgatory by W. B. Yeats (2003)
The Hollow in the Sand by Brendan Ellis (2002)
A Brief Taste of Lightning by Malcolm
Hamilton (2002)

See also Venues

*photo: Sandra O Malley in Birdie Birdie by Michael Harding,
2004 © James Connolly, PicSell8*

Cahoots NI

109 – 113 Royal Avenue
Belfast BT1 1FF
Northern Ireland
tel: + 44 (0)28 9043 4349
fax: + 44 (0)28 9043 4339
email: info@cahootsni.com
web: www.cahootsni.com

artistic director: Paul McEneaney
education and outreach: Louise McFetridge

Cahoots NI is a professional children's touring theatre company, based in Belfast. Our aims are: to produce high quality large-scale work for children to tour main stage spaces throughout Northern Ireland; to develop audiences of young children and to provide inspiring theatrical experiences for young children; to encourage appreciation of the arts in children from all sections of society and to develop meaningful links with the communities in which the company works; to expand the imagination and stimulate the artistic creativity of children; to work with experienced and highly regarded professional artists and in doing so contribute to the cultural economy of the region.

Cahoots blend physical theatre with other art forms including circus skills, magic, music, illusion, mime and black light.

In addition to the major venues in Northern and Southern Ireland, Cahoots NI has performed at the Young @ Art Festival in Belfast, International Children's Festival in Edinburgh and will perform at the Seoul Performing Arts Festival for Young Audiences in Summer 2004. The company has also produced Christmas shows for the Lyric Theatre, Belfast.

Alongside their performance schedule, Cahoots run education and outreach workshops for children in schools throughout the year.

recent productions:
The Starcatcher by Paul Bosco McEneaney and Zoë Seaton (co-production with Lyric Theatre, 2003)
A Fairy's Tale by Paul Bosco McEneaney (2003)
The Blizzard Wizard by Paul Bosco McEneaney and Zoë Seaton (2002)
Buster by Paul Bosco McEneaney (2002)

photo: Cressida Decarree in Buster by Paul Bosco McEneaney, 2002 © Chris Hill

Calipo
Theatre Company

Barlow House
Narrow West Street
Drogheda, Co. Louth
Republic of Ireland
tel: + 353 (0)41 983 7455
fax: + 353 (0)41 984 3109
email: info@calipo.ie
web: www.calipo.ie

artistic director: Darren Thornton
company manager: Collette Farrell

Calipo Theatre Company was founded in 1994 in Drogheda by former members of the Droichead Youth Theatre. Combining the exuberant energy of club culture with the stylistic approach of the movies, Calipo mixes the conventional with the unconventional in order to promote theatre as the vibrant and exciting artform that it is. By maintaining the traditional elements of theatre, however, the company aims to produce work that will cross over and introduce new ideas to an older audience.

Community and Outreach is an important part of Calipo's work and the company has established a workshop policy to explore issues that are relevant to young people. The company produces an outreach programme in multi-media and drama with early school leavers and school goers. Calipo also has a team of associate artists who facilitate its outreach work and participate in all devising processes for the stage. The company aims to tour new work to suitable venues in Ireland and abroad.

recent productions:
Getting 2 Level 10 by Irma Grothuis (2001)
Makin' Hits by Martin Maguire and Darren Thornton (2000)
Xaviers by Martin Maguire, Barbara Carr, Yvonne Morgan and Darren Thornton (1999)
The Crow by J M O'Barr, adapted by Darren Thornton (1998)
Love is the Drug... devised by the company (1998)

photo: Conor Byrne in Xaviers by Martin Maguire, Barbara Carr, Yvonne Morgan and Darren Thornton, 1999
© Liam O'Callaghan

Calypso Productions

7 South Great George's Street
Dublin 2
Republic of Ireland
tel: + 353 (0)1 670 4539
fax: + 353 (0)1 670 4275
email: info@calypso.ie
web: www.calypso.ie

artistic director: Bairbre Ní Chaoimh
company manager: Kerry West
administrator: Selina O'Reilly

Calypso Productions is an award-winning, Dublin-based theatre company. It aims to push the boundaries of theatrical creativity while producing challenging new plays that address the way people's lives are affected by contemporary issues of social justice and human rights.

We believe passionately that theatre with its vast imaginative resources can be a crucial catalyst for change in society. We are constantly seeking ways in which our productions can be made more accessible, inclusive and engaging for people from a wide variety of cultural, racial and socio-economic backgrounds.

recent productions:
Five Kinds of Silence by Shelagh Stephenson (2004)
Mixing it on the Mountain by Maeve Ingoldsby (2003)
Stolen Child by Bairbre Ní Chaoimh and Yvonne Quinn (2003)
Guess Who's Coming for the Dinner by Roddy Doyle (2002)
The Asylum Ball by Gavin Kostick (2000)

photo: Five Kinds of Silence by Shelagh Stephenson, 2004
© Tom Lawlor

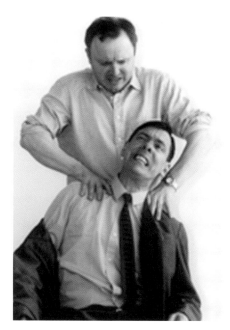

Civic Theatre

Tallaght
Dublin 24
Republic of Ireland
tel: + 353 (0)1 462 7460
fax: + 353 (0)1 462 7478
email: civictheatred24@eircom.net
web: www.civictheatre.ie

director: Bríd Dukes
administrator: Kerry Hendley

The Civic Theatre is primarily a receiving venue for professional productions of contemporary Irish and international work in theatre, dance, opera and music.

The theatre also produces a minimum of two new productions per year in the main auditorium. In the Loose End studio space, the Civic Theatre co-produces a series of new works with emerging theatre companies.

The Civic Theatre tours its in-house productions to other receiving venues throughout Ireland, average length of tour is two weeks.

recent productions:
The Sunshine Boys by Neil Simon (2004)
The Odd Couple by Neil Simon (2003)
The Big Friendly Giant by Roald Dahl, adapted by David Wood (2002)
Attaboy, Mr. Synge! by Deirdre Kinahan (2002)

See also Venues

photo: Michael James Ford and Nicholas Grennell in The Odd Couple by Neil Simon © Orla Murray

Corcadorca
Theatre Company

11-12 Marlboro Street
Cork
Republic of Ireland
tel/fax: + 353 (0)21 427 8326
email: info@corcadorca.com
web: www.corcadorca.com

Since it was founded in 1991, Corcadorca has created almost 30 productions in theatres and more unusual spaces. The company demonstrates its commitment to new writing through regular commissioning and the biennial Corcadorca Playwright Award.

artistic director: Pat Kiernan
company manager: Fin Flynn
administrator: Oonagh Montague

Corcadorca is a text-based company committed to creating theatre of the highest quality for Cork and beyond. Corcadorca interacts with the city and its people on a physical and artistic basis by nurturing and developing local artists through an accessible, professional environment and creating site-specific work in culturally significant areas of the city.

recent productions:
Snap by Ger Bourke (2003)
Love, devised (2003)
Mix it Up by Raymond Scannell (2002)
Amy the Vampire (& her Sister Martina) by Gavin Quinn (2002)
Bruen's Twist by Eamonn Sweeney (2002)

photo: Maria Tecce in *A Midsummer Night's Dream* by William Shakespeare, 2001 © Mike McSweeney, Provision

The Corn Exchange

43-44 Temple Bar
Dublin 2
Republic of Ireland
tel: + 353 (0)1 679 6444
fax: + 353 (0)1 679 6284
email: info@cornexchange.ie
web: www.cornexchange.ie

artistic director: Annie Ryan
general manager/producer: Sarah Durcan

Founded in 1995, The Corn Exchange is an independent theatre production company dedicated to developing theatre that is adventurous, visceral and alive. Specialising in a renegade version of Commedia dell'Arte, The Corn Exchange has also developed site-specific work as well as more traditional narrative theatre and collaborates with international practitioners of various disciplines in exchanges to explore the boundaries of theatre and what is possible within it.

The Company's reputation was established through its early productions based in Commedia dell'Arte and the multi-award winning productions of *Car Show, Foley, Lolita* and *Mud*.

The Corn Exchange is committed to artistic exchange on a national and international basis and to establishing long-term working relationships with practitioners throughout Ireland and abroad. The company has toured extensively throughout Ireland, the UK and the East Coast of America.

recent productions:
Mud by Maria Irene Fornes (2003)
Lolita by Nabokov, adapted by Michael West (2002)
Foley by Michael West (2000)
The Seagull by Michael West (1999)
Car Show by various authors (1998-2001)

photo: Andrew Bennett and Ruth Negga in Lolita by Nabokov, adapted by Michael West, 2002 © Paul McCarthy

Druid

Flood Street
Galway
Republic of Ireland
tel: + 353 (0)91 568660
fax: + 353 (0)91 563109
email: info@druidtheatre.com
web: www.druidtheatre.com

artistic director: Garry Hynes
managing director: Fergal McGrath
administrator: Yvonne Corscadden
administration executive: Michelle Corcoran

Founded in 1975, Druid is recognised as one of the pioneers of the modern cultural development of Ireland in the last quarter of a century. From its Galway home, it has led the way in the development of Irish theatre, performing in its Chapel Lane home, elsewhere in Galway, Ireland and beyond.

Druid has toured extensively at home and abroad (including visits in recent years to London, Sydney, Washington D.C. and New York), making the company one of the best known in the English-speaking theatre world.

Druid today continues to be acclaimed for its award-winning work on the dynamic Irish repertoire, offering new productions of classics as well as nurturing the work of a new generation of Irish writers. Writers associated with Druid include Tom Murphy, Geraldine Aron, Owen Mc Cafferty, Christian O'Reilly and in 1996 Druid gave Martin McDonagh his professional premier with its production of *The Beauty Queen of Leenane*. Writers currently under commission include Enda Walsh and Eugene O'Brien.

As a pioneer of the regional touring circuit, Druid remains committed to its national audience. For example, the company's first production of 2004 (*The Playboy of the Western World*) performed to over 35,000 people in ten locations across Ireland visiting many of the small communities and locations close to the heart of Synge's vision.

recent productions:
The Playboy of the Western World
by J.M. Synge (2004)
Sharon's Grave by John B. Keane (2003)
Sive by John B. Keane (2002)
The Good Father by Christian O'Reilly (2002)
My Brilliant Divorce by Geraldine Aron (2001)

photo: Anne-Marie Duff and Cillian Murphy in The Playboy of the Western World by J.M. Synge, 2004 photograph Keith Pattison

DubbelJoint Theatre Company

BIFHE
Whiterock Road
Belfast BT12 7PH
Northern Ireland
tel: + 44 (0)28 9020 2222
fax: + 44 (0)28 9020 2223
email: maura@dubbeljoint.com
web: www.dubbeljoint.com

artistic director: Pam Brighton
co-ordinator: Maura Brown
outreach officer: Oliver Corr
marketing officer: Flair Campbell

The company is committed to the exploration of pertinent and contemporary issues within Ireland, in particular the North of Ireland, through theatrical productions. Since its origin, DubbelJoint has produced at least one major production each year, written or adapted by members of the company. These plays have toured a great variety of local, national and international venues, from church halls, community centres, to the Grand Opera House, Belfast, and New York, bringing theatre to large numbers of people, many of whom may not have experienced it before.

DubbelJoint is an award-winning company and is one of the leading independent theatre producers in Belfast. It has a strong commitment to community venues, particularly in areas that suffer from social, economic and cultural disadvantage and to local writing, and through these, strives to democratise theatre and make it accessible to all. We have traditional links with Féile an Phobail, having premiered a new play in the Festival every year since 1993.

recent productions:
A Cold House by Brian Campbell and Laurence McKeown (2003)
Black Taxis by Brian Moore (2003)
Paddy On The Road by Brian Moore (2002)
Working Class Heroes by Brenda Murphy (2002)

164,632

photo: Bill Heyland, Vincent Higgins and Susie Kelly in A Cold House by Brian Campbell and Lawrence McKeown, 2003

Everyman Palace Productions

15 MacCurtain Street
Cork
Republic of Ireland
tel: + 353 (0)21 450 1673
fax: + 353 (0)21 450 2820
email: palace@oceanfree.net
web: www.everymanpalace.com

artistic director: Patrick Talbot
theatre manager Brendan Galvin
marketing manager: Patricia O'Sullivan
technical manager: Mark Donavan

Everyman Palace Productions is the in-house production company of the Everyman Palace Theatre.

recent productions:
The Glass Menagerie by Tennessee Williams (2004)
Side by Side by Sondheim (2004)
Bouncers by John Godber (2003)
Flynnie by Michael McAuliffe, adapted from the book (2003)
Who's Afraid of Virginia Woolf? by Edward Albee (2003)

See also Venues

photo: Liam Heffernan in The Good Thief by Conor McPherson, 2002 © Janice O'Connell, F22 Photography

Fishamble
Theatre Company

Shamrock Chambers
1-2 Eustace Street
Dublin 2
Republic of Ireland
tel: + 353 (0)1 670 4018
fax: + 353 (0)1 670 4019
email: info@fishamble.com
web: www.fishamble.com

artistic director: Jim Culleton
general manager: Ciara Flynn
**marketing & development
officer:** Cerstin Mudiwa
literary officer: Gavin Kostick

Fishamble is dedicated to the discovery, development and production of excellent new work for the theatre. It presents this work in exciting and dynamic productions for audiences in Dublin, throughout Ireland and internationally. The company's body of work includes numerous award-winning plays by both emerging and established playwrights. Its Playwright Development Initiative includes a series of courses, readings and competitions through which vibrant and pioneering work is brought to the stage.

Fishamble is committed to bringing its work to audiences throughout Ireland and overseas. In recent years, Fishamble has engaged in a number of very rewarding collaborations with theatre companies, venues and festivals in Ireland and internationally.

recent productions:
Tadhg Stray Wandered In by Michael Collins (2004)
Shorts by various authors (2003)
The Buddhist of Castleknock by Jim O'Hanlon (2002)
Still by Rosalind Haslett (Meeting House Square, 2002)
Contact by Jeff Pitcher and Gavin Kostick (2002)

*photo: Eamonn Owens in Tadhg Stray Wandered In by
Michael Collins, 2004 © Colm Hogan*

Focus Theatre

6 Pembroke Place
off Pembroke Street
Dublin 2
Republic of Ireland
tel box office: + 353 (0)1 676 3071
tel admin: + 353 (0)1 671 2417
email: focustheatre@eircom.net

artistic director: Joe Devlin
administrator: Alastar MacAongusa
head of studio: Tim McDonnell

Since its foundation by the late Deirdre O'Connell in 1967, Focus Theatre has been a centre for the learning and the practice of the Stanislavski System, incorporating a weekly actors' training workshop, The Stanislavki Studio, now led by Tim McDonnell.

Focus continues to build on its established reputation as a producer of the best of European and international, as well as Irish, drama and new writing, with particular emphasis on plays which explore the human condition and inter-personal relationships.

recent productions:
Very Heaven by Ann Lambert (2004)
Proof by David Auburn (2003)
The Gallant John-Joe by Tom MacIntyre (2003)
Talking Through His Hat by Michael Harding (2003)
Stuck by David Rubinoff (2003)

See also Venues

photo: Hazel Dunphy in Proof by David Auburn, 2003
© Sean Brady

Galloglass Theatre Company

30 Parnell Street
Clonmel,
Co. Tipperary
Republic of Ireland
tel: + 353 (0)52 26797
fax: + 353 (0)52 27270
email: admin@galloglass.ie
web: www.galloglass.ie

artistic director: Caroline FitzGerald
general manager: Jim Myers

Galloglass Theatre Company was founded in 1990 and since 2003 is under the artistic direction of Caroline FitzGerald. It presents two to three shows per year, all of which tour extensively.

The company's artistic policy is to present plays of merit from the Irish and European repertoire in productions that embrace quality and professionalism, thereby encouraging audience development and interest in Clonmel and on tour.

The company is committed to touring nationally and internationally, with the productions designed to perform in venues of all sizes.

recent productions:

The Desert Lullaby by Jennifer Johnston (2004)
Fred and Jane by Sebastian Barry (2003)
Ghost Story by Fergus and Conor Linehan (2003)
My Children My Africa by Athol Fugard (2003)

See also Venues

photo: Geraldine Plunkett and Eileen Colgan in The Desert Lullaby by Jennifer Johnston, 2004 © John Crowley

The Gate Theatre

Cavendish Row
Dublin 1
Republic of Ireland
tel (box office): + 353 (0)1 874 4045
tel (admin): + 353 (0)1 874 4368
fax: + 353 (0)1 874 5373
email: info@gate-theatre.ie
web: www.gate-theatre.ie

director: Michael Colgan
deputy director: Marie Rooney
head of production: Teerth Chungh
theatre manager: Eamon Kenny

The management's principal aim is the ongoing viability of the Gate, and within that context it pursues a standard of excellence in producing new Irish plays, together with classics from the Irish and world repertoire.

The Gate Theatre is a 371-seat proscenium arch theatre, situated in a Georgian building, which celebrated its 75th anniversary in 2003. The theatre has undergone a continuous process of renovation and upgrading to ensure the preservation of the 18th-century building while at the same time providing technical and audience facilities suitable for a world-class theatre.

Performances take place all year round, and in recent years the theatre has undertaken a considerable amount of international touring, resulting in an increasingly high profile, not only for the work of the Gate, but for Irish theatre as a whole.

recent productions:
The Price by Arthur Miller (2004)
Dancing at Lughnasa by Brian Friel (2004)
Jane Eyre by Charlotte Bronte, adapted by Alan Stanford (2003)
Waiting for Godot by Samuel Beckett (2003)
The Importance of Being Earnest by Oscar Wilde (2003)

photo: Risteard Cooper and Lia Williams in The Eccentricities of a Nightingale by Tennessee Williams, 2003 © Tom Lawlor

Graffiti
Theatre Company

The Weighmaster's House
2 Church Street
Shandon
Cork,
Republic of Ireland
tel: + 353 (0)21 439 7111
fax: + 353 (0)21 439 7110
email: graffiti@eircom.net
web: www.graffiti.ie

artistic director: Emelie FitzGibbon
financial administrator: Jennifer O'Donnell
tour manager: Olan Wrynn
outreach officer: Geraldine O'Neill

Graffiti has been providing top quality educational theatre productions to young audiences for 20 years. In that time, the company's productions have been seen by over a million young people in Ireland and abroad.

Graffiti's artistic policy is to provide a range of excellent work for its target audiences and to offer a service to the youth, particularly of the Munster area, by extending the range and availability of children's and young people's theatre and workshops.

Productions tour to early learning, primary and post-primary schools in Munster and South Leinster. Irish-language productions tour to Gaelscoileanna in that area.

recent productions:
Jackie – an Ospidéal by Sarah FitzGibbon (2004)
Fishy Tales by Enda Walsh (2004)
Walking the Tightrope by Mike Kenny (2003)
Céim ar Chéim by Mike Kenny (2003)
Striking Distance by Raymond Scannell (2002)

photo: Raymond Scannell, Anne Fitzpatrick and Simon Delany in Striking Distance by Raymond Scannell © Jorg Koster

An Grianán
Theatre Productions

Port Road
Letterkenny,
Co. Donegal
Republic of Ireland
tel: + 353 (0)74 9123288
fax: + 353 (0)74 9120665
email: patriciamcbride@eircom.net
web: www.angrianan.com

director: Patricia McBride
administrator: Helene McMenamin

Since its foundation in 1999 An Grianán Theatre has produced work in-house and for touring. The theatre aims to maintain a professional theatre production base in Donegal offering work of the highest artistic standards. An Grianán produces classic work from the modern Irish, European and American canon.

An Grianán's work is available for touring to middle and large scale venues throughout Ireland. The theatre and its productions aim to offer a platform for the wealth of talent from Donegal and to celebrate the distinctive culture of the North-West corner of the island. An Grianán is interested in establishing partnerships with other theatre companies and venues throughout the country.

recent productions:
The Little Mermaid, adapted by Simon Sharkey (2003)
The Twits by Roald Dahl, adapted by David Wood (2002)
Dancing at Lughnasa by Brian Friel (2002)
Hansel and Gretel (2001)
Oíche Ghealaí by Cathal Ó Searcaigh, adapted from *Salome* (2001)

See also Venues

photo: Morna Regan and Dessie Gallagher in Dancing at Lughnasa by Brian Friel, 2002 © Declan Doherty

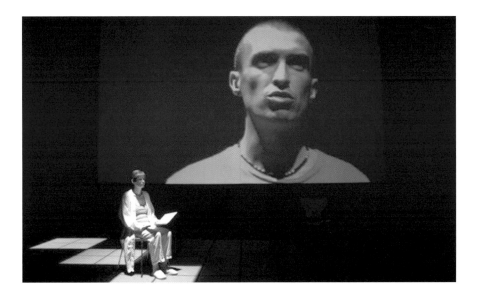

Gúna Nua
Theatre Company

74 Dame Street
Dublin 2
Republic of Ireland
tel/fax: + 353 (0)1 675 9921
email: info@gunanua.com
web: www.gunanua.com

artistic directors: Paul Meade, David Parnell

Gúna Nua Theatre was founded in 1998. Since that time it has become one of Ireland's leading independent theatre companies, with a reputation for innovative, accessible, quality work.

Gúna Nua has at its core the following principles: to create new work for the stage; to develop a working method which enables the full involvement of theatre practitioners from different disciplines at the earliest possible stage in the play-making process; to use this working method for the creation of new work, and to adapt this working method for the theatrical production of existing texts; to use modern theatre techniques to bring a vibrant, dynamic and, above all, entertaining form of storytelling to the stage; to achieve excellence in performance through intelligence, integrity and passion; to produce work which is contemporary in thinking and which reflects the concerns and interests of the times, in order to attract a new theatre-going audience.

recent productions:
The Real Thing by Tom Stoppard (2004)
Skin Deep by Paul Meade (2003)
Taste by David Parnell (2002)
Scenes From a Water Cooler by Paul Meade and David Parnell (2001)
The Importance of Being Earnest by Oscar Wilde (co-production with Civic Theatre, Tallaght, 2001)

photo: Jennifer O'Dea and Mark O'Halloran in Skin Deep by Paul Meade, 2003

Island
Theatre Company

Church Street
King's Island
Limerick
Republic of Ireland
tel: + 353 (0)61 410433
fax: + 353 (0)61 400997
email: info@islandtheatrecompany.ie
web: www.islandtheatrecompany.ie

artistic director: Terry Devlin
general manager: Alice Kennelly

From its base in Limerick, Island Theatre
Company produces two to three shows per
year, tours nationwide and has a developing
outreach programme. The company produces
a mixture of new writing as well as plays
from the existing repertoire.

All of Island's productions are designed for
touring. The company currently tours
throughout Ireland, North and South.

recent productions:
Lovers by Brian Friel (2004)
The Quiet Moment by Mike Finn (2002)
Faith Healer by Brian Friel (2002)
Our Town by Thornton Wilder (2001)
The Taming of the Shrew by
William Shakespeare (2001)

photo: Barry McGovern in Faith Healer by Brian Friel, 2002
© Arthur Gough

Kabosh

Old Museum Arts Centre
7 College Square North
Belfast BT1 6AR
Northern Ireland
tel: + 44 (0)28 9024 3343
fax: + 44 (0)28 9023 1130
email: info@kabosh.net
web: www.kabosh.net

artistic director: Karl Wallace
general manager: Sinead Coll
projects manager: Azucena Avila

Founded in 1994, Kabosh is committed to innovation in theatre practice and producing cutting-edge theatre. In particular, the company focusses on experimenting both visually and physically, integrating text and music with precision movement to create stories.

Kabosh produces both installation performance (touring and site specific) as well as main stage productions which tour Ireland, the UK and Europe year round.

recent productions:
Todd by Conor Mitchell (2004)
Rhinoceros by Eugene Ionesco (2003)
Mojo-Mickybo by Owen McCafferty (2003)
Sleep Show devised by Karl Wallace (2001)
Orianna devised by Karl Wallace and Rachel O'Riordan (2001)

photo: Sonya Kelly, Karl O'Neill and Jo Donnelly in Rhinoceros by Eugene Ionesco, adapted by Martin Mooney, 2003 © John Baucher

Loose Canon
Theatre Company

26 South Frederick Street
Dublin 2
Republic of Ireland
tel/fax: + 353 (0)1 677 6956
email: info@loosecanon.com
web: www.loosecanon.com

artistic director: Jason Byrne
administrator: Kate McSweeney

Loose Canon Theatre Company was founded in 1996. Performances over the last eight years reflect an evolutional approach to creating theatre. The company places a high value on investigation, research and experiment.

We wish to express what cannot be expressed in words, considering theatrical those thoughts which escape spoken language. Everything filling the stage, that can be shown and materially expressed, is intended first to appeal to the senses, and not primarily to the mind. We do not reject text, our aim is to re-interpret rather than illustrate.

recent productions:
Fragments of a Dead Performance I,
devised (2003)
Hedda Gabler by Henrik Ibsen (2003)
The Duchess of Malfi by John Webster (2002)
Macbeth by William Shakespeare (2001)
In the Dark Air of a Closed Room, devised
by the company (2000)

*photo: Deirdre Roycroft in Fragments of a Dead Performance
III (Medea Material), devised, 2003 © Ros Kavanagh*

Lyric Theatre

55 Ridgeway Street
Stranmillis
Belfast BT9 5FB
Northern Ireland
tel: + 44 (0)28 9038 5685
fax: + 44 (0)28 9038 1395
email: info@lyrictheatre.co.uk
web: www.lyrictheatre.co.uk

artistic director: Paula McFetridge
general manager: Mike Blair

The Lyric is Northern Ireland's only full-time producing theatre, presenting the finest in new writing, contemporary Irish drama and international classics.

It produces distinctive professional drama that explores the diversity of cultural values in the north through a clear and consistent aesthetic vision. The Lyric's mission includes specific initiatives to commission new work, train professionals, develop audiences and collaborate with other arts organisations. It is committed to providing regular employment opportunities for indigenous professional practitioners.

As the Lyric has an essential role to play in representing the cultural voice of the north further afield, it recognises the importance of local, national and international touring.

The Lyric acknowledges the importance of increasing access to high-quality theatre for all members of our society. Facilities include: 6 wheelchair spaces in the main auditorium; lift access; an induction loop system and a minicom booking service. Each production has signed and audio-described performances

as well as touch tours for visually impaired young people during the Christmas season. The theatre has a full-time education officer who co-ordinates workshops, post-show discussions, student placement opportunities and education packs for each production.

recent productions:
True West by Sam Shepard (2004)
The Weir by Conor McPherson (2004)
Ghosts by Ibsen, adapted by
Conall Morrison (2003)
The Starcatcher by Paul Bosco McEneaney
and Zoe Seaton (2003)
New Year's Eve Can Kill You by Marie Jones (2003)

photo: Declan Conlon in True West by Sam Shepard, 2004
© Chris Hill Photographic

The Machine

SFX City Theatre
23 Upper Sherrard Street
Dublin 1
Republic of Ireland
tel: + 353 (0)1 855 4090
fax: + 353 (0)1 855 4671
email: director@sfx.ie
web: www.sfx.ie

artistic director: Michael Scott
technical director: Paul Hyland
administration/marketing: Myra Geraghty

The primary role of The Machine's work is the exploration of theatre form and the investigation of the ability of live theatre to excite, debate, inform and develop society.

The Machine seeks to create a theatre space where the continuing debate on theatre form can be investigated. The company manages and performs in the SFX City Theatre, a space it also makes available to other companies whose work informs this debate.

recent productions:
Shirley Valentine by Willy Russell (2004)
The Snowman by Raymond Briggs (2003)
The Matchmaker by John B. Keane (2003)
The Field by John B. Keane (2003)
The Vagina Monologues by Eve Ensler (2003)

See also Venues

photo: Mary McEvoy in Shirley Valentine by Willy Russell, 2004 © Valerie O'Sullivan

Macnas

Black Box
Dyke Road,
Galway
Republic of Ireland
tel: + 353 (0)91 561462
fax: + 353 (0)91 563905
email: admin@macnas.com
web: www.macnas.com

Macnas is a performance company with a community arts ethos and the underlying belief that the creative experience is open to everyone and that artistic activities should not be elitist. The company is committed to developing its own highly visual style in traditional and non-traditional venues, indoors and outdoors, at home and overseas.

general manager: John Ashton
performance director: Judith Higgins
financial controller: Edel Gorman
community & training
co-ordinator: Dave Donovan

Macnas brings together a blend of imagination, passion, wit and self-confidence in a variety of settings: in theatres; on streets; in communities; in schools and in non-traditional performance spaces.

recent productions:
The Mysteries, adapted by Mikel Murfi & Richard Hayhow, with text by Vincent Woods (2003)
Gráinne Mhaol, adapted by Kathi Leahy & Patricia Forde (2002)
The Lost Days of Ollie Deasy by Mikel Murfi (2000)
Diamonds in the Soil, devised by Patrick O'Reilly in association with the company (1998)
The Dead School by Patrick McCabe (1998)

See also Street Theatre/Circus Companies

photo: Midie Corcoran in The Lost Days of Ollie Deasy by Mikel Murfi, 2000 © Joe Shaughnessy

Meridian Theatre Company

11-12 Marlboro Street
Cork
Republic of Ireland
tel: + 353 (0)21 427 6837
fax: + 353 (0)21 427 9134
email: meridtc@iol.ie

artistic director: Johnny Hanrahan
company manager: Bridget Cleary
project co-ordinator: Sue Baker

Meridian produces interdisciplinary new work. This work incorporates music, video and other related media as part of a long-term experiment in theatrical form. The company is currently developing a working structure which will facilitate the development of projects over several years in co-production with national and international partners.

recent productions:
Croon by Daphne Wright & Johnny Hanrahan (2004)
Beats n' Pieces by Raymond Scannell (2003)
Racoon by Tom Hall (2003)
Mind That 'Tis My Brother by Gaye Shortland (2002)
White Woman Street by Sebastian Barry (2002)

photo: Cindy Cummings in Croon by Daphne Wright and
Johnny Hanrahan, 2004 © Tom Lawlor

Operating Theatre

38 Moyne Road
Ranelagh
Dublin 6
Republic of Ireland
tel: + 353 (0)86 816 5288/ (0)86 233 2560
fax: + 353 (0)1 496 2516
email: alicurran@eircom.net

artistic directors: Olwen Fouere, Roger Doyle
producer: Ali Curran

Operating Theatre creates performance-based work with music as a core element. In its 23-year history, Operating Theatre has produced a diverse portfolio of work using processes which have included the integration of music technology with original composition, found and commissioned texts and live performance.

The company's work has been presented in both conventional and non-theatrical environments.

recent productions:
Passades devised by the company, (2004)
Chair by Olwen Fouere, in collaboration with Roger Doyle and Johnny Hanrahan (2001)
Angel/Babel by Roger Doyle, Olwen Fouere and Leon Ingulsrud (1999)

photo: Olwen Fouere in Chair by Olwen Fouere, Roger Doyle and Johnny Hanrahan, 2001 © Amelia Stein

Ouroboros
Theatre (Ireland)

*(previously known as
The Theatreworks Company)*

112 St Stephen's Green
Dublin 2
Republic of Ireland
tel/fax: + 353 (0)1 405 4944
email: Ouroboros@eircom.net
web: www.ouroboros.ie

artistic director: Michael Caven
resident set designer: Ferdia Murphy
resident costume designer: Sinead Cuthbert

Formed in 1995, and based in Dublin,
Ouroboros (till mid-2004 known as The
Theatreworks Company) is dedicated to
producing at least one main-stage scale
production a year, along with a range of
training workshops for actors.

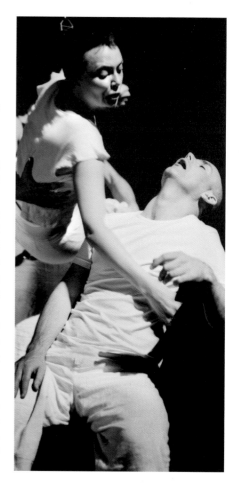

The company's artistic policy is to produce
works rarely, if ever, seen in Ireland. We seek
to offer our audience an exciting and
enriching experience by choosing texts that
tell epic and transforming tales of the
profundity of the human spirit. We seek to
produce these works in a vision that utilises a
total theatre language, comprising a dynamic
synthesis of realistic and stylised performance
techniques that is developed through music,
design and image, to a form that is capable of
transporting and affecting our audience
through an act of the collective imagination.

recent productions:
Macbeth by William Shakespeare
(in association with Second Age, 2003)
Tales from Ovid adapted by Michael Caven (2002)
Richard III by William Shakespeare (2001)
Mutabilitie by Frank McGuinness (2000)
Anna Karenina by Helen Edmundson (1999)

*photo: Liz Schwarz and Jude Sweeney in Tales from Ovid
adapted by Michael Caven, 2002 © Ros Kavanagh*

Pan Pan

43 Upper George's Street
Dun Laoghaire
Co. Dublin
Republic of Ireland
tel: + 353 (0)1 280 0544
fax: + 353 (0)1 230 0918
email: info@panpantheatre.com
web: www.panpantheatre.com

artistic directors: Gavin Quinn, Aedín Cosgrove
general manager: Aoife White

Aedín Cosgrove and Gavin Quinn founded Pan Pan in 1993. The company's style of theatre mixes contemporary attitude with personal feelings, how we see the world yesterday and sometimes, near the end of a performance, how we see it today. As a group of artists, Pan Pan has developed an individual aesthetic that has grown from working in theatre performance for the last eleven years. We work in the exploration of new forms, a new approach and experiments with time, space, music and performance.

Over the years, Pan Pan has toured extensively, both at home and abroad. As a result, the company has built up strong links with venues and festivals all over Europe, South Korea and Australia.

recent productions:
Mac-Beth 7 by Shakespeare (2004)
For The First Time Ever by Gavin Quinn (2003)
Deflowerfucked by Pan Pan (2001)
Standoffish by Pan Pan (2000)
Mr. Staines by Dermot Healy (1999)

photo: Mac-Beth 7 by Gavin Quinn, adapted from Macbeth by William Shakespeare, 2004 © Gavin Quinn

The Passion Machine

27 Mountjoy Square
Dublin 1
Republic of Ireland
email: passionmachine2@hotmail.com

artistic director: Paul Mercier
general manager: Anne Gately

The Passion Machine is based in Dublin and was founded in 1984. The company is a project-based operation, staging only original Irish work, and is committed to a wholly indigenous populist theatre that depicts, challenges and celebrates the contemporary Irish experience.

recent productions:
Diarmuid and Gráinne by Paul Mercier
(in association with Abhann Productions, 2001)
It Come Up Sun by Joe O'Byrne (2000)
We Ourselves by Paul Mercier (2000)
Native City by Paul Mercier (1998)
Fully Recovered by Anto Nolan (1998)

photo: Eanna McLiam and Emily Nagle in Diarmuid and Grainne by Paul Mercier, 2001 © Derek Speirs

Prime Cut Productions

285a Ormeau Road
Belfast BT7 3GG
Northern Ireland
tel/fax: + 44 (0)28 9064 5101
email: primecut@btconnect.com
web: www.primecutproductions.co.uk

artistic director: Jackie Doyle
development manager: Emma Jordan
financial & administration manager: Edel Magill

Prime Cut Productions was formed in 1992
with the aim of producing contemporary
international drama to the highest standards.
The company is actively committed to
promoting the talents of playwrights
throughout the world. The company's unique
style continues to make international drama
accessible and entertaining.

Prime Cut tours throughout Ireland in the
autumn and spring to venues ranging
between 100 and 300 seats in capacity. The
company also tours internationally. Previous
venues have included the Bush Theatre,
London, West Yorkshire Playhouse and Arhus
Festival, Denmark.

recent productions:
Neil LaBute's *The Mercy Seat*/Harold Pinter's
Ashes to Ashes (2004)
After Darwin by Timberlake Wertenbaker (2003)
Gagarin Way by Gregory Burke (2003)
The Chance adapted by Jackie Doyle (2002)

*photo: Patrick O'Kane and Michelle Fairley in Ashes To Ashes
by Harold Pinter, 2004 © Chris Hill*

Quare Hawks

The Market House
Market Street
Monaghan
Republic of Ireland
tel: + 353 (0)47 77809
fax: + 353 (0)47 71113
email: info@quarehawks.com
web: www.quarehawks.com

artistic director: Liam Halligan
company secretary: Melanie Brick

Quare Hawks was formed in 1999, with the motivation that theatre is an actor's art. First and last. The company has three aims – to create original pieces of theatre that arise from, and have relevance to, a specific area and a given community; to

incorporate skills and techniques from international theatre practitioners; and to introduce new and/or neglected plays from home and abroad.

Quare Hawks tours Ireland and abroad with an emphasis on work that challenges conventions, prejudices and perceptions.

recent productions:
Winter Came Down by Michael McCudden (2003)
Leaving by Philip Osment (2002)
Cracked, devised, based on Hanna Greally's book, *Bird's Nest Soup* (2001)
The Undertaking by Philip Osment (2000)

photo: Diane O'Keeffe, Dawn Fleming and Liz Keller in
Cracked, devised, 2001 © Hannah Smolenska

Red Kettle
Theatre Company

Meeting House Lane
Waterford
Republic of Ireland
tel: + 353 (0)51 879 688
fax: + 353 (0)51 857 416
email: info@red-kettle.com
web: www.come.to/redkettle

artistic director: Ben Hennessy
executive director: Mary Boland
administrator: Catherine Collins

The artistic policy of Red Kettle, founded in 1985, is to produce theatre in Waterford, throughout Ireland and where possible, overseas. Whilst including work from the existing repertoire, the company specialises in commissioning new Irish plays for adults and children.

The company is fully committed to creating, through its children's company, Little Red Kettle, a platform whereby children can participate actively in the theatre process and to make theatre accessible and attractive to young audiences.

In addition to productions at its home base, Red Kettle tours Ireland and abroad.

recent productions:
The Castlecomer Jukebox by Jimmy Murphy (2004)
The True Story of Urcú by Liam Meagher and Ben Hennessy (2003)
Hummin' by Tony Guerin (2002)
The Kings of the Kilburn High Road by Jimmy Murphy (2002)
The Queen and Peacock by Loughlin Deegan (2001)

photo: The Castlecomer Jukebox by Jimmy Murphy, 2004
© Gerry O'Carroll

Replay Productions

Old Museum Arts Centre
7 College Square North
Belfast BT1 6AR
Northern Ireland
tel: + 44 (0)28 9032 2773
fax: + 44 (0)28 9032 2724
email: replay@dircon.co.uk
web: www.replayproductions.org

artistic director: Richard Croxford
general manager: Brona Whittaker

Established in 1988, Replay is dedicated to providing high quality theatre that entertains, educates and stimulates children and young people, and to supporting and inspiring the adults that work with and care for them. In addition to high performance standards, all Replay projects provide unique curriculum support, encourage increased understanding, development and learning (at school level and in life skills) and promote concepts of cultural identity and diversity.

Within its extensive touring programme of productions, workshops and related activities, Replay specialises in commissioning new writing for young audiences, and also serving the needs of young people with disabilities. More recently, the company has focussed on skills development, offering training in drama for writers, artists, teachers and youth leaders. Replay tours its work throughout Northern Ireland, and occasionally further afield. While performing predominantly in schools, the company also performs limited runs in public venues.

recent productions:

Flaming Fables by Mary McNally (2004)
Striking Distance by Raymond Scannell (2003)
The Millies by Nicola McCartney (2003)
Little Lou Tells a Story by Sarah FitzGibbon (2002)
Almost Human by Robert Rigby (2002)

photo: Ruairi Tohill in Striking Distance by Raymond Scannell, 2003 © John Boucher

Rough Magic Theatre Company

5-6 South Great George's Street
Dublin 2
Republic of Ireland
tel: + 353 (0)1 671 9278
fax: + 353 (0)1 671 9301
email: info@rough-magic.com
web: www.rough-magic.com

artistic director: Lynne Parker
executive producer: Loughlin Deegan
administrator: Elizabeth Whyte
literary manager: Christine Madden

Rough Magic was founded in 1984. The company's artistic policy is to commission, develop, produce and promote new work for the stage, in an international context. This includes world premières of new Irish plays, Irish premières of major plays from the contemporary international scene, and international touring and collaboration.

Rough Magic's wide-ranging work to date includes over 40 Irish premières, the professional debuts of many Irish writers, and extensive tours throughout Ireland, the UK and beyond.

recent productions:
Words of Advice for Young People by Ioanna Anderson (2004)
Take Me Away by Gerald Murphy (2004)
Olga by Laura Ruohonen, in a new version by Linda McLean (2003)
Shiver by Declan Hughes (2003)
Copenhagen by Michael Frayn (2002)

*photo: Aidan Kelly in Take Me Away by Gerald Murphy, 2004
© Pat Redmond*

Second Age
Theatre Company

74 Dame Street
Dublin 2
Republic of Ireland
tel: + 353 (0)1 679 8542
fax: + 353 (0)1 670 7926
email: info@secondage.com
web: www.secondage.com

artistic director: Alan Stanford
general manager: Linda Keating

Founded in 1989, Second Age Theatre Company produces to the highest standards plays that are on the syllabus for the Junior and Leaving Certificate English examinations. In direct response to the demand from over 2,000 English teachers on the company's mailing list, the majority of productions are usually from the works of Shakespeare.

In addition, the company regularly tours throughout Ireland and provides post-show workshops along with educational resource notes for the teachers about the plays and the productions.

recent productions:
Hamlet by William Shakespeare (2004)
Macbeth by William Shakespeare
(in association with Ourobouros, 2003)
Romeo and Juliet by William Shakespeare (2002)
Macbeth by William Shakespeare (2002)
King Lear by William Shakespeare (2001)

photo: Rory Keenan and Emily Nagle in Hamlet by William Shakespeare, 2004 photography: Annika Johanssen

Storytellers Theatre Company

Third Floor
5 Aston Quay
Dublin 2
Republic of Ireland
tel: + 353 (0)1 671 1161
fax: + 353 (0)1 671 1159
email: storytel@indigo.ie
web: www.storytellerstheatrecompany.com

artistic director: Mary Elizabeth Burke-Kennedy
company manager: Joan Mallon

Since its inception in 1986, Storytellers Theatre Company has brought a new dimension to Irish Theatre. Storytellers brings to the stage large-scale dramas drawn from diverse literary sources, sometimes creating new plays from stories that have never been dramatised, sometimes revisiting and revitalising classic theatre pieces. A repertoire of plays has been created, drawn from popular stories, myths, legends and novels from Irish and international sources.

To perform this repertoire, the company has developed a unique ensemble style which incorporates a mix of well-established players with talented newcomers. The playing is bold, direct, ironic and playful with an intense focus on the actor as storyteller. This style demands an alert, imaginative engagement between the audience and actors. It is particularly appropriate in Ireland where the cultural heritage is rich in storytelling.

Storytellers is committed to touring throughout Ireland and has done so annually for the last ten years. The company continues to develop a multi-layered outreach programme for school children and teachers to ensure the continued engagement of young audiences.

recent productions:
Rashomon by Ivor Benjamin (2004)
Hansel and Gretel by Mary Elizabeth Burke-Kennedy (2003)
Antigone by Sophocles, new version by Conall Morrison (2003)
Women in Arms by Mary Elizabeth Burke-Kennedy (2002)
The Grapes of Wrath by John Steinbeck, adapted by Frank Galati (2001)

photo: Eoin Lynch in Rashomon by Ivor Benjamin, 2004

Taibhdhearc na Gaillimhe

Amharclann Náisiúnta na Gaeilge

An tSráid Láir
Gaillimh
Éire
tel: + 353 (0)91 562024
fax: + 353 (0)91 563195
email: eolas@antaibhdhearc.com
web: www.antaibhdhearc.com

artistic director: Darach Mac Con Iomaire

Taibhdhearc na Gaillimhe is the national Irish Language theatre and produces five major productions a year. Our aim is to develop and promote Irish language theatre throughout the country and the majority of our productions are new works which reflect the vibrancy of new Irish language writing.

Central to Taibhdhearc na Gaillimhe's vision is the provision of quality theatre for young people to develop their interest in all aspects of the theatre. Na Crosáin, An Taibhdhearc's

Youth Theatre caters for young people in the western region and enables them to participate in a range of different productions.

Fuadar Feabhra & Scáilí Samhna are initiatives set up by An Taibhdhearc to encourage new writing. Four experimental productions are produced each November giving new writers, actors and directors a chance to experience the challenges of staging new work in a professional environment.

Taibhdhearc na Gaillimhe tours four productions a year to venues nationally.

recent productions:
An Béal Bocht by Myles na gCopaleen, adapted by Darach Mac Con Iomaire (2004)
Cúigear Chonamara by Mícheál Ó Conghaile (2003)
Scaoil Leis An gCaid by Breandán M. Mac Gearailt (2003)
Níor Mhaith Linn Do Thrioblóid by Joe Steve Ó Neachtain (2003)
Cré na Cille by Máirtín Ó Cadhain, adapted by Macdara Ó Fátharta (2002)

photo: Marc Mac Lochlainn & Darach Ó Dubháin in An Béal Bocht by Myles na gCopaleen © Andrew Downes

TEAM Educational Theatre Company

4 Marlborough Place
Dublin 1
Republic of Ireland
tel: + 353 (0)1 878 6108/872 1192
fax: + 353 (0)1 874 8989
email: team@eircom.net
web: www.teamtheatre.ie

artistic director: Martin Murphy
general manager: Lisa Heaney
education officer: Muireann Ahern
production manager: Roy Murray

For almost 30 years, Team has been at the forefront of theatre-in-education in Ireland. The company aims to produce work for children and young people to high artistic standards, primarily in their own formal learning environment, that: provides an authentic experience which resonates with their own lives; challenges them to feel, think, interact and do within the dramatic context; and opens them to the potential of theatre.

The company works with up to 10,000 students over 30 weeks of touring every year in Dublin, the North East, the North West and the Midlands.

recent productions:
The Making of Antigone Ryan by Martin Murphy (2003)
Jack Fell Down by Michael West (2003)
Black Ice by Thomas McLaughlin (2002)
Bumbógs & Bees by Frances Kay (2002)
Burning Dreams by Frances Kay (2001)

photo: Peter Daly in Black Ice by Thomas McLaughlin, 2002
© Kevin McFeely

Tinderbox Theatre Company

Imperial Buildings
72 High Street
Belfast BT1 2BE
Northern Ireland
tel: + 44 (0)28 9043 9313
fax: + 44 (0)28 9032 9420
email: info@tinderbox.org.uk
web: www.tinderbox.org.uk

artistic director: Michael Duke
general manager: Appointment pending
administrator: Kerry Woods
outreach director: John McCann

Tinderbox develops, commissions and produces dynamic new theatre plays that resonate strongly with audiences in Belfast, Northern Ireland and beyond. The company provides professional expertise and innovative programmes to inspire, nurture and support both emerging and established playwrights, and offers a specialised and versatile Outreach Programme to increase the value of its plays and productions for the communities it serves.

Tinderbox tours productions selectively when they are best suited to regional, national and international audiences.

recent productions:
Revenge by Michael Duke (2004)
The Chairs by Eugène Ionesco, a new version by Owen McCafferty (2003)
Massive by Maria Connolly (2002)
Caught Red Handed by Tim Loane (2002)
No Place Like Home devised by the company, text by Owen McCafferty (2001)

photo: Kieran Ahern and Gemma Burns in Revenge by Michael Duke, 2004. photograph Phil Smyth

Town Hall Theatre

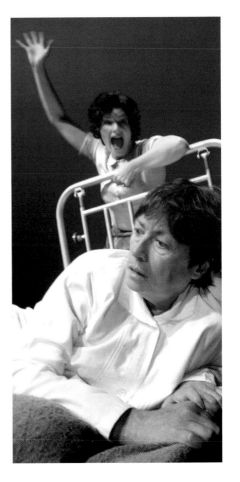

Courthouse Square
Galway
Republic of Ireland
tel: + 353 (0)91 569755
fax: + 353 (0)91 569664
email: tht@galwaycity.ie
web: www.townhalltheatregalway.com

manager: Mike Diskin

The Town Hall Theatre was opened in 1995. It is the largest and best attended theatre in the west of Ireland. Since 1998, the Town Hall has mounted several in-house productions each year.

The policy of Town Hall Theatre is to engage with the needs of the audiences attending venues on the regional theatre circuit by producing quality shows which are clearly targeted at general or niche markets. All productions tour subject to demand from other Irish venues.

recent productions:
Stained Glass at Samhain by Patricia Burke Brogan (2002)
Ualach an Uaignis by Martin McDonagh, translated by Micheál Ó Conghaile (2002)
Our Lady of Sligo by Sebastian Barry (2002)
Country and Irish by Jon Nee (2002)
A Doll's House by Henrik Ibsen, adapted by Frank McGuinness (2000)

See also Venues

photo: Fedelma Cullen and Emma McIvor in Our Lady of Sligo by Sebastian Barry, 2002 © Aengus McMahon

Upstate Theatre Project

Barlow House
West Street
Drogheda, Co. Louth
Republic of Ireland
tel: + 353 (0)41 984 4227
fax: + 353 (0)41 984 4232
email: admin@upstate.ie
web: www.upstate.ie

artistic director: Declan Gorman
drama development officer: Declan Mallon

Established in 1997, Upstate is a national/international touring company and a regional drama development initiative contained within a single, integrated project. The company operates across a range of inter-linked programme strands: Upstate Live, producing professional productions and touring; Upstate Local, engaging in regional and cross-border arts development and participation projects; Upstate Learning, providing local training and third-level arts education modules; Upstate Lab, focussing on artform and repertoire development. Upstate is committed to aesthetic innovation and to social-political enquiry and change through art. By presenting devised dramas, commissioned works and new versions of classics and by interactive and imaginative engagement with communities and diverse artists, Upstate pursues innovative, entertaining, thoughtful theatre for contemporary audiences.

Most Upstate Live productions are developed for cross-border and national touring circuits, but may later tour internationally, e.g. Epic was seen at Traverse Theatre, Edinburgh, following a cross-border/Ireland tour in 2002. The company is open to imaginative approaches in relation to co-productions, site-specific commissions for festivals etc.

recent productions:
Epic by Declan Gorman (2001)
The Countrywoman by Paul Smith, adapted by Elizabeth Kuti (2000)
Macbeth by William Shakespeare (1999)
Hades by Declan Gorman (1998)
The Weavers by Gerhart Hauptmann, in a version by Declan Gorman (1997)

photo: Sinead Douglas and Brendan McCormack in Epic by Declan Gorman, 2002 © Douglas Robertson

Yew Tree Theatre

O'Rahilly Street
Ballina
Co. Mayo
Republic of Ireland
tel: + 353 (0)96 71238
fax: + 353 (0)96 73113
email: yew@indigo.ie
web: www.yewtreetheatre.com

artistic director: John Breen

Yew Tree Theatre is a non-venue based production company that tours new Irish plays and plays from the popular Irish and international repertoire.

The company produces narrative driven work that focuses on function rather than form. It is committed to developing relationships with artists and organisations in the West and North-West and in developing new audiences for their work. Yew Tree is open to forming strategic partnerships with companies that have similar policies.

Yew Tree Theatre tours throughout Ireland and, following the success of Alone it Stands, is developing a significant international network.

recent productions:
Charlie by John Breen (2003)
The Playboy of the Western World by J.M. Synge (co-production with Cork Opera House, 2003)
Grand by Max Hafner (2002)
Big Maggie by John B. Keane (2000)
Alone It Stands by John Breen (1999)

photo: Alone It Stands by John Breen, 1999 © Paul McCarthy

Gillian Beauchamp in Dance Theatre of Ireland's production of
As A Matter of Fact by Robert Connor and Loretta Yurick.
photo: Kieran Hartnett, photos courtesy of Dr. Paul Eckman

Ballet Ireland

Agher
Summerhill
Co. Meath
Republic of Ireland
tel/fax: + 353 (0)46 955 7585
email: balletireland@eircom.net
web: www.balletireland.com

managing director: Anne Maher
artistic director: Günther Falusy

Ballet Ireland was founded in 1998. It is a full-time organisation whose aims include performing, developing and promoting ballet of the highest quality. The company has a classical repertoire and also produces new works in the neo-classical idiom.

Its educational unit, initiated in 1999, has developed a comprehensive educational programme for which it received an AIB Better Ireland Awards grant in 2003. It includes an annual summer school, workshops held onstage, lecture demonstrations, master classes, and an Associate programme.

Ballet Ireland pursues a policy of extensive touring, both nationally and internationally.

recent productions:
Ballet Fireworks 2 by various choreographers (2004)
Ballet Fireworks by various choreographers (2002)
Sleeping Beauty by Günther Falusy (2002)
Nutcracker by Günther Falusy (2001)
Swan Lake by Günther Falusy (2001)

photo: Cressida Merritt-Webb in Les Sylphides, Ballet Fireworks, 2002 Photographer: Günther Falusy

CoisCéim Dance Theatre

First and Second Floor
14 Sackville Place
Dublin 1
Republic of Ireland
tel: + 353 (0)1 878 0558
fax: + 353 (0)1 878 0813
email: info@coisceim.com
web: www.coisceim.com

artistic director: David Bolger
general manager: Jenny Traynor
administrator: Nicola Dunne

CoisCéim Dance Theatre exists to create innovative and challenging dance theatre that is both enjoyable and accessible to a wide section of the community. It aims to use the cultural wealth of literature, music and dance talent in Ireland to develop a style of dance theatre that is unique in the context of modern European dance. CoisCéim's creations aim to be adventurous, cutting edge, and accessible to those unfamiliar with contemporary dance.

Since its formation in 1995, the company has presented 16 critically acclaimed stage productions to both national and international audiences. In 2002, the company's first film, Hit and Run, premiered at the International Dance Festival Ireland in Dublin and has gone on to win several major awards, including the Paula Citron Award for Choreography for the Camera and the Award for Creative Excellence at the Dance on Camera Festival, New York 2003.

recent productions:
Swept by David Bolger (2003)
Mermaids by David Bolger (2003)
When Once is Never Enough/The Rite of Spring by David Bolger (2002)
Ballads by David Bolger (2001)
Boxes by David Bolger & Sean Jeremy Palmer (2000)

photo: Diane O'Keeffe and David Bolger in Swept by David Bolger, 2003 © Hugo Glendinning

Cork City Ballet

56 Clevedon
Kilmoney
Carrigaline
Co. Cork
Republic of Ireland
tel: + 353 (0)21 437 5155
email: corkcityballet@yahoo.com

artistic director: Alan Foley

Cork City ballet exists to present quality ballet to the highest possible standards by offering a wide-ranging repertoire that includes new and lesser-known works as well as the established classics.

Our policy is to provide performance opportunities and employment for Irish dancers, choreographers, teachers and practitioners. We strive to build on our existing international relationships, thus creating valuable exchange opportunities and absorbing the international culture of dance into Irish ballet, whilst extending the public's understanding and enjoyment of dance.

One of the signature elements of Cork City Ballet has been the incorporation of contemporary and modern dance into its classical foundation to create new and relevant ballets for our time.

recent production:
Ballet Spectacular 2004 by Alan Foley (2004)

photo: Alan Foley and Monica Loughman in Cork City Ballet's
Ballet Spectacular 2004 © Kieran Tobin.

Daghdha Dance Company

University of Limerick
Limerick
Republic of Ireland
tel: + 353 (0)61 202804/(0)86 3887402
fax: + 353 (0)61 202943
email: mail@daghdha.ie
web: www.daghdha.ie

artistic director: Michael Klien
general manager: Roisin Kinsella
education officer: Vicky O'Brien

Daghdha is a professional contemporary dance company whose primary focus is the creation and production of original choreographic works. The company is committed to the production of artistically distinctive, high quality, contemporary Irish works.

The company also runs an extensive education programme that strives to increase the awarness, understanding and practice of dance as a means of expression and imagination. The company is involved in a variety of innovative projects that range from primary school residencies through to collaborations at university level.

Daghdha tours nationally and continues to build a strong international profile by touring in America, Asia and Eastern Europe.

recent productions:
Once Beneath The Skin by Michael Klien (2004)
Empty Shells by Davide Teringo & Angi Smalis (2004)
Im Fett by Michael Klien (2004)
The Dying Swan by Michael Klien, from *Trath Na gCos* (2004)
Einem by Michael Klien (2003)

photo: Angi Smalis in Im Fett by Michael Klien, 2004
© Gravity and Grace

Dance Theatre of Ireland

Centre for Dance, Bloomfields
Lower George's Street
Dun Laoghaire, Co. Dublin
Republic of Ireland
tel: + 353 (0)1 280 3455
fax: + 353 (0)1 280 3466
email: danceire@iol.ie
web: www.dancetheatreireland.com

artistic directors: Robert Connor & Loretta Yurick
company manager: Megan Stack
centre & outreach contact: Paula O'Shaughnessy

Dynamic and multi-faceted, Dance Theatre of Ireland creates, produces and tours dance theatre and digital dance. While their work has increasingly incorporated new technologies, it continues to embrace the search for vocabularies and collaborations which enlighten the process of being human.

The company's co-productions and international tours (France, Netherlands, Germany, USA, Switzerland) are supported by embassies and agents in Europe. DTI tours to all major venues in Ireland and by invitation to international dance and digital art festivals in Europe and America. The company also collaborates with eminent international choreographers (Charles Cre Ange, Philippe Saire, Rui Horta) creating work strong in visual and emotional impact.

President Mary McAleese opened the company's Centre for Dance in Dun Laoghaire where DTI are now based and where the company offers a diverse programme of classes for professionals and the public. The company's educational work takes place in a wide range of community and school settings through the very popular, award-winning outreach programme, DANCE POP, offering increased access to workshops, performances and discussions.

recent productions:
Between You & Me by Robert Connor & Loretta Yurick, Willi Dorner, Philippe Saire, Marie-Françoise Garcia & Alexandre Iseli (2004)
As a Matter of Fact by Loretta Yurick & Robert Connor (2003)
The Simulacra Stories by Joanne Leighton (2002)
PRISM by Robert Connor & Loretta Yurick (2002)
Evidence by Robert Connor & Loretta Yurick (2001)

photo: Gillian Beauchamp in As A Matter of Fact by Robert Connor and Loretta Yurick, 2003. photo Kieran Hartnett, photos courtesy of Dr. Paul Eckman

Fabulous Beast Dance Theatre

Dublin
Republic of Ireland
tel: + 353 (0)86 085 0030
or + 44 (0)20 7288 1296
fax: + 44 (0)20 7288 1296
email: info@fabulousbeast.net
web: www.fabulousbeast.net

artistic director: Michael Keegan-Dolan

recent productions:
Giselle by Michael Keegan-Dolan (2003)
The Flowerbed by Michael Keegan-Dolan (2000)
Fragile by Michael Keegan-Dolan (1999)
The Good People by Michael Keegan-Dolan (1998)
Sunday Lunch by Michael Keegan-Dolan (1997)

photo: Giselle by Michael Keegan-Dolan, 2003 © Michael Keegan-Dolan

Fluxusdance

Riverbank Arts Centre
Main Street
Newbridge
Kildare
Republic of Ireland
tel: + 353 (0)86 820 1328
fax: + 353 (0)45 520264
email: cathy@fluxusdance.com

artistic director: Cathy Kennedy

Fluxusdance is a dance production company based in Kildare. Collaboration and interaction with emerging digital technologies is a strong tenet of the company's work as well as nationwide programmes of access through FLEx (Fluxusdance Local Experience).

recent productions:
You Can't Kill a Button by Cathy O'Kennedy (2002)
Súil Eile by Cathy O'Kennedy (2001)
Giselle: The Presence of the Past by Cathy O'Kennedy (2001)
Morphic Fields by Cathy O'Kennedy (2000)

photo: Rebecca Waters and Jennifer Fleenor in Morphic Fields by Cathy O'Kennedy, 2000 © Adrian Melia

Irish Modern Dance Theatre

SFX City Theatre
23 Upper Sherrard Street
Dublin 1, Republic of Ireland
tel: + 353 (0)1 874 9616
fax: + 353 (0)1 878 7784
email: imdt@iol.ie
web: www.irishmoderndancetheatre.com

artistic director: John Scott
administrator: Elisabetta Bisaro

Irish Modern Dance Theatre is a company whose policy is to create and commission new works and expand the experience of dance theatre for audiences and performers in Ireland. To that end, their work has played with every theatrical and dance convention.

IMDT has developed an audience with a curiosity for modern dance in a country known more for its literary traditions and text-based drama. John Scott promotes dialogue with international choreographers: from workshops with Thomas Lehmen (2003/4), Meredith Monk and Pablo Vela (2001), Chris Yon (2003) to commissions of new work: Thomas Lehmen (2004), John Jasperse (2002), Chris Nash (2000), Seán Curran (1998), Fabrice Dugied (1997) and John Wisman (1995). He has also helped facilitate workshops with Deborah Hay (2003).

IMDT performs in every possible location throughout Ireland, north and south. International performances include Danspace Project at St Marks Church, New York; l'Étoile du Nord, Paris; Unga Atalante and Pusterviksteatern, Göteborg, Sweden; and Varna Festival, Bulgaria.

John Scott, born in Dublin, trained at the Irish National College of Dance and Dublin City Ballet where he worked with Anna Sokolow. He subsequently worked with Meredith Monk in Quarry and Yoshiko Chuma in Reverse Psychology and studied with Susan Buirge, Anne Crosset, Andy De Groat and Janet Panetta. His own choreographic work plays with different performance situations, from theatres to museums, restaurants, shop windows and train stations. He uses performers of different styles, ages and backgrounds, and is currently working on a project with survivors of torture from the Centre for Care for the Survivors of Torture.

recent productions:
Left and Right by John Scott (2002)
Rough Air by John Scott (2001)
Off the Wall by John Scott (2000)
That Place, Those People by Sean Curran (1999)
Intimate Gold by John Scott (1999)

photo: Justine Doswell and Philip Connaughton in Rough Air by John Scott, 2001 © Hugo Glendenning

Myriad Dance

South Slob Road
Drinagh South
Drinagh
Co. Wexford
Republic of Ireland
tel: + 353 (0)53 40975/(0)86 876 3552
fax: + 353 (0)53 40975
email: info@myriaddance.com
web: www.myriaddance.com

directors: Deirdre Grant, Brid Malone

Myriad Dance was formed in 1999 in Wexford by Deirdre Grant and Brid Malone. The company produces new innovative contemporary dance work in a variety of different performance settings – outdoors, site-specific, adapted theatre spaces for local and national audiences. The company also promotes Dance Development Initiatives in the south east region, running the Pulse Youth Dance Programme alongside Wexford County Council since 2001.

recent productions:
Scramble by Deirdre Grant (2002)
In An Instant by Deirdre Grant (2001)
Shortcuts & Storylines by Deirdre Grant
and Brid Malone (2000)
Broken Masque by Deirdre Grant (1999)

photo: Scramble by Deirdre Grant, 2002 photograph Paddy Grant

Rex Levitates Dance Company

First Floor
74 Dame Street
Dublin 2
Republic of Ireland
tel: + 353 (0)1 671 1736
email: admin@rexlevitates.com
web: www.rexlevitates.com

artistic directors: Jenny Roche, Liz Roche
company manager: Sally Ebert

Rex Levitates is a dynamic young company committed to producing entertaining, innovative and throught provoking contemporary dance works, which constantly explore and question the world we live in.

recent productions:
Resuscitate by Liz Roche (2004)
Bread and Circus by Liz Roche (2003)
Their Thoughts Are Thinking Them by Rex Levitates (2002)
Senses by Liz Roche (2002)
Trip Down by Liz Roche (2001)

photo: Grant McLay and Liz Roche in Their Thoughts Are Thinking Them by Rex Levitates, 2002 © Fionn McCann

Siamsa Tíre
The National Folk Theatre

Town Park
Tralee
Co. Kerry
Republic of Ireland
tel: + 353 (0)66 712 3055
fax: + 353 (0)66 712 7276
email: siamsatire@eircom.net
web: www.siamsatire.com

artistic director: Oliver Hurley
general manager: Marianne Kennedy

Siamsa Tíre was established as the National Folk Theatre of Ireland in 1974. The company exists to represent Irish folk culture in its many forms, through the medium of theatre. Its artistic policy is to present Irish folk life in a contemporary fashion, through the use of music, song, dance, mime and movement.

Siamsa Tíre tours to venues throughout Ireland, North and South, and overseas from February to March and from November to December.

recent productions:
Oileán by Oliver Hurley (2003)
Samhain by Oliver Hurley (2001)
Oisín by Oliver Hurley (2000)
Clann Lir by John Sheehan (1999)

See also Venues

photo: Oileán – Celebrating the Blasket Islands by Cindy Cummings, 2003 © Valerie O'Sullivan

subsidised opera companies

Chris Steele and Sebastian O'Shea Farren in Opera Theatre Company production of The Turn of the Screw by Britten © Anthony Wood

Castleward Opera

737 Lisburn Road
Belfast BT9 7GU
Co. Antrim
Northern Ireland
tel: + 44 (0)28 9066 1090
fax: + 44 (0)28 9068 7081
email: info@castlewardopera.com
web: www.castlewardopera.com

artistic director: Ian Urwin
general manager: Hilda Logan
administrator: Helen McCready

Main season runs from the end of May to the end of June when two operas are performed in Castle Ward, Strangford, Co. Down – a National Trust property on the shores of Strangford Lough.

recent productions:
La Rondine by Puccini (2003)
Tosca by Puccini (2003)
La Belle Helene by Offenbach (2002)
Lucia di Lammermoor by Donizetti (2002)
The Marriage of Figaro by Mozart (2001)

Photo: La Rondine by Puccini, 2003 © Stanley Matchett MBE

Opera Ireland

The Schoolhouse
1 Grantham Street
Dublin 8
Republic of Ireland
tel: + 353 (0)1 478 6041
fax: + 353 (0)1 478 6046
email: info@operaireland.com
web: www.operaireland.com

artistic director: Dieter Kaegi
chief executive: David Collopy
development director: Nicola Moore
**marketing/communications
executive:** Lisa Irvine

Opera Ireland produce two seasons of opera
per year in spring and winter. Each season
comprises two full-scale operas on alternate
nights at the Gaiety Theatre.

recent productions:
Tosca by Puccini (2004)
Jenufa by Janacek (2004)
Norma by Bellini (2003)
Don Giovanni by Mozart (2003)
Queen of Spades by Tchaikovsky (2002)

*Photo: Stefania Spaggairi and Marcel Vanaud in Tosca by
Puccini, 2004 © Patrick Redmond*

Opera Theatre Company

Temple Bar Music Centre
Curved Street
Dublin 2
Republic of Ireland
tel: + 353 (0)1 679 4962
fax: + 353 (0)1 679 4963
email: info@opera.ie
web: www.opera.ie

artistic director: Annilese Miskimmon
chief executive: Andrew McLellan
technical director: Patrick McLaughlin
marketing manager: Sorcha Carroll

Opera Theatre Company has been touring professional opera to venues throughout Northern Ireland and the Republic since 1986. The company has a reputation for bold, innovative programming with equal emphasis on new and established works, and seeks to bring together the most talented Irish and international music and theatre practitioners. Through the impact of its productions, as well as during residencies and special events, the company seeks to attract new audiences of all ages to the art form.

International appearances have included the major festivals at Edinburgh, Melbourne and Perth as well as invitations to the Czech Republic and the Brooklyn Academy of Music, New York.

recent productions:
The Cunning Little Vixen by Janacek (2004)
The Turn of the Screw by Britten (2004)
La Cenerentola by Rossini (2003)
Thwaite by Jurgen Simpson & Simon Doyle (2003)
Ariodante by Handel (2003)

Photo: Chris Steele and Sebastian O'Shea Farren in The Turn of the Screw by Britten, 2004 © Anthony Woods

Wexford
Festival Opera

Theatre Royal
High Street
Wexford
Republic of Ireland
box office: + 353 (0)53 22144
tel: + 353 (0)53 22400
fax: + 353 (0)53 24289
email: info@wexfordopera.com
web: www.wexfordopera.com

artistic director: Luigi Ferrari
chief executive: Jerome Hynes
administrator: Phil Keeling

For over 50 years, the Irish coastal town of
Wexford has showcased this festival of rare
opera, which boasts a reputation as
international as its audience.

The narrow, ancient Viking streets and tiny,
atmospheric theatre set the scene for over 40
daytime events as well as 18 evening
performances of three major productions. The
productions are rehearsed and performed only
in Wexford, with the Wexford Company of
artists, drawn from all over the world,
participating in many of the events day and
night.

recent productions:
Die Drie Pintos by Von Weber/Mahler (2003)
María Del Carmen by Granados (2003)
Svanda Dudák by Weinberger (2003)
Il Giuramento by Mercadante (2002)
Mirandolina by Martinu (2002)

*Photo: Larisa Kostyuk in Svanda Dudák by Jaromir
Weinberger © Derek Speirs*

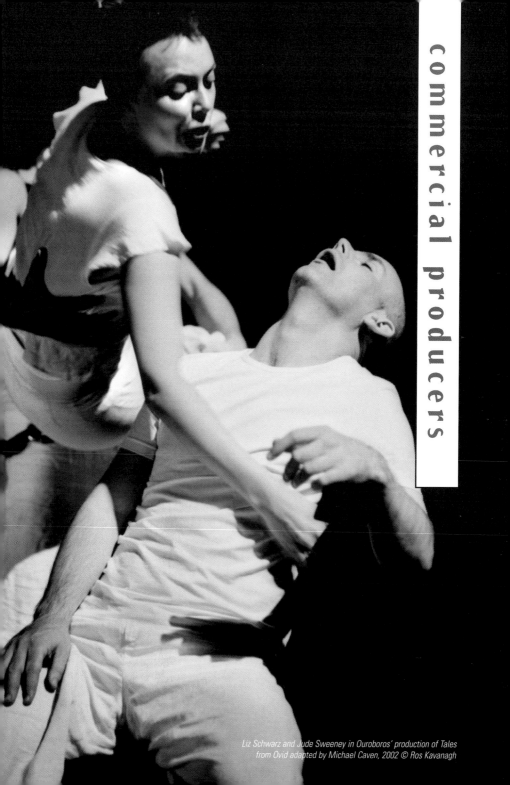

commercial producers

Liz Schwarz and Jude Sweeney in Ouroboros' production of Tales
from Ovid adapted by Michael Caven, 2002 © Ros Kavanagh

Abhann Productions

23 Mary Street Little
Dublin 7, Republic of Ireland
tel: + 353 (0)1 889 4900
fax: + 353 (0)1 889 4992
email: info@riverdance.com
web: www.riverdance.com
senior executive producer (Riverdance):
Julian Erskine
executive producer (new projects):
Ronan Smith

Class Acts Promotions (Ireland) Ltd

39 Wellington Park
Belfast BT9 6DN, Northern Ireland
tel: + 44 (0)28 9068 1041
fax: + 44 (0)28 9068 7747
email: info@classactsprom.com
web: www. classactsprom.com
director: Trevor McClintock

Cork Opera House

Emmet Place
Cork, Republic of Ireland
tel: + 353 (0)21 427 4308
fax: + 353 (0)21 427 6357
email: info@corkoperahouse.ie
web: www.corkoperahouse.ie
executive director: Gerry Barnes

Edward Farrell Productions

Irishtown, Athlone
Co. Westmeath, Republic of Ireland
tel: + 353 (0)90 647 4418/647 5518
fax: + 353 (0)90 647 8818
producer: Edward Farrell

Gaiety Theatre Ltd

South King Street
Dublin 2, Republic of Ireland
tel: + 353 (0)1 677 1717
fax: + 353 (0)1 677 1921
email: info@gaietytheatre.net
web: www.gaietytheatre.net
executive director: John Costigan

Gerry Sinnott

44 Blackburne Square, Rathfarnham Gate
Dublin 14, Republic of Ireland
tel: + 353 (0)1 492 8060/(0)87 241 1684
fax: + 353 (0)1 492 8061
producer: Gerry Sinnott

Lane Productions

9-17 St. Andrew's Street
Dublin 2, Republic of Ireland
tel: + 353 (0)1 679 7760
fax: + 353 (0)1 679 7552
email: bcashe@eircom.net
web: www.andrewslane.com
directors/producers: Pat Moylan/Breda Cashe

Noel Pearson Productions
Ferndale Films

4-6 Haddington Road
Dublin 4, Republic of Ireland
tel: + 353 (0)1 660 5411
fax: + 353 (0)1 660 5543
mobile: + 353 (0)86 8555 468
email: ferndale@dublin.com,
info@ferndalefilms.com
web: www.ferndalefilms.com
head of production: Anne Marie Naughton

Pat Egan Management

Merchants Court, 24 Merchants Quay
Dublin 8, Republic of Ireland
tel: + 353 (0)1 679 7700
fax: + 353 (0)1 679 7495
email: pategan@clubi.ie
director: Pat Egan

Tony Byrne Productions

C/o Tivoli Theatre
Francis Street, Dublin 8
Republic of Ireland
tel: (+) 353 (0)1 475 0962
fax: (+) 353 (0)1 475 0962
email: albyrne@indigo.ie
contact: Tony Byrne

Conor Lovett in Gare St Lazare's production of The Beckett Trilogy, 2001 © Marilyn Kingwill

AboutFACE Theatre Company

17 Pine Valley Avenue, Rathfarnham, Dublin 16, Republic of Ireland
tel: + 353 (0)87 414 4884 **fax:** + 353 (0)1 491 0628
email: aboutface@eircom.net **web:** www.aboutfacetheatrecompany.com
artistic directors: Anna Olson, Paul Nugent, Alan Walsh **executive producer:** Karl Walsh
AboutFACE enacts strong narrative-driven texts, with a current focus on new American work.
recent productions: *Boy Gets Girl* by Rebecca Gilman (2003) *Featuring Loretta* by George F. Walker (2003)

Angel Exit

30 Sandycove Road, Sandycove, Dublin, Republic of Ireland
tel: + 353 (0)87 246 4125 **email:** info@angelexit.com **web:** www.angelexit.com
artistic directors: Acushla Bastible, Tamsin Fessey
Founded in Paris, 2001, by graduates of the prestigious Ecole Lecoq, Angel Exit is an international
physical theatre ensemble dedicated to the production of dynamic and accessible new theatre.
recent productions: *Bolt Upright* (2003) *Imaginary Prisons* (2001)

Asylum Productions

c/o Triskel Arts Centre, Tobin Street, Cork, Republic of Ireland
tel: + 353 (0)21 427 5875/(0)87 294 7270 **email:** asylumtheatre@hotmail.com
artistic director: Donal Gallagher
Asylum seeks to bring the best of contemporary, cutting edge theatre to the local, national
and international stage. Also, through our international youth programme, we aim to use
theatre as a 'development tool' – creating work that is vibrant, engaging and relevant to
youth, in order to ensure a future generation of theatre-goers.
recent productions: *Bedbound* by Enda Walsh (2003) *Standing Room Only* devised by various authors (2003)

B*spoke

email: Bspoketheatreco@aol.com
producers: Jane Brennan, Alison McKenna
recent productions: *The Drunkard* by Tom Murphy, after WH Smith and A Gentleman (2003)
Sophocles' *Electra* in a version written and directed by Frank McGuinness (2002)

Balor Theatre Company

The Balor Theatre, Ballybofey, Co. Donegal, Republic of Ireland
tel: + 353 (0)74 913 0424 **fax:** + 353 (0)74 913 1840
email: balordcagroup@eircom.net **web:** www.balortheatre.com
project co-ordinator: Mark McCollum
BITE is fundamentally a theatre-in-education company whose main aim is to use theatre as an
educational tool to impact positively on individual lives. *See also Venues*

Bare Bodkin Theatre Company

1 Watergate Street, Navan, Co. Meath, Republic of Ireland
tel: + 353 (0)46 907 4877/(0)86 853 4205 **email:** odeaterry@hotmail.com
artistic director: Terry O'Dea **administrator:** Val Keogh
Bare Bodkin's artistic policy is to produce specifically commissioned new work and work from
the repertoire at its base in County Meath. The company also aims to tour nationally and
internationally where possible.
recent productions: *Our Childhood Country* by John and Tommy McArdle (2004) *Spoonface
Steinberg* by Lee Hall (2002)

Bare Cheek Theatre Company
Elliot Farm, Old Boley, Barntown, Co. Wexford, Republic of Ireland
tel: + 353 (0)53 34459 **email:** t.mccleanefay@ucc.ie **web:** www.barecheektheatre.com
artistic director: Tony McCleane-Fay **company administrator:** Monika McCleane
Bare Cheek's artistic policy is to produce dynamic and visual theatre that involves all the senses of
the audience by presenting challenging, contemporary work with universal themes. The Company
also runs County Wexford Youth Theatre and operates drama schools in Wexford and Cork.
recent productions: *Someone Who'll Watch Over Me* by Frank McGuinness (2001) *Innocence* by
Frank McGuinness (2002) *See also Youth Theatre Groups*

BDNC Theatre Ltd
11 Russell Avenue East, East Wall, Dublin 3, Republic of Ireland
tel: +353 (0)1 874 8977 **email:** lmurphydub@hotmail.com
artistic director: Ciarán Taylor **administrator:** Lisa Murphy
BDNC Theatre was established in 2002 to produce new, existing and devised work of
contemporary relevance to Irish audiences. Since then, they have created five diverse and
successful shows, touring in Northern and Southern Ireland and the Czech Republic, and
represent Ireland at the Prague Fringe 2004.
recent productions: *Hyde and Jekyll* devised by Ciarán Taylor and company (2003) *Wheel* devised
by Ciarán Taylor and company (2003)

Be Your Own Banana
48 Seven Oaks, Frankfield, Douglas, Cork, Republic of Ireland
tel: + 353 (0)86 604 2327 **email:** Byobanana@hotmail.com **web:** homepage.eircom.net/~byob
artistic director: Brian Desmond
BYOB was founded, in January 2000, as an independent theatre company specialising in
researching comic technique and in producing original, comedic theatre. The company's style is
influenced by Keith Johnstone, the Commedia dell'Arte, silent cinema clowning, Grotowskian
physical theatre and traditional Irish storytelling.
recent productions: *The Ballad of Badger Bickle's Youngfella* by Brian Desmond and Alan Collins
(2002) *De Bogman* by Brian Desmond and Mairtin de Cogain (2001)

Beg, Borrow and Steal Theatre Company
35 Leinster Avenue, North Strand, Dublin 3, Republic of Ireland
tel/fax: + 353 (0)1 855 7154 **email:** applause@eircom.net
director: Maggie Biggs **artistic director:** Paul Maher
Beg, Borrow and Steal touring company makes work for street theatre and for children. The company
also produces Samhain, Dublin's Hallowe'en Parade which celebrates Ireland's Celtic heritage.

Belfast Theatre Company
207 Russell Court, Claremont Street, Belfast BT9 6JX, Co. Antrim, Northern Ireland
tel: + 44 (0)28 9059 6814 **fax:** + 44 (0)28 9059 6814 **email:** patrick.scully207@ntlworld.com
director: Paddy Scully
The company's artistic policy is to promote new and innovative drama, especially from Northern Ireland.

Bewley's Café Theatre
2nd Floor, Grafton Street, Dublin 2, Republic of Ireland
tel: + 353 (0)86 878 4001 **email:** bewleyscafetheatre@eircom.net **web:** www.bewleys.com
company director: Michael James Ford **administrator:** Maureen Loughran
Bewley's Café Theatre is Dublin's only permanent, year-round venue for lunchtime drama. The company presents a wide variety of theatre with a particular emphasis on comedy and new Irish writing.
recent productions: *Just A Little One* by Karen Egan and Susannah de Wrixon (2004) *Lost Letters of a Victorian Lady* by Michelle Read (2004) *See also Venues*

Black Box Theatre Company
'Vienna', Conary Upper, Avoca, Co.Wicklow, Republic of Ireland
tel/fax: + 353 (0)402 30799 **email:** bbox@indigo.ie **web:** www.blackbox-theatreco.com
artistic director: Patrick David Nolan **administration contact:** Rebecca Roper
Black Box is dedicated to new Irish writing and plays that have a contemporary relevance. Current projects include 'Dublin – May 17th 1974 – Monaghan 2004', a commemoration of the Dublin-Monaghan bombings.
recent productions: *Loco County Lonesome* by Patrick McCabe (2001) *Didi's Big Day* by Paul Walker (2000)

The Bone Ensemble
Magoola, Dripsey, Co. Cork, *or* c/o Granary Theatre, Mardyke, Cork, Republic of Ireland
tel: +353 (0)21 743 4900/490 4436 **email:** theboneensemble@yahoo.co.uk **web:** www.granary.ie
artistic directors: Adam Curtis, Jill Dowse
The Bone Ensemble produces innovative new work using a collaborative process, devising and commissioned new writing.
recent productions: *Again*, text by Craig Baxter and the company (Granary co-production, 2004)

Boomerang Theatre Company Ltd
c/o Sullivan's Quay National School, Cove Street, Cork, Republic of Ireland
tel: +353 (0)21 484 0422 **fax:** +353 (0)21 431 6826
email: info@boomerang-theatre.com, trishedelstein@eircom.net
director: Trish Edelstein
Boomerang Theatre Company Ltd was established in 2001 with a policy to co-produce with other European theatre companies. Since its first production with Lost Baggage, the company has toured extensively around Europe. The company is interested in exploring new ways of working in the theatre and always works in a multi-disciplinary fashion.
recent productions: *Searching For The Enemy* by Gerald Bauer (2004) *The Picture of Dorian Gray* by Oscar Wilde, adapted by John Osborne (2003)

Bruiser Theatre Company
306 Beersbridge Road, Belfast BT5 5DY, Co. Antrim, Northern Ireland
tel: + 44 (0)28 9028 7257 **email:** info@bruisertheatrecompany.com **web:** www.bruisertheatrecompany.com
artistic director: Lisa May **company manager:** Stephen Beggs
Since its inception in 1997, Bruiser has aimed to produce exciting, innovative and highly physical theatre, presenting existing texts using physical theatre techniques. Bruiser's theatre is flexible and easily transportable, allowing plays to be performed in a wide variety of spaces to target as wide an audience as possible.
recent productions: *The School for Scandal* by Richard Brinsley Sheridan (2004) *Blood Wedding* by Federico Garcia Lorca (2003)

Catastrophe
28 Carraig Mor, Lackagh, Co. Galway, Republic of Ireland
tel: + 353 (0)86 408 9074 **email:** galwaycatastrophe@hotmail.com
artistic director: Paul Hayes **resident playwright:** Josh Tobiessen
Catastrophe was founded in the summer of 2001 by three graduates of the recently formed MA
in Drama and Theatre Studies at NUI, Galway. The company's work combines original scripts
with a physically engaging acting style to create their own brand of dark comedy.
recent productions: *Kidnapping the Rileys* by Josh Tobiessen (2004) *In the Bedroom* by
Anthony Caleshu (2003)

Centre Stage
99 Fitzroy Avenue, Belfast BT7 1H4, Co. Antrim, Northern Ireland
tel: + 44 (0)28 9024 9119 **fax:** + 44 (0)28 9028 3749
email: admin@centre-stage.biz **web:** www.centre-stage.biz
artistic director: Roma Tomelty
Centre Stage produces works by classic Ulster writers pre-1969 and the best of international
work rarely seen in Ulster.
recent productions: *Little Miss Muffet* (2004) *Married Bliss* (2002)

Classic Stage Ireland
The Helix, DCU, Glasnevin, Dublin 9, Republic of Ireland
tel: +353 (0)1 700 7772 **fax:** +353 (0)1 700 7773 **email:** csi@thehelix.dcu.ie **web:** www.thehelix.ie
artistic director: Andy Hinds **associate director:** Marie-Louise O'Donnell
Classic Stage Ireland devotes itself exclusively to the presentation of the great world classics.

Common Currency Theatre Company
Flat 3, 16 Vessey Place, Dun Laoghaire, Co. Dublin, Republic of Ireland
tel: + 353 (0)87 288 5410 **email:** commoncurrency@yahoo.com
directors: Louise Drumm, Leticia Agudo
Common Currency endeavours to address the common experience of Europeans through the
currency of theatre, producing work that is challenging and accessible to Irish audiences.
recent productions: *Trainspotting* by Irvine Welsh, adapted by Harry Gibson (2001) *1900* by
Alessandro Baricco, translated by Marella Boschi (2000)

Crazy Dog Audio Theatre Company
91 Mount Drummond Square, Harold's Cross, Dublin 6, Republic of Ireland
tel: + 353 (0)1 497 3017 **email:** info@crazydogaudiotheatre.com **web:** www.crazydogaudiotheatre.com
artistic director: Roger Gregg
Crazy Dog Audio Theatre has produced internationally acclaimed radio series which combine the
highest production values with richly layered comic surrealism, literary parody and broad slap-stick.
Crazy Dog is also featured on the digital network XM Radio's Sonic Theater.
recent productions: *The Apocalypse of Bill Lizard* by Roger Gregg (2004) *Beyond the Back of Beyond*
by Roger Gregg (2003)

Crooked House Theatre Company

Riverbank Arts Centre, Main Street, Newbridge, Co. Kildare, Republic of Ireland
tel: + 353 (0)87 275 9420/(0)45 448309 **fax:** + 353 (0)45 432490
email: crookedhouse@riverbank.ie **web:** www.crookedhouse.ie
artistic director: Peter Hussey **production manager/designer:** Ciaran Aspell
Crooked House develops new work for theatre in the absurdist tradition of Beckett and
Ionesco. They also stage classical texts and provide theatre-in-education programmes.
In addition, they have premiered new work by leading international playwrights.
recent productions: *Boat Memory* by Laline Paul (2004) *Karamazoo* by Philip Ridley (2004)
See also Youth Theatre Groups

Cyclone Productions

Cliffside, Weavers Point, Crosshaven, Co. Cork, Republic of Ireland
tel: + 353 (0)21 483 1948 **fax:** + 353 (0)21 483 1948 **email:** cycloneproductions@eircom.net
artistic director: Peadar Donohoe **administrator:** Brenda Roche
Cyclone's artistic policy is to explore theatre pieces using an innovative style and a thought-
provoking intensity.
recent productions: *Play the Piano Drunk* by Jon Whitty (Granary Theatre co-production, 2002)
Sex, Drugs, Rock and Roll (2000)

Dark Horse Theatre Company

22 Ballyboden Crescent, Rathfarnham, Dublin 16, Republic of Ireland
tel: + 353 01 495 0112/(0)87 123 1163 **email:** darkhorsetheatre@eircom.net
artistic director: Robin Keogh **production manager:** Deirdre McSweeney
Dark Horse's artistic policy is to produce plays relevant to minority groups but universal in theme.
recent productions: *Don't Take Your Coat Off!* by Robin Keogh (2003) *Kilt* by Jonathan Wilson (2003)

Decadent Theatre Company

Woodlawn, Ballinasloe, Co. Galway, Republic of Ireland
tel: + 353 (0)87 765 4374 **email:** decadenttheatreco@hotmail.com
artistic director: Andrew Flynn **administrator:** Grainne O'Byrne
Decadent's artistic policy is to produce and promote contemporary Irish drama.
recent productions: *The Weir* by Conor McPherson (2003) *Lovers* by Brian Friel (2002)

Dionysos Theatre Company

22 Lower Camden Street, Dublin 2, Republic of Ireland
tel: + 353 (0)1 478 9580 **fax:** + 353 (0)1 478 9580 **email:** dionysostheatre@yahoo.co.uk
artistic director: Helena Lewin
Formed in 2001, Dionysos formed a strong connection with Scandinavian drama. The company
works to produce exciting performances and to collaborate with other theatre companies as
well as with other art forms. Future plans include The Ghost Sonata by August Strindberg, with
a new translation and original music.
recent productions: *Mosaic* by Anthony Minghella (2003) *The Stronger* by August Strindberg (2002)

Djinn Productions
tel: + 353 (0)87 679 0885 **email:** djinntheatre@yahoo.com
artistic director: Ursula Rani Sarma **producer:** Kate Neville
Djinn Productions was founded in Cork in 1999 by writer/director Ursula Rani Sarma and producer Kate Neville. This small company is based on the belief that new writing is central to contemporary theatre. Through our productions, we aim to constantly challenge the boundaries of the medium, producing work which is innovative yet accessible.
recent productions: *Blue* by Ursula Rani Sarma (Project co-production, 2003) *Blue* by Ursula Rani Sarma (Cork Opera House co-production, 2000)

Donal O'Kelly Productions
33 Palmerston Road, Rathmines, Dublin 6, Republic of Ireland
tel: + 353 (0)87 673 4773 **email:** donalokelly@eircom.net **director:** Donal O'Kelly
Donal O'Kelly is a playwright and actor with an international reputation who has performed productions of his own solo plays in Ireland, the UK, Europe, North America and Australia.
recent productions: *Bat The Father Rabbit The Son* by Donal O'Kelly (2003) *The Hand* by Donal O'Kelly (2003)

Down to Earth Theatre Company
Tower 4, Fumbally Court, Fumbally Lane, Dublin 8, Republic of Ireland
tel: + 353 (0)1 416 3672 **email:** monikadte@esatclear.ie
artistic director: Shane O'Doherty **administrator:** Sandra Upton
Down to Earth aims to develop environmental and social awareness through the combination of visual, musical and textual theatre within the community. The company's interests lie in promoting the benefits of theatre as a social and cultural learning process available to the community at large.
recent productions: *The Treasure Hunt* by Joe O'Donnell (2003) *The Round Tuit* by Joe O'Donnell (2001)

The Dublin Theatre Company
2 The High Road, Kilmainham, Dublin 8, Republic of Ireland **tel:** + 353 (0)1 679 4336
directors: Tony Chestermon, Carmel White **artistic director:** Ronan Wilmot
Formed in 1997, the Dublin Theatre Company's artistic policy is to present great Irish and international theatre and drama. The company is resident at Temple Bar's The New Theatre.

Fly by Night Theatre Company
22 Daniel Street, Dublin 8, Republic of Ireland **tel:** + 353 (0)1 453 9110/288 6586
producer: Richard Brennan
Fly by Night commissions and produces new Irish playwriting. The company operates a collective artistic directorship.

Gare St Lazare Players Ireland
c/o Lovetts, Well Road, Cork, Republic of Ireland *and* 10 Vieille Cote, 78270 Mericourt, France.
tel: +33 (0)1 3479 3674/+353 (0)87 742 1917 **fax:** +33 (0)1 3479 3750
email: loverty@ wanadoo.fr **web:** www.garestlazareplayers.com **artistic director:** Judy Hegarty-Lovett
Gare St Lazare Players is an international company based simultaneously in Ireland and France with workshop/rehearsal facilities outside Paris. The company was founded in Chicago by Bob Meyer in 1983 and moved to France in 1988. Judy Hegarty Lovett and Conor Lovett have been running the Irish operation since 1995. The company rehearses either in Cork or in Mericourt, France and tends to tour Ireland and then internationally.
recent productions: *Swallow* by Michael Harding (2003) *Lessness* by Samuel Beckett (2002)

Glass Ceiling Theatreworks

35 Ava Gardens, Belfast BT7 3BW, Co. Antrim, Northern Ireland
tel: + 44 (0)28 9064 6034 **email:** janice_kennedy@belfastinstitute.co.uk
company manager: Janice Kennedy
Non-subsidised, we work on a project to project basis. Our aim is two-fold: to create professional opportunity for actors and artists who are completing training and wish to establish a career in theatre, and to put other creative artforms (dance, music, art) into the arena of theatre to create multi-performance events.

Granary Productions

Granary Theatre, Mardyke, Cork, Republic of Ireland
tel/fax: + 353 (0)21 490 4276 **email:** granary@ucc.ie **web:** www.granary.ie
artistic director: Tony McCleane-Fay **technical manager:** Kath Geraghty
Granary produces and presents new and experimental work by artists across disciplines. The programme combines work in theatre, performance, dance, live art, installation, and music, with a lively critical programme of PERFORUM talks, workshops and artist's presentations.
recent productions: *Again*, text by Craig Baxter and the Bone Ensemble company (co-production with the Bone Ensemble, 2004) *Face to the Wall* by Martin Crimp (2004) *See also Venues.*

Impact Theatre Company

Basement 18, The Crescent, O'Connell Avenue, Limerick, Republic of Ireland
tel: + 353 (0)61 316399 **email:** impacttheatrecompany@eircom.net
artistic director: Patrick Burke
Based at new venue i space, Impact Theatre Company is committed to the development of new talent of theatre artists and practitioners, with particular emphasis on new writing, in Limerick city.
recent productions: *Billy and Budd* by Padraig Meehan (2003) *Effigy* by Brona Titley (2002) *See also Venues.*

Indian Ink Theatre Company

26A Cliftonville Road, Belfast BT14 6JY, Northern Ireland
tel: +44 (0)7703 175790 **fax:** +44 (0)28 9075 1584
email: kinsella1@hotmail.com **web:** www.indianinktheatre.co.uk
artistic director: Julie Kinsella
Indian Ink tours small-scale productions throughout Ireland, aiming to produce accessible, entertaining theatre and to encourage and promote a variety of new work, particularly involving women in the arts.
recent productions: *Secs and the City* by Julie Kinsella (2003) *The Numbers Game* by Julie Kinsella (2000)

Inis Theatre

25 Ardlui Park, Blackrock, Co. Dublin, Republic of Ireland
tel: + 353 (0)86 248 6695/(0)86 387 2391 **email:** info@inistheatre.com **web:** www.inistheatre.com
artistic directors: Iseult Golden, Carmel Stephens **director-in-residence:** David Horan
Inis Theatre focuses primarily on adaptation, specifically on adapting non-theatrical art-forms for the stage. To date, the company has created three original shows inspired, in turn, by poetry, the novel and film genres. To this end, techniques are employed from a variety of theatrical traditions including Commedia d'Ell Arte, Clown and Music Hall.
recent productions: *To Kill a Dead Man* by Kevin McGee (2003) *Lady Susan* by Jane Austen, adapted by the company (2001)

Iomha Ildanach
Crypt Arts Centre, Dublin Castle, Dublin 2, Republic of Ireland
email: info@cryptartscentre.org **web:** www.cryptartscentre.org
artistic director: John O'Brien **executive director:** Niall O Sioradain
Íomhá Ildánach's artistic policy is to create new and original theatre within an Irish cultural context. The company also engages in audience development activities through research and performance in a variety of areas and organises ongoing training and development for its members.
recent productions: *The Lysistrata Project* by Aristophanes (2003) *The Designated Mourner* by Wallace Shawn (2002)

Janus Theatre Company
Railway House, Desert, Enniskeane, Co. Cork, Republic of Ireland
tel: + 353 (0)23 47015 **email:** ianbel@eircom.net
artistic director: Belinda Wild **writer in residence:** Ian Wild
Janus produces original work devised and written by the company with a strong visual and musical focus, as well as imaginative interpretations of theatre classics.
recent productions: *Spaghetti Western* by Janus Theatre Company (2003) *Reds Under The Beds* by Janus Theatre Company (2001)

Knickerbocker Glories
1 Mulroy Road, Cabra, Dublin 7, Republic of Ireland
tel: + 353 (0)1 868 9827/(0)87 210 1333 **email:** fergusw@gofree.indigo.ie
artistic director: Sinead Beary **company manager:** Fergus Walsh
Knickerbocker Glories formed in July 1999, and are committed to promoting theatre for young audiences. Its policy is to produce fun, engaging, thought-provoking theatre for children. The aim is to give children a magical experience of live theatre that will promote a desire to create some magic of their own.
recent productions: *The Little Prince,* adapted from the tale by Antoine de Saint-Exupéry (2000/2001) *There's a Whale on the Clothesline!* by Sinead Beary and Fergus J. Walsh (2002/2003)
See also Spotlight Theatre Company.

La Scène d'Ouessant
formerly known as Hana-Bi Theatre Company
College Gate, Apt 56, Townsend St, Dublin 2, Republic of Ireland
tel: + 353 (0)86 879 5801 **email:** louessant@hotmail.com
artistic director: Laurent Salaùn
Our artistic aim is to bring well-known European playwrights to Dublin who deal with themes such as solitude, racism, homophobia, sex, violence, exclusion, difficulty to express a demand and the impossibility to escape from Desire. The company is an association of artists (Irish, Greek, French) who have been working in Dublin for more than 7 years and who want to express their personal artistic view on the Irish society they are living in.
recent productions: *Water Drops on Burning Rocks* by R.W. Fassbinder (2004) *In the Solitude of Cotton Fields* by B.M. Koltes (2003)

Lambert Puppet Theatre

Clifton Lane, Monkstown, Co. Dublin, Republic of Ireland
tel: + 353 (0)1 280 0974 **fax:** + 353 (0)1 280 4772
email: info@lambertpuppettheatre.com **web:** www.lambertpuppettheatre.com
creative director: Eugene Lambert
The Lambert Puppet Company, established 1972, creates puppet theatre for adults and children. The company's policy is to provide quality puppet entertainment for the whole family. With a repertoire of over 30 productions, the Lambert operates all year round with public and schools performances. *See also Venues and Irish Festivals.*

The Little Sisters of Tragedy

12 Leinster Street East, Dublin 3, Republic of Ireland
tel: + 353 (0)1 855 0843 **email:** mwale@ireland.com
artistic co-ordinator: Mark Wale
The Little Sisters of Tragedy are physical comedians with conscience. The company handcrafts new shows that re-invent clowning and commedia traditions. The Little Sisters of Tragedy utilise boundless visual and vocal ingenuity rooted in the performer/audience relationship.
recent productions: *Bad Sunday* by Mark Wale (2002) *Leave It To Me* devised by the company (1998)

Locus Theatre Company

Basement 6, Haigh Terrace Dun Laoghaire Co Dublin
tel: +353 (0)1 284 4804/(0)87 750 2597
email: carriemac2003@yahoo.com **web:** www.summersiti.org
artistic director: Caroline McSweeney **producer:** Lisa Fitzpatrick
Locus Theatre Company is committed to the creation of new work. Its primary focus is on creating work through the ensemble process. Narrative is sourced from the actor and performed in innovative visual theatrical forms.
recent productions: *Action,* devised (2003) *Faces For Places,* devised (1997)

Medaza Productions

54 St Kevin's Square, Cork, Republic of Ireland
tel: + 353 (0)87 971 1573 **email:** medazzatheatre@hotmail.com
artistic directors: Padraig Trehy, Jon Whitty **administrator:** Susan Burke
Medaza is dedicated to producing creative, entertaining and original work, plays and films which will dramatically challenge and examine contemporary society and artistic practice.
recent productions: *Play the Piano Drunk* by Jon Whitty (Granary co-production, 2002) *Twinkletoes* by Jennifer Johnston (2001)

Mentl Productions

10 Norwood Court, Rochestown Road, Cork, Republic of Ireland
tel: + 353 (0)86 833 7840 **fax:** + 353 (0)21 427 0670
email: mentlproductions@hotmail.com **web:** www.mentlproductions.com
artistic director: Edward Coughlan **executive producer:** Siofra Hegarty
Mentl's artistic policy is to create work that challenges actors, directors and audiences.
recent productions: *Homefront* by Ciaran Creagh (Eclipse Productions co-production, 2003) *Schizo* by Edward Coughlan (2001)

MorWax Productions
57 Windfield Gardens, Clybaun Road, Galway, Republic of Ireland
tel: + 353 (0)91 523469 **email:** pdeburca@hotmail.com
artistic director: Peadar De Burca **producer/stage manager:** Monika Radlak
Founded in 2001, MórWax productions cover the whole spectrum of theatre: shows for children, students, adults, traditional theatre, experimental and original.
recent productions: *The Plough and the Stars* by Sean O'Casey (2003) *Psycho* adapted from Hitchcock's film by Peadar de Burca (2003)

nervousystem
40 Kenilworth Park, Harold's Cross, Dublin 6W, Republic of Ireland
tel: +353 (0)86 369 5295 **email:** nervousystem@ziplip.com
artistic director: Aiden Condron **producer/company writer:** Jeffrey Gormly
nervousystem was born out of a series of fora held in 2001 at the Crypt Arts Centre, Dublin Castle. The resulting theatre collective works on a full-time basis in the field of performance research and development, placing the actor at the centre of the dramatic experience and focussing primarily on the relationship between actors and audience.
recent productions: *Fireface: The Cuchulainn Plays* by W.B. Yeats (2004)

Noggin Theatre Company
Skerry Cross, Dromone, Oldcastle, Co. Meath, Republic of Ireland
tel: + 353 (0)44 66550 **email:** aliceb@esatclear.ie
artistic director: Alice Barry **company director:** Steve Neale
Formed in 2000, Noggin Theatre Company's artistic policy is to explore motivating themes through new writing and to make theatre entertaining, available and accessible to a wider community, including rural areas and young people.
recent productions: *Rum and Raisin* by Alice Barry and Deirdre Kinahan (2003) *Summer Fruits* by Deirdre Kinahan (2003)

North Face Theatre Company
19 Princess Park, Whitehead, Carrickfergus, Co. Antrim BT38 9QY, Northern Ireland
tel: + 44 (0)28 9335 3075 **fax:** + 44 (0)28 9335 3075
email: mail@northfacetheatre.com **web:** www.northfacetheatre.com
artistic director: Sean Caffrey
North Face Theatre Company's artistic policy is to present new writing and other plays that span the gulf between the two communities in Northern Ireland. The company also aims to encourage new audiences for theatre and to tour throughout Ireland, North and South.
recent productions: *Deceptive Imperfections* by Gary Mitchell (2003) *Lonely Baby* by Sean Caffrey (2003)

Openmind Theatre Company
Coláiste an Chraoibhin, Fermoy, Co. Cork, Republic of Ireland
tel: + 353 (0)25 31633 **fax:** + 353 (0)25 32748 **email:** omorrison@c-chraoibhin.ie
artistic contact: Geraldine Canning **administration:** Olive Morrison
Openmind Theatre Company was formed from a Post Leaving Certificate NCVA Performing Arts Course. The company is particularly interested in working with students through performance and touring abroad.
recent productions: *Red Riding Hood* (2001) *The Playboy of the Western World* (2000)

The Performance Corporation
111 Rail Park, Maynooth, Co. Kildare, Republic of Ireland
tel: + 353 (0)1 628 6319 **email:** performancecorporation@europe.com
artistic director: Jo Mangan **associate writer:** Tom Swift
The Performance Corporation was founded in 2002 with a view to creating live performances that are truly cross-artform, interactive and enjoyable! Audience is key, and the company aims to work with a core creative group of performers and designers to engage and entertain audiences whilst provoking and challenging them at the same time.
recent productions: *The Butterfly Ranch* by Tom Swift (2004) *The 7 Deadly Sins* by Tom Swift and Jo Mangan (2003)

Playgroup
2 Laurel Villas, Mardyke, Cork, Republic of Ireland
tel: +353 (0)87 633 3015 **email:** playgrouptheatre@hotmail.com
artistic directors: Tom Creed, Hilary O'Shaughnessy
Playgroup are committed to producing high-quality contemporary theatre which is challenging, often provocative, but always entertaining. Our main interests lie in new Irish writing, devised work, and major contemporary international plays in translation.
recent productions: *Crave* by Sarah Kane (Granary co-production, 2003) *Soap!* by Lynda Radley and Ciaran Fitzpatrick (2003)

Plush Theatre Productions
1 Northumberland Court, Haddington Road, Ballsbridge, Dublin 4, Republic of Ireland
tel: + 353 (0)1 667 7961/ (0)86 8484448 **fax:** + 353 (0)1 667 7961
email: plushtp@eircom.net
company directors: Gabrielle Breathnach, Jean O'Dwyer
Plush Theatre Productions was established in 1997 with the aim of producing high quality productions focussing on women's roles.
recent productions: *Who's Afraid of Virginia Woolf?* by Edward Albee (2002) *Abigail's Party* by Mike Leigh (1999)

Poc Productions
32 Manor Court, Knocnacarra, Co. Galway, Republic of Ireland
email: pocteo@eircom.net
company members: Paul Brennan, Diarmuid de Faoite
POC productions was formed in 2001 to produce the multi award winning show, Pádraic Ó Conaire. Since 2001, the company has been evolving a new methodology, combined with a holistic approach to the individual, the theatre and our own cultural heritage, to produce new works in Irish and English that ring true to our evolving human and national psyche.
recent productions: *Herman* by Paul Brennan, translated by Michael O Conghaile and Gabriel Rosenstock (2004) *Paris, Texas* by Diarmuid de Faoite, adapted from Wim Wenders' film (2003)

Púca Puppets
77 The Village, Raheny, Dublin 5, Republic of Ireland
tel/fax: + 353 (0)1 832 9594 **email:** pucapuppets@eircom.net **artistic director:** Niamh Lawlor
Púca Puppets specialises in puppet theatre for both adults and children. Drawing from theatre and visual art disciplines and informed by research or community art practice, the work is usually devised through a collaborative process.
recent productions: *A Puppet Passion* by Niamh Lawlor (2003) *Peg! Peig!* devised by Niamh Lawlor, Helene Hugel and Margot Jones, (Temple Bar Properties co-production, 2001)

PurpleHeart Theatre Company
56 Lynnwood, Dundrum, Dublin 14, Republic of Ireland
tel: + 353 (0)87 248 7177/(0)87 677 8530 **email:** purpleheart_theatrecompany@oceanfree.net
artistic director: Stuart Roche **executive producer:** Alan King
PurpleHeart is committed to presenting acclaimed plays from international writers to an Irish audience. These texts aim to provoke, embrace, reflect, and articulate the interests and needs of a contemporary audience. The company has revived its productions for touring through Ireland North and South since its inception in 1999.
recent productions: *Coyote on a Fence* by Bruce Graham (2003) *rundown* by Mark O'Rowe (2003)

Queen of Sheba Productions
56 Fitzwilliam Square, Dublin 2, Republic of Ireland
tel: + 353 (0)1 662 2594 **fax:** + 353 (0)1 676 2310
director: Eithne McGuinness
Queen of Sheba's artistic policy is to produce plays that engage an audience on an emotional and political level.
recent productions: *Typhoid Mary* by Eithne McGuinness (1997, revived 2004). *Limbo* by Eithne McGuinness (2001)

Ransom Productions
15 Church Street, Belfast BT1 1PG, Co. Antrim, Northern Ireland
tel: +44 (0)28 9096 4320 **email:** info@ransomproductions.co.uk **web:** www.ransomproductions.co.uk
artistic director: Rachel O'Riordan **writer in residence:** Richard Dormer
Ransom Productions was formed in 2002 by Rachel O'Riordan and Richard Dormer. The company aims to produce new writing in a physical, dynamic and highly skilled format. Ransom's next production is Protestants by Robert Welch, also to be directed by Rachel O'Riordan and performed by Richard Dormer. It will premiere in the Cathedral Quarter Arts Festival, Belfast, October 2004.
recent productions: *Hurricane* by Richard Dormer (2002)

Rattlebag Theatre Company
21 Lower Beechwood Avenue, Ranelagh, Dublin 6, Republic of Ireland
email: rattlebagtheatre@eircom.net
artistic director: Joe Devlin
Rattlebag Theatre Company was founded by Joe Devlin in 1990 to produce small-scale international work. By the late 1990s, the company had expanded into classical theatre, new writing and has developed a policy for experimentation and exploration of a broader theatrical vocabulary to encompass physical, visual and music theatre.
recent productions: *Measure for Measure* by William Shakespeare (2002) *Irish Men 2* devised by Joe Devlin and company (2002)

The Read Company
30-31 Wicklow Street, Dublin 2, Republic of Ireland **tel/fax:** + 353 (0)1 672 6130
email: admin@readco.ie **web:** www.readco.ie
artistic directors: Tara Derrington, Michelle Read
READCO aims to encourage the exploratory journey of the playwright and the director, harness the spontaneous impulse of the actor and enhance the audience's experience of theatre as a live medium.
recent productions: *The Other Side* by Michelle Read (2003) *Living Space* by Improvisation (2001)

Red Moon Theatre

Theatre Workshop Ireland, Yoletown Studios, Killinick, Co. Wexford, Republic of Ireland
tel: + 353 (0)53 35014/(0)86 086 1449 **email:** theatreworkshopireland@oceanfree.net
directors: Michael Way, Irene Wright
Red Moon is an independent professional theatre-in-education company touring educational drama, TIE and classes, workshops and projects in art and drama to schools and community centres. The company also organises community theatre projects and facilitates in-service programmes for teachers.
recent productions: *An t-Oilean* (2001/2002) *The Great Windfall* (2001/2002)

Red Rua Theatre Company

c/o Teach Mhuire, Tivoli Terrace North, Dun Laoghaire, Co. Dublin, Republic of Ireland
tel: + 353 (0)86 2468028/(0)86 6071759 **fax:** + 353 (0)1 286 9607 **email:** redruatheatre@hotmail.com
artistic director: Mary Kelly-Borgatta
This Wicklow-based theatre company develops new work, often site-specific to the county, as well as conducting extensive, innovative exploration of classical texts. The company also acts as a springboard for young writers, actors, designers and technicians.
recent productions: *Heartbreak House* by George Bernard Shaw (2003) *You and Whose Army* by Margaret Cohen and Judy Russell (2003)

Riff Raff Theatre

Theatre Workshop, Yoletown Studios, Killinick, Co. Wexford, Republic of Ireland
tel: + 353 (0)53 35014/(0)86 086 1449 **email:** theatreworkshopireland@oceanfree.net
directors: Michael Way, Irene Wright
Riff Raff Theatre is an independent professional fringe theatre, touring throughout Ireland, North and South, and overseas. The company produces dynamic and cinematic, ensemble-based theatre art.
recent productions: *Burning History* (2001/2002) *me.com* (2001/2002)

Riverrun Theatre Company

Thomond, Mitchelsfort, Watergrasshill, Co. Cork, Republic of Ireland
tel: + 353 (0)21 488 9238/(0)87 238 2891 **email:** riverrun1@eircom.net
artistic director: Michael McCarthy
Riverrun Theatre Company aims to produce high quality international classic plays, including Tennessee Williams' *A Streetcar Named Desire* and Peter Shaeffer's *The Royal Hunt of the Sun*.
recent productions: *A Tale of Ansty and the Tailor*, adapted by Michael McCarthy (2003) *Dancing for Men/Bitch Goddess*, double bill by Mark Safranko (2002)

The Road Show Theater

Lucas House, Ballindooley, Galway, Republic of Ireland
tel: + 353 (0)87 130 0776 **email:** info@roadshowtheater.com **web:** www.roadshowtheater.com
director: Jessamyn Fiore
Founded in January 2003, The Road Show Theater is a group of American, Irish and English theatre artists committed to performing new work that combines powerful drama with original live music.
recent productions: *Keep* by Meghan Kennedy (2004) *The Mysterious World of Birds* by Jessamyn Fiore (2003)

rondo theatre company
11 Sperrin Road, Dublin 12, Republic of Ireland
tel: + 353 (0)1 456 1190/(0)86 262 3035 **email:** soobootoo@hotmail.com
artistic advisor: Sue Mythen
Founded in 1997, rondo aims to produce new work with a strong emphasis on a dynamic physicality.
recent productions: *Stone Ghosts* by Sue Mythen (2001) *Eleven Fifty Eight* by Rowan Tully (1997)

Semper Fi
Unit 18B Goldenbridge Industrial Estate, Inchicore, Dublin 8, Republic of Ireland
email: wpaul@gofree.indigo.ie **artistic director:** Karl Shiels **producer:** Paschal Friel
Formed in November 1999, our purpose is to create significant and hopefully profound theatre
out of unexpected tales, dangerous texts, within site-specific locations. By moving the safety
net of established parameters, Semper Fi aims to make theatre bold, at times spontaneous and
fun, at others dark and disturbing.
recent productions: *Slaughter* by Heiner Muller (2003) *Ladies and Gents* by Paul Walker (2002)

Shadowbox Theatre Company
88 Clover Hill, Bray, Co. Wicklow, Republic of Ireland
tel/fax: +353 (0)1 276 5091 **email:** shadowbox-theatre@oceanfree.net
artistic directors: Frieda Hand, Gemma Gallagher
Shadowbox was formed in 1998 when it recognised the need for high quality professional arts work
for people who have little access to mainstream arts activity in Ireland. The company has developed
a core group of actors with intellectual disability who create pieces of theatre for performance.
recent productions: *MAZE* devised by the company (2004) *BAOBABS* devised by the company (2002)

Shake the Speare Theatre Company
The Fit Up, Morette, Emo, Portlaoise, Co. Laois, Republic of Ireland
tel: + 353 (0)87 821 0560 **email:** cabrini@eircom.net **web:** www.shakethespeare.com
artistic director: Cabrini Cahill
Shake the Speare is a young, vibrant theatre company committed to theatre work of
physicality, music and poetry. The company is resident at The Fit Up, its own purpose-built
rehearsal space, where collaboration and training are at the core of their work.
recent productions: *Sleeping a Love Song* by Michael Harding (2002) *Bog Dances* by Michael
Harding (2000)

Sidetrack Theatre Company
19 Erris Road, Cabra, Dublin 7, Republic of Ireland **tel:** + 353 (0)87 271 1346
artistic director: Sinead Culbert **administration:** Gary Egan
Sidetrack is committed to performing works by playwrights seldom seen on the Irish stage,
especially British and American authors such as Mike Leigh, Joe Orton and Tennessee Williams.

Siren Productions

171 The George, Charlotte Quay Dock, Ringsend Road, Dublin 4, Republic of Ireland
tel: + 353 (0)1 667 6630 **email:** sacartmell@aol.com
artistic director: Selina Cartmell
Siren Productions aims to find new definitions of theatre through taking rarely performed plays, new writing, devised and classic work into unexpected performance spaces. Siren Productions aims to become a home for nurturing new talent and working with established artists, exploring relationships between combined art forms, welcoming a diverse field of creative partnership.
recent productions: *La Musica* by Marguerite Duras (2003) *Fando & Lis* by Fernando Arrabal (2003)

Skehana

110a Liosmór, Cappagh Road, Gaillimh, Republic of Ireland
tel: + 353 (0)91 592700 **fax:** + 353 (0)91 592723 **email:** marymcp@eircom.net
producer: Mary McPartlan
Skehana was established in 1991, initially to produce Mysogynist, written by playwright Michael Harding, and featuring Tom Hickey in a solo performance. It continues to develop relationships with established writers and actors, allowing them to work in an open and collaborative environment where new writing can be explored and existing texts can be revisited and revitalised. Skehana's touring policy is to use only one or two actors in streamlined productions that can travel to small centres and unusual venues such as community halls, cafes, canteens, halting sites, prisons, wherever we can.
recent productions: *On The Way Out* by Tom MacIntyre (2002) *The Gallant John-Joe* by Michael Harding (2000)

Smashing Times Theatre Company

Coleraine House, Coleraine Street, Dublin 7, Republic of Ireland
tel: + 353 (0)1 865 6613 **fax:** + 353 (0)1 873 5283
email: smashingtimes@eircom.net **web:** www.smashingtimes.ie
artistic director: Mary Moynihan **company manager:** Freda Manweiler
Smashing Times has fostered its own process of creativity to engage with local audiences, bringing real meaning to the term 'access', using professional and community theatre practices to support voices struggling to be heard. The company creates original performances to explore a range of social and political themes relevant to people's lives and to encourage cross-border and cross-community communication.
recent productions: *May Our Faces Haunt You* by Mary Moynihan (2003) *A Journey through the Markets* by Paul Kennedy (2003)

Sneaky Productions

2 Baroda Parade, Belfast BT7 3AD, Co. Antrim, Northern Ireland **tel:** + 44 (0)28 9022 0785
email: info@sneakyproductions.com **web:** www.sneakyproductions.com
artistic director: Jonathan Harden **production manager:** Ellie Botwood
Our aim is to produce work that is not bound by genre, to create theatre that excites our audiences, and attracts first-time theatre-goers to both conventional and extraordinary performance spaces. In doing this, we aspire to offer experience and support to a new generation of actors, writers, composers, musicians, directors and technical staff, encouraging them to further their craft within Northern Ireland, while at the same time providing opportunities to work outside the province, showcasing its rich artistic talent.
recent productions: *The Young Man with the Cream Tarts* by Declan Feenam and Lisa McGee (2004) *Jump!* by Lisa McGee (2003)

Sole Purpose Productions
The Playhouse, Artillery Street, Derry BT48 6RG, Northern Ireland
tel/ fax: + 44 (0)28 7127 9918 **email:** solepurpose@mac.com
artistic directors: Patricia Byrne, Dave Duggan
Sole Purpose Productions uses the discourse of theatre and imagination to investigate social and public issues. The company produces new work for theatre and non-theatre venues, performing locally, nationally and internationally.
recent productions: *Don't Say A Word* by Patricia Byrne (2004) *The Recruiting Office* by Dave Duggan (2004)

Spanner in the Works Theatre Company
56 Divis Drive, Glen Road, Belfast BT11 8AA, Co. Antrim, Northern Ireland
tel/fax: + 44 (0)28 9061 2106 **email:** patricia.downey@talk21.com
artistic director: Patricia Downey
Spanner in the Works is an all-female theatre company that works with both rural and urban sides of society. They also aim to address social concerns through the medium of drama and the arts. The company tours its own devised pieces around Ireland.
recent productions: *Nature or Nurture,* devised by the company (2004)

Spike Productions
1 Chester Road, Ranelagh, Dublin 6, Republic of Ireland
tel: + 353 (0)1 496 7465 **fax:** + 353 (0)1 491 3105 **email:** spikep@eircom.net
artistic director: Alan Kinsella **secretary:** Katherine Murphy
Spike Productions' artistic policy is to produce new or innovative theatrical pieces. The company also facilitates foreign companies to produce theatre in Ireland.
recent productions: *Decadence* by Stephen Berkoff (2004) *Creatures* by Alex Bonstein and Lee Maddeford (2000)

Spotlight Theatre
1 Mulroy Road, Cabra, Dublin 7, Republic of Ireland
tel: + 353 (0)1 868 9827/(0)87 210 1333 **email:** fergusw@gofree.indigo.ie
artistic director: Sinead Beary **company manager:** Fergus Walsh
Spotlight Theatre was formed in 1997 and aims to serve as a platform for emerging new talent by encouraging the development of skills relating to all aspects of the theatrical process, including writing, performance, direction and production.
recent productions: *It Just Came Out* by Christian O'Reilly (2001) *Oleanna* by David Mamet (2001)
See also Knickerbocker Glories Theatre Company.

The Stomach Box Theatre
11 Aubrey Park, Shankill, Co. Dublin **email:** thestomachbox@hotmail.com
directors: Dylan Tighe, Seán Og, Phil MacMahon
The Stomach Box fuses live-art and performance to produce theatre where the visual is paramount. We believe all art forms can be used to create a distinctly theatrical experience.
recent productions: *Amnon and Tamar* (2 Samuel 13:01), devised by the company (2003)

Tall Tales Theatre Company

Unit 1, Guinness Enterprise Centre, Taylor's Lane, Dublin 8, Republic of Ireland
tel: + 353 (0)1 410 0801 **fax:** + 353 (0)1 410 0987 **email:** talltales@oceanfree.net
artistic director: Deirdre Kinahan **company manager:** Eileen Sheridan
The Tall Tales programme of theatre focusses on new female writing, devised works and
contemporary drama, often touring their productions nationally.
recent productions: *Rum and Raisin* by Alice Barry and Deirdre Kinahan (2003) *Saint Oscar* by
Terry Eagleton (2003)

Teatro Punto

92 Cnoc an Oir, Letteragh, Galway, Republic of Ireland
tel: +353 (0)91 860727/(0)86 816 4201 **email:** info@teatropunto.com
manager: Pat McElligott **actor/director:** Carlos Garcia Estevez
Teatro Punto was created in Paris in 1998 by practitioners from Italy, England, Ireland,
Switzerland, France and Spain. Our work is a fusion of all cultures in the company. Influences
range from mediaeval minstrelsy and jesting through Commedia dell'Arte to modern clowning.
Audience contact is also critical to our style of theatre,.
recent productions: *Don't Sleep!!!* by Teatro Punto (2003/2004) *It's Too Arty...* by Teatro Punto (2003)

Thinking Image

The Rock, Kinsale, Co. Cork, Republic of Ireland
tel: 353 (0)86 401 8304 **email:** calduggan@yahoo.com
director: Cal Duggan
Thinking Image is dedicated to the integrity of the written word made visible.
recent productions: *The Yellow Wallpaper* by Charlotte Perkins Gilman, adapted by Cal Duggan (2004)

Two Chairs Company

21 Bridgewater Quay, Islandbridge, Dublin 8, Republic of Ireland
tel: + 353 (0)1 679 1120 **email:** twochairs@eircom.net
directors: Nuala Hayes, Ellen Cranitch
Two Chairs Company was founded to explore words and music in a variety of settings, with minimal
use of set and lighting design. They have developed a style of music and storytelling performance
which appeals to all ages, and have performed at festivals throughout Ireland and overseas in
theatrical and non-theatrical venues.
recent productions: *The Confessions, the Truth and the Lies of an Old Reprobate* by Joe O'Neill,
adapted by Nuala Hayes (2003) *Scéalta Shamhna* (2000)

Tyger Theatre Company

c/o Galway Arts Centre, Dominick Street, Galway.
tel: +353 (0)87 291 9852/(0)86 881 1095 **email:** TYGERGalway@hotmail.com
directors: Jessica Curtis, Aideen O'Donnell
Tyger was founded in 2001 by a group of individuals who were involved in Galway Youth Theatre's performance and production courses. We felt that as a group we had the necessary skills to mount our own original productions alongside the work we were doing at GYT. Our primary aim is to introduce new and original work to Galway's theatre-going public. We have adapted one film, written and developed three of our own productions and staged new and original work by two established playwrights thus far.
recent productions: *Frozen* by Bryony Lavery (2004) *Wait A While* by Christian O'Reilly (2004)

Wallfly Productions

51 Bellevue Road, Glenageary, Co. Dublin, Republic of Ireland
tel/fax: + 353 (0)1 285 1021 **email:** wallfly2000@hotmail.com
artistic director: Tom O'Leary **producer:** Donna Eperon
Wallfly Theatre Company was set up with the intention of producing intimate and exciting theatre. Its emphasis is centred on strong dramatic characters and their profound effect on each other.
recent productions: *Consenting Adults* by Dermot Bolger (2002) *Toyer* by Gardnar McKay (1999)

Yeats Theatre Company

14 Lord Edward Street, Sligo, Republic of Ireland
tel/fax: + 353 (0)71 914 6622 **email:** eddiehenry@eircom.net
directors: Edmund Henry, Walter McDonagh **administrator:** Lillian O'Hara
Yeats Theatre Company performs the plays of W.B. Yeats and related productions integrating traditional music, poetry and song.
recent productions: *Thirst* by Flann O'Brien (2003) *The Pot of Broth* (2003)

CCAT @ABERYSTWYTH ARTS CENTRE AND TEMPLE BAR
CULTURAL CO-OPERATION AND TOURING

FINANCIAL AND PRACTICAL SUPPORT FOR TOURING SHOWS OR EXHIBITIONS IN THE INTERREG REGION OF WALES.

CCAT WELCOMES APPLICATIONS IN ALL ARTFORMS.

ONGOING 'GO SEE' AWARDS ARE ALSO AVAILABLE TO DEVELOP RELATIONSHIPS WITH WELSH PRACTITIONERS OR ORGANISATIONS.

MORE INFORMATION: WWW.CCAT.IE
EMAIL: CCAT@TEMPLEBAR.IE TEL: +353 1 677 2255

CCAT @ ABERYSTWYTH ARTS CENTRE AND TEMPLE BAR
IS PART-FUNDED BY IRELAND WALES INTERREG PROGRAMME

Rebecca Walter in Catapult Dance's production of XYZ
by Rebecca Walters © Fionn McCann

Catapult Dance

8 Lisburn Street, Dublin 7, Republic of Ireland
tel: +353 (0)86 375 0260 **email:** rebewalt@yahoo.com
artistic director: Rebecca Walter
Catapult Dance Company was founded in March 2001 by artistic director Rebecca Walter.
The company has premiered seven new works to date, performing in usual and unusual venues
throughout Ireland. The company has also drawn cross artform audiences through collaboration
with Dublin-based bands and composers including Double Adaptor, Hugh O'Neill and Justin
Carroll. Catapult has toured extensively in Ireland.
recent productions: *Home Disco* by Rebecca Walter (2003) *Please put your wild finger away* by
Rebecca Walter (2003)

Echo Echo Dance Theatre Company

The Playhouse, 5-7 Artillery Street, Derry BT48 6RG, Northern Ireland
tel/fax: + 44 (0)28 7126 2162 **email:** info@echoechodance.com
artistic directors: Steve Batts, Ursula Laeubli
Based in Derry, Echo Echo Dance Theatre Company is the only full-time independent professional
dance company in Northern Ireland. In existence since 1991, it was first established in Holland
by artistic directors Ursula Laeubli and Steve Batts, who performed, taught and directed all over
Europe, before relocating to the North in 1997. Echo Echo exists to produce professional dance-
theatre productions and to promote interest in and participation in dance and movement at all
levels, basing its practice on a wide interest in movement influences from outside the main
dance traditions as well as within.
recent productions: *Under Observation* by Ursula Laeubli (2003) *Tenderised* by Steve Batts (2003)

Flock Dance Company

Claddagh House, Killeenaran, Kilcolgan, Co. Galway, Republic of Ireland
tel: + 353 (0)91 796902 **email:** carolang@aol.com **web:** www.flockdance.org
director: Jim Rooney **artistic director:** Carol Langstaff
It is the aim of Flock Dance Company to inspire people through evocative yet accessible dance with
a dance company of professional and semi-professional dancers drawn primarily from the community
and which presents original works which are professionally presented to the highest standards.
recent productions: *Go! Move! Shift!* by Carol Langstaff (2004) *Joy!* by Carol Langstaff (2003)

half/angel

20 Plunkett Chambers, 21-23 Oliver Plunkett Street, Cork, Republic of Ireland
tel: + 353 (0)21 490 5650 **fax:** + 353 (0)21 490 5650 **email:** jools@halfangel.ie **web:** www.halfangel.ie
artistic directors: Jools Gilson-Ellis, Richard Povall
half/angel is a performance production company based in Cork, formed in 1995 by Jools
Gilson-Ellis and Richard Povall. half/angel has developed a distinctive body of work,
characterised by a poetic use of old, new and emerging technologies, with platforms including
CD-ROM, installation and performance.
recent productions: *Spinstren* by Jools Gilson-Ellis and Richard Povall (2002) *The Secret Project*
by Jools Gilson-Ellis and Richard Povall (1999)

New Balance Dance Company

23 Goatstown Road, Dublin 14, Republic of Ireland
tel: + 353 (0)1 660 5765 **email:** ennebrow@hotmail.com
artistic director: Adrienne Brown
New Balance is a contemporary dance company that produces original works of dance, working with composers, poets, dancers and actors. The company favours long-term collaborative partnerships with an emphasis on research and exploration leading to external performance.
recent productions: *Voices* by Adrienne Brown (2002) *Colmcille* (in association with the Institute for Choreography and Dance, 2000)

Rebus

Granary Theatre, The Mardyke, Cork, Republic of Ireland
tel/fax: 021 490 4272 **email:** info@granary.ie **web:** www.granary.ie (under 'projects')
artistic director: Cindy Cummings
A Cork-based performance/research group, supported by the Granary Theatre, who practise dance improvisation in live perfomance under the direction of Cindy Cummings. Current members are Maggie Harvey, Nick Bryson, Chloe de Buyl and Cindy Cummings, Tom Creed and Tony McCleane-Fay.
recent productions: *oneyearon* devised by the company (2004) *Rebus....adventures in new dance performance*, devised by the company (2003)

This Torsion Dance Theatre

3 Clonsilla Park, Dublin 15, Republic of Ireland
tel: +353 (0)87 637 0567 / +44 (0)7940 676571 **email:** niamhtir_na_nog@hotmail.com
artistic director: Niamh Condron
This Torsion Dance Theatre was set up in 2001 with a desire to explore and expand on movement and performance possibilities. The interest in performance lies in the belief that the aesthetic journey can shed light on certain truths about the human condition and that no other pre-existent language can express what the individual mover expresses. With the ideology that the body speaks with a loud honesty, This Torsion has created a number of short works for various platforms and festivals.
recent productions: *WhiteWASH* by Niamh Condron (2003) *2b* by Niamh Condron (2003)

Co-Opera

5 Abbey Road, Athenry, Co. Galway, Republic of Ireland
tel: + 353 (0)87 641 4762 **email:** michaelbhunt@eircom.net
artistic director: Michael Hunt
Co-Opera tours opera productions nationally and internationally, aiming to make the artform as accessible and widely available as possible. Most of our productions are drawn from the mainstream operatic repertoire. We have been in existence since 1998, touring fully staged productions of opera in small-scale musical versions to all areas of Ireland. International touring includes Carmen (Corby, UK) and Madama Butterfly (Faroe Islands International Festival).
recent productions: *Cosi Fan Tutte* by Mozart (2003) *Tonight, Lola Blau* by Kreisler (2003)

PJT INSURANCE SERVICES LTD

17 Main Street, Swords, Co. Dublin, Ireland

Specialist Insurance Brokers to Irish Theatre

Theatres and Venues
Arts Centres
Touring Theatre Companies
Youth Drama

If you need an insurance quotation speak to the experts.

Contact Peter Thomas or Claire Dumbrell for Theatres, venues and arts centres
Contact Emma O'Sullivan for touring theatre companies, youth drama and
amateur drama societies

Phone: (353) 1 840 1254 **Fax:** (353) 1 813 1070 **Email:** info@pjtins.ie

Irish Brokers Association Member
PJT Insurance Services Ltd is a multi-agency intermediary regulated by
The Irish Financial Services Regulatory Authority

street theatre / circus companies

Spraoi's production of Jonah, 2003

The Beat Initiative

9-11 Ballymacarrett Road, Belfast BT4 1BT, Co. Antrim, Northern Ireland
tel: + 44 (0)28 9046 0863 **fax:** + 44 (0)28 9046 0865
email: info@belfastcarnival.org **web:** www.belfastcarnival.org
director: David Boyd **performance director:** Christina Nelson
The Beat Initiative is a carnival arts company, providing training, community workshops,
performances and events. The company is known for working with large numbers of participants to
create large-scale outdoor events such as the Belfast Carnival. Stage performances have included
Our Town (Millennium Dome, 2000) with 240 young people. Beatstyle is the Beat Initiative's own
young people's performance group. They have produced carnival-based performances in most of
Belfast's large venues and worked in collaboration with groups from Carlingford to Cork.

Belfast Circus School

23-25 Gordon Street, Belfast BT1 2LG, Co. Antrim, Northern Ireland
tel: + 44 (0)28 9023 6007 **fax:** + 44 (0)28 9023 6007 **email:** carol@belfastcircus.org
director: Will Chamberlain **administrator:** Carol Napier
The Belfast Circus School features a wide range of circus performers providing colourful
walkabout and mind-boggling shows.

Buí Bolg

Whitemill Industrial Estate, Wexford, Republic of Ireland
tel: + 353 (0)53 23183 **fax:** + 353 (0)53 24984 **email:** buibolg@iol.ie **web:** www.buibolg.com
artistic director: Colm Lowney **sales and marketing:** Stephanie Hayes
Buí Bolg is now in its 11th year servicing the Irish festival industry. The company employs ten
full-time staff, working in design, construction, costume and administration. Innovation,
inspiration and determination have been the driving force behind Buí Bolg's success, enabling
them to prove extremely popular with both festival organisers and audiences alike. New designs
are added to their extensive selection of puppets, costumes and floats each year offering a greater
choice to clients. The company provide a wide range of services including community parades/
workshops, walkabouts, floats, installations and commissions. Buí Bolg has successfully branched
into the corporate market in recent years; however, their core activities remain festival-based.

Inishowen Carnival Group

4 Bridge St. Cafe, Bridge Street, Carndonagh, Co. Donegal, Republic of Ireland
tel: + 353 (0)74 937 3375 **fax:** + 353 (0)74 937 3374
email: inishowencarnivalgroup@hotmail.com **web:** www.carndonagh.com/carnival
designer: Mark Hill **co-ordinator:** Kevin O'Neill
The Inishowen Carnival Group seeks to provide access to community arts to as wide a range of
people as possible, and maintain quality in performance, design and creation.

Macnas

Black Box, Dyke Road, Galway, Republic of Ireland
tel: + 353 (0)91 561462 **fax:** + 353 (0)91 563905
email: admin@macnas.com **web:** www.macnas.com
performance director: Judith Higgins **general manager:** John Ashton
Macnas brings together a blend of imagination, passion, wit and self-confidence in a variety of settings: in theatres; on streets; in communities; in schools and in non-traditional performance spaces. Macnas is a performance company with a community arts ethos and the underlying belief that the creative experience is open to everyone and that artistic activities should not be elitist. The company is committed to developing its own highly visual style in traditional and non-traditional venues, indoors and outdoors, at home and overseas.
recent productions: *The Mysteries,* adapted by Mikel Murfi and Richard Hayhow, with text by Vincent Woods (2003) *Gráinne Mhaol,* adapted by Kathi Leahy and Patricia Forde (2002)
See also Subsidised Drama Companies.

Spraoi

The Studios, Carrickpherish, Waterford, Republic of Ireland
tel: + 353 (0)51 841808 **fax:** + 353 (0)51 858023 **email:** info@spraoi.com **web:** www.spraoi.com
director: T.V. Honan **artistic directors:** Dermot Quinn, Mike Leahy
Spraoi is a festival and production company, and the company bring their vast experience of street theatre and spectacle to bear on their large-scale indoor and outdoor productions. It is a full-time festival and production company, employing seven full-time, and many more on a contract basis throughout the year. To celebrate its 10th birthday in 2002, the company embarked on its most ambitious project to date – the construction of its own purpose-built studios. In January 2003, Spraoi moved into its new base, the first building in Ireland dedicated solely to the development of street arts.
recent productions: *Siege,* St Patrick's Day parade, Dublin (2004) *Jonah,* Spraoi Studios, Waterford (2003) *See also Irish Festivals.*

The Umbrella Project

Unit 2, Enterprise Centre, Childers Road, Limerick, Republic of Ireland
tel: + 353 (0)61 317220 **fax:** + 353 (0)61 317223
email: umbrellaproject@eircom.net **web:** www.umbrellaproject.ie
artistic director: Jim Woodlock
The Umbrella Project is the premier street theatre company in the Mid-West region. The company exists to provide entertainment and participation in street pagents as well as fostering a strong community involvement in the arts.

*Morna Regan and Dessie Gallagher in An Grianán's production of
Dancing at Lughnasa by Brian Friel © Declan Doherty*

Amharclann na Carraige/ Theatre on the Rock

B.I.F.H.E. Whiterock Road
Belfast BT12 7PH, Northern Ireland
tel: + 44 (0) 28 9020 2222
fax: + 44 (0) 28 9020 2223
email: maura@dubbeljoint.com
web: www.dubbeljoint.com
co-ordinator: Maura Brown
programming policy: Amharclann na Carraige is home to Dubbeljoint and JustUs Theatre Company but is also available to other companies on request.
terms: Rental
seats: 200-400
stage type: Flexible
stage dimensions: Height 10.36m; width 9.75m; depth 6.4m

Andrews Lane Theatre

9-17 St Andrew's Lane,
Dublin 2, Republic of Ireland
box office: + 353 (0)1 679 5720
tel: + 353 (0)1 679 7760
fax: + 353 (0)1 679 7552
email: info@andrewslane.com
web: www.andrewslane.com
artistic director: Pat Moylan
technical manager: Eva Walsh
programming policy: The theatre's policy is to present the best of established and emerging Irish and international theatre. With a studio and main space, the theatre facilitates large and small-scale work.
terms: Rental
main auditorium:
   seats: 220 **stage type:** Proscenium arch
   stage dimensions: Height to grid 3.5m; width 9.76m; depth 4.88m
studio:
   seats: 72 **stage type:** Studio
   stage dimensions: Height to grid 2.46m; width 8.76m; depth 5.18m
See also Commercial Producers.

Ardhowen Theatre

Dublin Road, Enniskillen
Co. Fermanagh, Northern Ireland
box office: + 44 (0)28 6632 5440
tel: + 44 (0)28 6632 3233
fax: + 44 (0)28 6632 7102
artistic director: Eamonn Bradley
technical supervisor: Tom Sharkey
programming policy: Ardhowen runs a mixed programme of events which includes touring dance and theatre companies from Ireland and abroad, and youth drama and youth dance programmes and workshops.
terms: Box office split, Guarantee, Guarantee/ split, Rental
theatre by the lakes:
   seats: 290 **stage type:** Proscenium arch
   stage dimensions: Height to grid 7.48m; width 10.8m; depth 12.82m
gallery bar:
   seats: 100 **stage type:** Flexible
studio:
   seats: 50 **stage type:** Studio

Ards Arts Centre

Townhall, Conway Square, Newtownards,
Co. Down BT23 4DB, Northern Ireland
tel: + 44 (0)28 9181 0803
fax: + 44 (0)28 9182 3131
email: arts@ards-council.gov.uk
web: www.ards-council.gov.uk
arts officer: Eilis O'Baoill
arts centre co-ordinator: Jill Graham
programming policy: The centre programmes approximately four drama works and two dance works per annum including an annual Christmas production for children. Ards Arts Centre seeks to develop its moderately conservative rural audience base through strategic selection of contemporary local productions and long-term development.
terms: Guarantee, Rental
seats: 100
stage type: Flexible
stage dimensions: Height to grid 4.47m; width 7.85m; depth 10.13m

The Ark

Eustace Street, Temple Bar,
Dublin 2, Republic of Ireland
tel: + 353 (0)1 670 7788
fax: + 353 (0)1 670 7758
email: info@ark.ie
web: www.ark.ie
director (acting): Belinda Moller
theatre programmer: Ronan Tully
programming policy: The Ark is principally a
producing house presenting its own productions
of original theatre and music theatre for
children. The venue occasionally acts as a
receiving venue, presenting innovative work
from around the world. The Ark's touring
division, The Mobile Ark, presents theatre,
concerts and visual arts programmes throughout
Ireland and beyond, on a year-round basis.
terms: Guarantee
seats: 150
stage type: In the round
stage dimensions: Height to grid 5.5m; width
10m; depth 8.7m
See also Subsidised Companies.

AXIS – Ballymun Arts and Community Resource Centre

Town Centre, Dublin 9, Republic of Ireland
tel: + 353 (0)1 883 2100
fax: + 353 (01) 883 2101
email: reception@axis-ballymun.ie
web: www.axis-ballymun.ie
artistic director: Raymond Yeates
programming policy: To present the work of
leading Irish artists and provide a rare opportunity
to see international work; to investigate education
and access activities; to develop new audiences,
especially young audiences; to develop a synergy
between the arts and community development.
terms: Box office split, Guarantee, Guarantee/
split, Rental
seats: 211
stage type: Proscenium arch with apron
stage dimensions: Height to grid 7m; width
8.5m; depth 6.5m

Backstage Theatre and Centre for the Arts

Farneyhoogan, Longford, Republic of Ireland
tel: + 353 (0)43 47888
fax: + 353 (0)43 47890
email: info@backstage.ie
web: www.backstage.ie
theatre manager: Mona Considine
stage manager: Sean Mulroy
programming policy: Backstage Theatre presents
a full and diverse programme including drama,
music, dance and the visual arts. The venue also
programmes exploratory or experimental works.
terms: Box office split, Guarantee, Guarantee/
split, Rental
seats: 212
stage type: Proscenium arch
stage dimensions: Height to grid 5.5m; width
12.5m; depth 7.63m

Ballyearl Arts and Leisure Centre

585 Doagh Road, Newtownabbey,
Co. Antrim BT36 5RZ, Northern Ireland
tel: + 44 (0)28 9084 8287
fax: + 44 (0)28 9084 4896
email: sbartley@newtownabbey.gov.uk
operations manager: Stephen Bartley
programming policy: This small-scale, intimate
venue programmes many local community
groups and amateur dramatic societies. The
venue is also available to touring productions.
terms: Rental
seats: 180
stage type: Flexible
stage dimensions: Height to grid 7m; width
12m; depth 6m

Balor Theatre

Main Street, Ballybofey, Co. Donegal
Republic of Ireland
tel/fax: + 353 (0)74 913 1840
email: balordcagroup@eircom.net
web: www.balortheatre.com
co-ordinator: Mark McCollum
supervisor: Kieran Quinn
programming policy: Balor Theatre presents in-house productions, local amateur groups and touring theatre. Venue hire can be arranged by contacting the Donegal Arts Officer *(see Arts Officers listing)* or directly with the theatre.
terms: Rental
seats: 162
stage type: Proscenium arch
stage dimensions: Height to grid 3.36m; width 8.23m; depth 5.94m
See also Partially/Non-Subsidised Drama Companies.

Bank of Ireland Arts Centre

Foster Place, Temple Bar, Dublin 2,
Republic of Ireland
tel: + 353 (0)1 671 2261
fax: + 353 (0)1 670 7556
email: boi.arts@boimail.com
web: www.boi.ie/artscentre
manager: Barry O'Kelly
arts administrator: Jenny Kirkwood
programming policy: The cultural programme includes theatre, the 'Classical Choice' Lunchtime Recital Series, evening charity recitals, art exhibitions, 'Out to Lunch' poetry readings and other social and cultural events.
terms: Rental
seats: 200
stage dimensions: Height to grid 4m; width 8m; depth 13m

Bank of Ireland Theatre

Áras na MacLéinn, National University of Ireland, Galway, Republic of Ireland
tel: + 353 (0)91 512062
fax: + 353 (0)91 512534
email: fionnuala.gallagher@nuigalway.ie
web: www.nuigalway.ie/arts_office
arts officer: Fionnuala Gallagher
programming policy: To showcase the best of Irish and international theatre and dance. Student productions are given priority during the academic year. Visiting companies are encouraged to give workshops.
terms: Box office split, Rental
seats: 80
stage type: Black box
stage dimensions: Height to grid 4m; width 13m; depth 8m

Bawnacre Centre

Irvinestown, Co. Fermanagh BT94 1EE,
Northern Ireland
tel: + 44 (0)28 6862 1177
fax: + 44 (0)28 6862 8082
chairperson: George Beacom
assistant manager: John Maguire
programming policy: The centre hosts a wide variety of dance, drama, arts and music events, courses and workshops.
terms: Box office split, Rental
main auditorium:
  seats: 850 **stage type:** Proscenium arch
  stage dimensions: Height to grid 8.53m; width 18.5m; depth 9.14m
minor hall:
  seats: 280 **stage type:** Flexible
small hall:
  seats: 100 **stage type:** Flexible

Belltable Arts Centre

69 O'Connell Street, Limerick, Republic of Ireland
box office: + 353 (0)61 319866
tel: + 353 (0)61 315 871
fax: + 353 (0)61 418 552
email: belltabl@iol.ie
web: www.belltable.ie
director: Peter McNamara
box office manager: Declan McLoughlin
programming policy: The Belltable Arts Centre is a point of access to the arts for the people of Limerick and its hinterland, providing a wide range of top quality artistic activity encompassing touring and local theatre, dance, film, music and visual arts.
terms: Box office split, Guarantee, Rental, Guarantee/split
seats: 257
stage type: Proscenium arch
stage dimensions: Height to grid 4.87m; width 7.16m; depth 10.21m
See also Irish Festivals.

Bewley's Café Theatre

Grafton Street, Dublin 2, Republic of Ireland
tel: + 353 (0)86 878 4001
email: bewleyscafetheatre@eircom.net
web: www.bewleys.com
director: Michael James Ford
administrator: Maureen Loughran
programming policy: Bewley's Café Theatre is Dublin's only permanent, year round venue for lunchtime drama. The venue primarily presents its own in-house productions but is occasionally available to other companies especially for cabaret and company in the evenings.
terms: Box office split, Rental
seats: 55
stage type: Raised platform
stage dimensions: Height to grid 4m; Width 3.9m; depth 3.5m
See also Partially/Non-Subsidised Drama Companies.

Birr Theatre and Arts Centre

Oxmantown Hall, Birr,
Co. Offaly, Republic of Ireland
box office: +353 (0)509 22911
tel: +353 (0)509 22893
fax: +353 (0)509 22894
email: birrtheatre@eircom.net
web: www.birrtheatre.com

venue manager: Michael Bowler
programming policy: Our policy is to bring a varied programme of art, entertainment and outreach projects to as wide a range of people as possible.
terms: Box office split, Guarantee/split, Rental
seats: 220
stage type: Flexible
stage dimensions: Height to grid 5m; width 7.3m; depth 4.8m

The Black Box

Dyke Road, Galway, Republic of Ireland
box office: + 353 (0)91 569777
tel: + 353 (0)91 569755
fax: + 353 (0)91 569 664
email: tht@galwaycity.ie
web: www.townhalltheatregalway.com
manager: Mike Diskin
technical manager: Peter Ashton
programming policy: To host large-scale shows, particularly those with inventive or unusual production demands.
terms: Box office split, Guarantee, Rental, Guarantee/split
seats: 100 – 600
stage type: Flexible
stage dimensions: Height to grid 12m; width 25m; depth 25m
See also Town Hall Theatre, Galway.

Briery Gap Cultural Centre

Macroom, Co. Cork, Republic of Ireland
box office: + 353 (0)26 41793
tel: + 353 (0)26 42421
fax: + 353 (0)26 41764
email: brierygap@eircom.net
web: www.macroom.ie
manager: Ann Dunne
technical manager: John Vaughan
programming policy: To present a wide range of programmes to appeal to all ages. Most events take place at weekends with preference for Sunday.
terms: Box office split, Guarantee, Rental, Guarantee/split
seats: 200
stage type: Proscenium arch
stage dimensions: Height to grid 3.66m; width 7.31m; depth 6.1m

The Burnavon Arts and Cultural Centre

Burn Road, Cookstown,
Co. Tyrone BT80 8DN, Northern Ireland
box office: + 44 (0)28 8676 9949
tel: + 44 (0)28 8676 7994
fax: + 44 (0)28 8676 5853
email: burnavon@cookstown.gov.uk
web: www.burnavon.com
manager: Tony McCance
administrator: Caroline Sheehy
programming policy: The venue programmes performances that have the capacity to appeal to a wide audience, educational productions and/or performances addressing social issues.
terms: Box office split, Guarantee, Rental, Guarantee/split
seats: 350
stage type: Proscenium arch
stage dimensions: Height to grid 8.5m; width 8.5m; depth 7.2m

Civic Theatre

Tallaght, Dublin 24, Republic of Ireland
box office: + 353 (0)1 462 7477
tel: + 353 (0)1 462 7460
fax: + 353 (0)1 462 7478
email: civictheatred24@eircom.net
web: www.civictheatre.ie
director: Brid Dukes
technical manager: Mick Doyle
programming policy: The Civic Theatre is mainly a receiving venue for professional productions of contemporary and classical work in theatre, dance and opera.
terms: Box office split, Guarantee, Rental, Guarantee/split
main auditorium:
  seats: 282 **stage type:** Proscenium arch
  stage dimensions: Height to grid 11.42m; width 10.04m; depth 8.33m
loose end studio:
  seats: 60 – 80 **stage type:** Studio
  stage dimensions: Not available

Clotworthy Arts Centre

Antrim Castle Gardens, Randalstown Road,
Antrim BT41 4LH, Northern Ireland
tel: + 44 (0)28 9442 8000
fax: + 44 (0)28 9446 0360
email: clotworthyarts@antrim.gov.uk
web: www.antrim.gov.uk
theatre programmer: Cathy McNally
technician: Michael McLaughlin
programming policy: Clotworthy Arts Centre is a receiving house for a broad range of small-scale professional theatre productions, hosting, on average, twelve to fifteen shows per year.
terms: Box office split, Guarantee
seats: 96
stage type: Proscenium arch
stage dimensions: Height to grid 4.26m; width 5.18m; depth 8.23m

Cork Opera House

Emmet Place, Cork, Republic of Ireland
box office: + 353 (0)21 427 0022
tel: + 353 (0)21 427 4308
fax: + 353 (0)21 427 6357
email: info@corkoperahouse.ie
web: www.corkoperahouse.ie
executive director: Gerry Barnes
technical manager: Chris Gaughan
programming policy: The aim of Cork Opera House is to serve its city and surrounding region as a municipal theatre, offering its audiences a varied, high quality programme which represents local, national and international developments in the performing arts. This service operates on two levels with a main auditorium of 1,000 seats and a studio theatre of 150 seats, the Half Moon Theatre, ensuring continuous activity without any seasonal closure. The artistic policy searches out plays, operas and dance of appropriate scale, standard and substance from the classical and contemporary repertoire for a major lyric theatre, while the studio theatre fosters a more experimental range of interdisciplinary projects, mixing drama with music and comedy, targeted at younger audiences.
resident theatre company: Cork Opera House
terms: Box office split, Guarantee, Rental, Guarantee/split

main auditorium:
   seats: 1000 **stage type:** Proscenium arch
   stage dimensions: Height to grid 18.29m;
   width 12.2m; depth 8.84m
half moon theatre:
   seats: 100 - 150 **stage type:** In the round
   stage dimensions: Height to grid 18.29m;
   width 3.65m; depth 2.13m
See also Commercial Producers.

Corn Mill Theatre and Arts Centre
Main Street, Carrigallen, Co. Leitrim
Republic of Ireland
tel: + 353 (0)49 433 9612
director: Sean McIntyre
programming policy: The Corn Mill Theatre
programmes both amateur and professional
productions.
terms: Box office split, Guarantee/split, Rental
seats: 180
stage type: Proscenium arch
stage dimensions: Height to grid 3.65m; width
7.31m, depth 4.28m

Courthouse Arts Centre
Main Street, Tinahely,
Co. Wicklow, Republic of Ireland
tel: + 353 (0)402 38529
email: tinahely@iol.ie
web: www.tinahely-courthouse.ie
artistic director: Sharon Corcoran
production manager: Magie Gallagher
programming policy: The Courthouse Arts Centre
is a multi-disciplinary arts centre based in a
renovated courthouse building (1843). The main
space is used for all activities, music, exhibitions,
a film society and theatre. Artistic policy with
regard to theatre favours the small-scale yet
highly professional productions. Within those
strictures, we are open to a wide range of work,
however experimental, shocking or otherwise
risky. The Courthouse co-produced *Women and
the Trojan Horse* by Sam Dowling and Nick Warren
with Praxis Theatre Company in 2003.
terms: Box office split, Guarantee, Guarantee/split
seats: 60 – 90
stage type: Flexible
stage dimensions: Height to grid 2.92m; width
4.76m; depth 5.53m

Crypt Arts Centre
Dublin Castle, Dame Street,
Dublin 2, Republic of Ireland
email: info@cryptartscentre.org
web: www.cryptartscentre.org
directors: John O'Brien, Niall O Sioradain
programming policy: The Crypt programmes new,
emerging and established companies, groups and
individuals.
terms: Box office split, Rental
seats: 80
stage type: Flexible
stage dimensions: Height to grid 2.75m; width
5m; depth 14.6m

Culturlann McAdam Ó Fiaich
216 Falls Road, Belfast BT12 6AH, Northern Ireland
box office: + 44 (0)28 9096 4180
fax: + 44 (0)28 9096 4189
email: eimear@culturlann.ie
events manager: Eimear Ní Mhathúna
programming policy: multi-purpose theatre,
gallery and workshop space. Own programme of
Irish language drama, music, and literature.
Facilities available for performance, rehearsal,
conference and workshops with priority given to
Irish language companies. Simultaneous
translation available.
terms: Rental
seats: 120 retractable
stage type: Flexible
stage dimensions: Height to grid 3.5m; width
10m; depth 8m
See also Subsidised Drama Companies.

The Dean Crowe Theatre and Arts Centre
Chapel Street, Athlone,
Co. Westmeath, Republic of Ireland
box office: + 353 (0)90 649 2129
tel/fax: + 353 (0)90 649 8414
email: deancrowetheatre@eircom.net
manager: Fionnuala O'Connell
programming policy: The theatre programmes a
mixture of professional and amateur theatre.
terms: Box office split, Guarantee, Rental
seats: 466
stage type: Proscenium arch
stage dimensions: Height 5.7m; width 9.2m;
depth 7.7m

Down Arts Centre

2-6 Irish Street, Downpatrick,
Co. Down BT30 6BN, Northern Ireland
tel: + 44 (0)28 4461 5283
fax: + 44 (0)28 4461 6621
email: mail@downartscentre.com
web: www.downartscentre.com
manager: Cathie McKimm
assistant arts officer: Amy Smyth
programming policy: To provide a diverse and
dynamic programme of events, exhibitions
and workshops for the people of Down
district and its visitors.
terms: Box office split, Guarantee, Rental
seats: 185
stage type: Proscenium arch
stage dimensions: Height to grid 3.96m; width
8.23m; depth 6m

Draíocht... a Centre for the Arts

The Blanchardstown Centre, Blanchardstown
Dublin 15, Republic of Ireland
box office: + 353 (0)1 885 2622
tel: + 353 (0)1 885 2610
fax: + 353 (0)1 824 3434
email: marketing@draiocht.ie
web: www.draiocht.ie
director: Emer McGowan
general manager: Jackie Ryan
marketing manager: Nicola Murphy
programming policy: A receiving house that
programmes local, national and international
shows from all performance disciplines. The
multi-purpose venue is used for a braod range of
activities including drama, dance, contemporary
visual arts and crafts, multi-media arts activities,
classical and traditional music, a programme of
activities for families and children, artists in
residence schemes, community outreach and
education projects, and much more.
terms: Box office split, Guarantee, Rental,
Guarantee/split
main auditorium:
  seats: 286 **stage type:** Proscenium arch
  stage dimensions: Height to grid 13.5m;
  width 13.41m; depth 11.58m
studio:
  seats: 96 **stage type:** Studio
  stage dimensions: Height to grid 5m; width
  12m; depth 10m

Droichead Arts Centre

Stockwell Street, Drogheda,
Co. Louth, Republic of Ireland
tel: + 353 (0)41 987 5140
fax: + 353 (0)41 984 2055
email: droiched@indigo.ie
director: Paul O'Hanrahan
technical assistant: John McGovern
programming policy: Our aim is to promote
professional, amateur and youth theatre through
our year-round theatre programme. The centre has
two buildings which enable it to nurture both the
creative process of theatre and the whole business
of theatrical production. We support two local
professional theatre companies, Upstate and
Calipo, a number of local amateur companies and
Droichead Youth Theatre.
terms: Box office split, Guarantee, Rental
seats: 160
stage type: Proscenium arch
stage dimensions: Height to grid 5m; width
7.57m; depth 10.37m

Drumlin House Theatre

Cooney's Row, Cootehill,
Co. Cavan, Republic of Ireland
tel: + 353 (0)49 555 2605
fax: + 353 (0)49 555 6058
chairperson: Hugh B. O'Brien
administrator: Breege O'Reilly
programming policy: Drumlin House Theatre
was primarily developed to provide a space for
in-house trainees to perform their work. The
venue is also rented to amateur groups and to
professional touring companies.
terms: Rental
seats: 210 maximum
stage type: Flexible
stage dimensions: Height to grid 4.3m; width
9.8m; depth 5.5m

Dublin Institute of Technology

Rathmines Road, Rathmines,
Dublin 6, Republic of Ireland
box office: + 353 (0)1 402 3515
tel: + 353 (0)1 402 3568
senior administrator: Fiona Howard
course chair in drama: Peter McDermott
programming policy: The venue is available
outside term time for independent projects or
within term for projects that can coincide with
coursework.
terms: Rental
seats: 60 – 80
stage type: Flexible
stage dimensions: Height to grid 4.5m; width
8m; depth 11m

Duchas Inis Oírr

Inis Oírr, Aran Islands,
Co. Galway, Republic of Ireland
tel/fax: + 353 (0)99 75150
email: inis_oirr@ireland.com
director: Val Ballance
programming policy: To stage small-scale
productions of dance and drama with priority
given to drama in Irish. Most shows are
programmed during the summer.
terms: Guarantee
seats: 80
stage type: Proscenium arch
stage dimensions: Height to grid 3.65m; width
4m; depth 3m

Dunamaise Arts Centre

Church Street, Portlaoise,
Co. Laois, Republic of Ireland
box office: + 353 (0)502 63355
tel: + 353 (0)502 63356
fax: + 353 (0)502 63357
email: info@dunamaise.ie
web: www.dunamaise.ie
director: Louise Donlon
technical manager: Nick Anton
programming policy: The Dunamaise Arts
Centre aims to present the best in professional
performance by touring companies and to
develop local and community arts performance.
Since it first opened its doors in May 1999, it
has presented work by all leading major Irish
theatre companies, including the Abbey, Druid,

Red Kettle, Island, Fishamble and Galloglass. It
also presents a wide range of music and dance
performance and is an important focal point for
community arts activity in the region.
terms: Box office split, Guarantee, Rental,
Guarantee/split
seats: 238
stage type: Proscenium arch
stage dimensions: Height to grid 6.5m; width
at pros 8.4m; depth 6.6m

Everyman Palace Theatre

15 MacCurtain Street, Cork, Republic of Ireland
box office: + 353 (0)21 450 1673
tel: + 353 (0)21 450 3077
fax: + 353 (0)21 450 2820
email: palace@oceanfree.net,
palacepress@eircom.net
web: www.everymanpalace.com
artistic director: Patrick Talbot
theatre manager: Brendan Galvin
programming policy: To present quality touring
and in-house productions.
terms: Box office split, Guarantee, Rental,
Guarantee/split
main auditorium:
   seats: 628 **stage type:** Proscenium arch
   stage dimensions: Height to grid 15.24m;
   width 7.31m; depth 5.48m
studio:
   seats: 100 **stage type:** Flexible
See also Subsidised Drama Companies.

The Factory Performance Space

Lower Quay Street, Sligo, Republic of Ireland
tel/box office: + 353 (0)71 917 0431
fax: + 353 (0)71 917 1100
email: info@blueraincoat.com
web: www.blueraincoat.com
artistic director: Niall Henry
company manager: Tara McGowan
programming policy: The Factory Performance
Space plays host to touring shows, workshops and
music recitals. Since re-opening in December 2000,
it has a new role as a theatrical research and
development facility, where companies from Ireland
and abroad come to workshop and perform.
seats: 85
stage type: End on
stage dimensions: Height to grid 5.5m; width
11.5m; depth 8.5m
See also Subsidised Companies.

Focus Theatre

6 Pembroke Place, Off Pembroke Street
Dublin 2, Republic of Ireland
tel/box office: 01 676 3071
email: focustheatre@eircom.net
artistic director: Joe Devlin
head of studio: Tim McDonnell
administrator: Alastar MacAongusa
programming policy: The Focus is available for
occasional rentals for music, alternative cabaret,
comedy and theatre. Also available as a
rehearsal space.
terms: Box office split, Rental
See also Subsidised Drama Companies.

The Forum Waterford

The Glen, Waterford, Republic of Ireland
box office: + 353 (0)51 871133
tel: + 353 (0)51 871111
fax: + 353 (0)51 871122
email: admin@forumwaterford.com
web: www.forumwaterford.com
theatre manager: Ciaran O'Neill
technical manager: Terry O'Neill
programming policy: The Forum programmes all
types of amateur and professional music, drama
and dance.
terms: Box office split, Guarantee, Rental,
Guarantee/split
the main room:
  seats: 550 **stage type:** Proscenium arch
  stage dimensions: Height to grid 4m; width
  15m; depth 8m
gallery theatre:
  seats: 300 **stage type:** Proscenium arch
  stage dimensions: Height to grid 4m; width
  15m; depth 12m
stage 2:
  seats: 200 **stage type:** Concert platform
  stage dimensions: Height to grid 4m; depth
  3.5m; width 6m

Friars Gate Theatre

Sarsfield Street, Kilmallock,
Co. Limerick, Republic of Ireland
tel: + 353 (0)63 98727
fax: + 353 (0)63 20180
email: friarsgate@eircom.net
web: www.friarsgate.net
manager: Caoimhe Reidy
programming policy: To present touring
professional theatre, dance and musical
companies from Ireland and overseas. Ongoing
education programme in drama, art and Irish
traditional music for children and adults.
terms: Box office split, Guarantee, Rental,
Guarantee/split
seats: 130
stage type: Proscenium arch
stage dimensions: Height to grid 3.96m; width
7.31m; depth 5.48m

Gaiety Theatre

South King Street, Dublin 2, Republic of Ireland
box office: + 353 (0)1 677 1717
tel: + 353 (0)1 646 8641
fax: + 353 (0)1 677 1921
email: info@gaietytheatre.net
web: www.gaietytheatre.net
executive director: John Costigan
theatre manager: Alan McQuillan
programming policy: Primarily a receiving house,
the variety of productions included in the season
encompasses: theatre, opera, dance, pantomime,
comedy and musicals. The annual pantomime is
produced in-house.
terms: Box office split, Guarantee/split, Rental
seats: 1137
stage type: Proscenium arch
stage dimensions: Height to grid 14.5m; width
8.3m; depth 9.5m
See also Commercial Producers.

Garage Theatre

St Davnet's Complex, Armagh Road,
Monaghan, Republic of Ireland
tel: + 353 (0)47 81597
fax: + 353 (0)47 81564
email: garagetheatre@eircom.net
administrator: Eileen Costello
technician: Charles Cawley
programming policy: A high-quality, year-round,
artistic programme presenting the best in
professional performance by national and
international touring companies and to develop
local and community productions.
terms: Box office split, Guarantee, Rental,
Guarantee/split
seats: 184
stage type: Proscenium arch
stage dimensions: Height to grid 4m; width
10m; depth 8.5m

Garter Lane Arts Centre

22a O'Connell Street, Waterford, Republic of Ireland
tel: + 353 (0)51 877153
box office: + 353 (0)51 855038
fax: + 353 (0)51 871570
email: boxoffice@garterlane.ie
web: www.garterlane.ie
artistic director: Caroline Senior
general manager: Lilly O'Reilly
programming policy: Garter Lane programmes
innovative theatre work that stimulates and
involves audiences, often involving outreach
/workshop initiatives. The venue is also actively
developing audiences for dance, frequently in
co-operation with local teachers. Runs are
usually one to three nights.
terms: Box office split, Guarantee, Rental,
Guarantee/split
seats: 180 – 240
stage type: Thrust stage, seating on three sides
stage dimensions: Height to grid 5m; width
6m; depth 9m

The Glens Centre

New Line, Manorhamilton,
Co. Leitrim, Republic of Ireland
tel: + 353 (0)71 985 5833
fax: + 353 (0)71 985 6063
email: info@theglenscentre.com
web: www.theglenscentre.com
artistic director: Anna Legge
chairman: Prin Duignan
programming policy: To present a quality
artistic programme, mixing all performance
disciplines from local, national and international
touring groups as well as producing children's
events and a community arts programme.
terms: Box office split, Guarantee, Rental,
Guarantee/split
seats: 130
stage type: Flexible
stage dimensions: Height to grid 4.26m; width
7.62m; depth 4.26m

Glór Irish Music Centre

Friar's Walk, Ennis, Co. Clare, Republic of Ireland
box office: + 353 (0)65 684 3103
programming policy: Glór programmes local
and touring productions from all performance
disciplines for adult and young audiences.
A particular focus is on Irish music under Glór's
remit as National Centre for the Performance
of Irish Music.
tel: + 353 (0)65 684 5370
fax: + 353 (0)65 684 5372
email: info@glor.ie
web: www.glor.ie
director: Katie Verling
programming manager: Fiona McCaffrey Jones
terms: Box office split, Guarantee, Rental
main auditorium:
   seats: 485 **stage type:** Proscenium arch
   stage dimensions: Height to grid 6.5m;
   width 24m; depth 7.6m
studio:
   seats: 65 **stage type:** Studio

An Grianán Theatre

Port Road, Letterkenny.
Co. Donegal. Republic of Ireland
box office: + 353 (0)74 912 0777
tel: + 353 (0)74 912 3288
fax: + 353 (0)74 912 0665
email: angrianan@eircom.net
web: www.angrianan.com
director: Patricia McBride
technical manager: Niall Cranney
programming policy: An Grianán Theatre offers
a platform to artists both professional and
amateur across the art forms as well as creating
a professional base for drama in Donegal by
producing work in-house.
terms: Box office split, Guarantee, Rental,
Guarantee/split
seats: 345
stage type: Proscenium arch with apron and infill
stage dimensions: Height to grid 13.2m; width
12.8m; depth 10.7m (excluding apron)
See also Subsidised Companies.

Granary Theatre

Mardyke, Cork, Republic of Ireland
box office: + 353 (0)21 490 4275
tel/fax: + 353 (0)21 490 4272
email: granary@ucc.ie
web: www.granary.ie
artistic director: Tony McCleane-Fay
technical manager: Kath Geraghty
programming policy: A small-scale black box
venue presenting in-house, local and touring
productions and innovative new work, the Granary
is also the central venue for the Cork Fringe
Festival. Granary produces and presents new and
experimental work by artists across disciplines. The
programme combines work in theatre, performance,
dance, live art, installation, and music, with a
lively critical programme of PERFORUM talks,
workshops and artists' presentations.
terms: Box office split, Guarantee, Rental
seats: 70 – 150
stage type: Flexible
stage dimensions: Height to grid 7.01m; width
10.87m; depth 12.19m
See also Partially/Non-Subsidised Drama Companies.

Grand Opera House

Great Victoria Street,
Belfast BT2 7HR, Northern Ireland
box office: + 44 (0)28 9024 1919
tel: + 44 (0)28 9024 0411
fax: + 44 (0)28 9023 6842
email: info@goh.co.uk
web: www.goh.co.uk
theatre director: John Botteley
technical manager: Anne Muldoon
programming policy: The Grand Opera House
presents a programme of the very best in live
theatrical performances and entertainment to
satisfy the widest range of tastes and ages.
terms: Box office split, Guarantee, Rental,
Guarantee/split
seats: 1021
stage type: Proscenium arch
stage dimensions: Height to grid 17.99; width
18.9m; depth 14.11m
See also Commercial Producers.

Hawk's Well Theatre

Temple Street, Sligo, Republic of Ireland
box office: + 353 (0)71 916 1518
tel: + 353 (0)71 916 1526
fax: + 353 (0)71 917 1737
email: joe_masterson@hotmail.com
web: www.hawkswell.com
general manager: Caroline Pilkington
marketing/front of house manager: Joe Masterson
technical manager: Nick McCall
programming policy: To present a year round
programme of quality, accessible drama and dance to
the people of the North-West region and its visitors.
terms: Box office split, Guarantee, Rental,
Guarantee/split
seats: 348
stage type: Proscenium arch
stage dimensions: Height to grid 6m; width
13.2m; depth 8.25m

The Helix

DCU, Collins Avenue, Glasnevin,
Dublin 9, Republic of Ireland
box office: +353 1 700 7000
tel: +353 1 7007077
fax: +353 1 7007110
email: info@thehelix.ie
web: www.thehelix.ie
director: Nick Reed
artistic programmer (the space): Marie-Louise O'Donnell
programming policy: The Helix comprises three different auditoria, The Mahony Hall, The Theatre and The Space, alongside a Visual Art Gallery. The venue aims to celebrate diversity of performance and culture within Ireland and around the world. Within twelve months of opening its doors, the Helix has welcomed orchestras from around the world, opera singers such as Dame Kiri Te Kanawa and Lesley Garrett, legendary singer-songwriters Van Morrison and Lou Reed, theatre from the US, UK, South Africa, Vietnam and of course Ireland.
terms: Guarantee
the mahony hall:
    seats: 1260 **stage type:** Concert platform
    stage dimensions: Height to canopy 10m; width 12m to 20m; depth 12m
the theatre:
    seats: 450 **stage type:** Proscenium arch
    stage dimensions: Height to grid 16m; width 22.5m; depth 11m
the space:
    seats: 140 **stage type:** Studio
    stage dimensions: Height to grid 6.5m; width 5.6m; depth 8.3m

i space

Basement 18, The Crescent, O'Connell Avenue, Limerick, Republic of Ireland
tel: +353 (0)61 316399
email: impacttheatrecompany@eircom.net
administrator: Ann Blake
programming policy: Impact Theatre Company presents its own productions here but i space is also available to other companies.
terms: Box office split, Rental
seats: 50
stage type: Flexible
stage dimensions: Height to grid 4m; width 4m; depth 3m
See also Partially/Non-Subsidised Drama Companies.

Institute for Choreography and Dance (ICD)

Firkin Crane, Shandon, Cork, Republic of Ireland
tel: + 353 (0)21 450 7487
fax: + 353 (0)21 450 1124
email: info@instchordance.com
web: www.instchordance.com
artistic director: Mary Brady
programming policy: The Institute for Choreography and Dance is a unique model for stimulating choreographic practice and dance research as a means of dance development. It provides space for interchange between choreographers to examine issues, work methodologies and goals particular to each, in a positive, challenging and practice-centered environment. ICD performances and presentations include work in progress, international seasons (spring/summer), and co-presentations of Irish-based companies and festivals.
terms: Box office split, Guarantee, Rental, Guarantee/split
seats: 240
stage type: Proscenium arch
stage dimensions: Height to grid 4.6m; width 9.5m; depth 9m

International Bar

23 Wicklow Street, Dublin 2, Republic of Ireland
tel: + 353 (0)1 677 9250
contact: Ann Donohoe, John Donohoe
programming policy: The venue is used primarily as a comedy and music venue, but is occasionally available for theatrical purposes particularly for lunchtime and early evening performances.
terms: Rental
seats: 50 – 75
stage type: Flexible
stage dimensions: Height 2m; width 3.3m, depth 2.1m

Island Arts Centre

Lagan Valley Island, Lisburn,
Co. Down BT27 4RC, Northern Ireland
email: arts.information@iac.lisburn.gov.uk
web: www.lisburncity.gov.uk
arts manager: Siobhan McCormick
arts centre co-ordinator: Christina Hurson
programming policy: The Island Arts Centre
promotes local and international visual and
performing arts talents with a core focus on
engaging children and young people as
audience members and interactive participants.
box office: + 44 (0)28 9250 9254
terms: Guarantee/split, Rental
main auditorium:
  seats: 400 **stage type:** Flexible
  stage dimensions: Height to grid 8m;
  width 16.5m
studio:
  seats: 100 **stage type:** Studio
  tel: + 44 (0)28 9250 9510
  fax: + 44 (0)28 9266 2679

Lambert Puppet Theatre

Clifton Lane, Monkstown,
Co. Dublin, Republic of Ireland
box office: + 353 (0)1 280 1863
tel: + 353 (0)1 280 0974
fax: + 353 (0)1 280 4772
email: info@lambertpuppettheatre.com
web: www.lambertpuppettheatre.com
director: Eugene Lambert
programming policy: The Lambert Puppet Theatre
creates its own in-house productions for children
and adults. The venue is also suitable for small-
scale outside productions.
terms: Rental
seats: 200 - 250
stage type: Flexible
stage dimensions: Height to ceiling 5m; width
5m; depth 3m
*See also Partially/Non-Subsidised Drama Companies and
Irish Festivals.*

Letterkenny Arts Centre

Central Library, Oliver Plunkett Road
Letterkenny, Co. Donegal, Republic of Ireland
box office: + 353 (0)74 912 0777
tel: + 353 (0)74 912 9186
fax: + 353 (0)74 912 3276
email: lkarts@indigo.ie
web: www.donegalculture.com
director: John M. Cunningham
assistant director: Derek O'Connor
programming policy: Letterkenny Arts Centre
currently consists of a single multi-purpose
space which is predominately used as a gallery,
with occasional small-scale performances,
usually educational or children's theatre, or as
part of a festival.
terms: Guarantee, Rental
seats: 80
stage type: Flexible
stage dimensions: Height to ceiling 2.5m;
width 15m; depth 9m

Liberty Hall

Eden Quay, Dublin 1, Republic of Ireland
box office: + 353 (0)1 872 1122
tel: + 353 (0)1 889 2640
fax: + 353 (0)1 889 2642
email: pmorris@siptu.ie
general manager: Tom Dunne
administrator: Pat Morris
programming policy: Liberty Hall programmes a
wide range of Irish and international work from
local groups through to international theatre,
music and conferences.
terms: Box office split, Rental
seats: 410
stage type: Proscenium arch with apron
stage dimensions: Height to grid 3.4m; width
12m; depth 8m

Linenhall Arts Centre

Linenhall Street, Castlebar,
Co. Mayo, Republic of Ireland
tel: + 353 (0)94 902 3733
fax: + 353 (0)94 902 6162
email: linenhall@anu.ie
web: www.thelinenhall.com
director: Marie Farrell
administrator: Maura Connolly
programming policy: The Linenhall Arts Centre
provides a wide range of arts activities for the
community, including music, theatre, dance, film
and poetry. Refurbished performance space open
since September 2002.
terms: Box office split, Guarantee, Rental
seats: 165
stage type: Flexible
stage dimensions: Height to ceiling 7.9m;
width 9m; depth 6.75m

The Market Place

Market Street, Armagh BT61 7AT, Northern Ireland
box office: + 44 (0)28 3752 1821
tel: + 44 (0)28 3752 1820
fax: + 44 (0)28 3752 1822
email: admin@marketplacearmagh.com
web: www.marketplacearmagh.com
theatre director: Jill Holmes
technical contact: Rodney Ellis
programming policy: The Market Place Theatre
and Arts Centre aims to present a diverse and
inspiring year-round programme of entertainment,
cultural outreach and arts activities, offering the
best available work from local, national and
international groups and artists.
terms: Box office split, Guarantee, Rental,
Guarantee/split
main auditorium:
  seats: 397 **stage type:** Proscenium arch
  stage dimensions: Height to grid 5.5m;
  width 10m; depth 10m
studio:
  seats: 120 **stage type:** Studio

Meeting House Square

Temple Bar Properties, 12 East Essex Street,
Dublin 2, Republic of Ireland
tel: + 353 (0)1 677 2255
fax: + 353 (0)1 677 2525
email: info@templebar.ie
web: www.templebar.ie
production manager: Rob Furey
head of cultural development: Grainne Millar
programming policy: Meeting House Square is a
flexible, multi-purpose outdoor performance
space featuring a 35mm projection screen,
projection booth and proscenium stage. Suitable
for all art forms and cinema presentations.
Standing room for 1,000 people. Also available
for commercial hire. Temple Bar Square and
streets are also available for use.
terms: Part guarantee
seats: 600
stage type: Proscenium arch
stage dimensions: Height to grid 5m; width
10m; depth 7m

Mermaid County Wicklow Arts Centre

Main Street, Bray, Co. Wicklow, Republic of Ireland
tel: + 353 (0)1 272 4030
fax: + 353 (0)1 272 4031
email: admin@mermaidartscentre.ie
web: www.mermaidartscentre.ie
artistic director: Aideen Howard
technical manager: Paul O'Neill
programming policy: To present the best of
national and international artistic practice in
dance, theatre, opera, music and visual art, and to
provide a forum for local artistic activity. Mermaid
is a receiving house. Performing arts are
programmed three to six months in advance. The
gallery is programmed up to 12 months in advance.
terms: Box office split, Guarantee, Rental,
Guarantee/split
seats: 242
stage type: Proscenium arch
stage dimensions: Height to grid 6m; width
11m; Stage depth 8.9m

The Millennium Forum Theatre and Conference Centre

Newmarket Street, Derry BT48 6EB,
Northern Ireland
box office: + 44 (0)28 7126 4455
tel: + 44 (0)28 7126 4426
fax: + 44 (0)28 7127 2799
email: DavidMcL@millenniumforum.co.uk
web: www.millenniumforum.co.uk
chief executive: David McLaughlin
technical manager: Jim Nelis
programming policy: Small, medium and large-scale drama, dance, musicals, concerts, variety, children's events, pantomime and opera productions.
terms: Box office split, Guarantee, Rental, Guarantee/split
seats: 371, 751 or 1027
stage type: Proscenium arch
stage dimensions: Height to grid 16.6m; width 25.7m; depth 12.85m

Moat Theatre

Abbey Street, Naas, Kildare, Republic of Ireland
tel: + 353 (0)45 883 030
fax: + 353 (0)45 883 032
email: info@moattheatre.com
web: www.moattheatre.com
administrator: Kathleen Smith
technical manager: Pat Callaghan
programming policy: Moat Theatre facilitates and fosters drama, music, dance, comedy and art to reach as wide an audience as possible.
terms: Rental
seats: 200
stage type: Proscenium arch
stage dimensions: Width 9.9m; depth 5.5m

Mullingar Arts Centre

Mount Street, Mullingar, Co. Westmeath,
Republic of Ireland
tel: + 353 (0)44 47777
fax: + 353 (0)44 47783
email: dharte@westmeathcoco.ie
web: www.mullingarartscentre.ie
director: Sean Lynch
pa to director: Derval Harte
programming policy: Mullingar Arts Centre's policy is to promote excellence and innovation in all art forms. The Centre is committed to promoting the arts through the educational aspects of its programme.
terms: Box office split, Guarantee, Rental, Guarantee/split
seats: 418
stage type: Proscenium arch
stage dimensions: Height to grid 5.5m; width 7m; depth 7m

The New Theatre

43 East Essex Street, Temple Bar,
Dublin, Republic of Ireland
tel: + 353 (0)1 670 3361
fax: + 353 (0)1 671 1966
email: sionnach@indigo.ie
artistic directors: Anthony Fox, Ronan Wilmot
administration contact: Maedbh McCullagh
programming policy: To promote excellence in theatre and to provide a platform for emerging and established playwrights.
terms: Rental
seats: 71
stage type: End on
stage dimensions: Height to grid 3.04m; width 5.2m; depth 4.2m

Newry and Mourne Arts Centre

1a Bane Arcade, Newry,
Co. Down BT35 6HP, Northern Ireland
tel: + 44 (0)28 3026 6232
fax: + 44 (0)28 3026 6839
email: mhughesarts@ukonline.com
director: Mark Hughes
technician: Eoin McCartan
programming policy: The centre is programmed
by the Newry and Mourne District Council; the
programme includes a broad range of amateur
and professional shows.
terms: Box office split, Guarantee, Rental,
Guarantee/split
seats: 125
stage type: Flexible
stage dimensions: Not available

Old Museum Arts Centre

7 College Square North,
Belfast BT1 6AR, Northern Ireland
box office: + 44 (0)28 9023 3332
tel: + 44 (0)28 9023 5053
fax: + 44 (0)28 9032 2912
email: gillian.mitchell@oldmuseum.co.uk
web: www.oldmuseumartscentre.org
director: Anne McReynolds
deputy director/live events programmer:
Gillian Mitchell
programming policy: OMAC has an ambitious,
innovative and risk-taking artistic programme
which is designed to promote new writing, devised
work, dance and physical theatre as well as music
and visual art. In addition to presenting the work
of established artists, we have a strong
commitment to supporting the work of new and
emerging artists without compromising artistic
integrity and quality. The live events programme
concentrates on presenting a mixture of local,
national and international work which has not
been previously seen in Northern Ireland, focussing
on that which is both innovative and accessible.
terms: Box office split, Guarantee, Rental,
Guarantee/split
seats: 90
stage type: Studio
stage dimensions: Height to grid 4.26m; width
7.92m; depth 6.4m

Olympia Theatre

72 Dame Street, Dublin 2, Republic of Ireland
box office: + 353 (0)1 677 7744
tel: + 353 (0)1 672 5883
fax: + 353 (0)1 672 5876
email: info@olympia.ie
web: www.olympia.ie
general manager: Brian Whitehead
stage manager: John Brogan
programming policy: Receiving theatre for plays,
musicals, opera, ballet, and music concerts.
Midnight concerts every Friday and Saturday.
terms: Box office split, Guarantee, Rental,
Guarantee/split
seats: 1242
stage type: Proscenium arch
stage dimensions: Height to grid 19.6m; width
10.5m; depth 10.6m

O'Reilly Theatre

Belvedere College, Great Denmark Street
Dublin 1, Republic of Ireland
box office: + 353 (0)1 858 6644
fax: + 353 (0)1 874 4374
email: manager@oreillytheatre.com
web: www.oreillytheatre.com
director: Mary Hickson
technical manager: Cormac Veale
programming policy: The aim of the O'Reilly
Theatre is to create a receiving venue that can
accomodate the diverse needs of the local,
national and international community in parallel
with the resident school community.
terms: Box office split, Guarantee, Rental,
Guarantee/split
main auditorium:
   seats: 392 – 530 **stage type:** Proscenium arch
   stage dimensions: Height to grid 8.9m;
   width 21m
the chapel:
   seats: 100-250 **stage type:** Flexible
   stage dimensions: Depth 8.5m; width 7.9m

Parochial Hall Theatre

Mary St, Clonmel, Co. Tipperary, Republic of Ireland
tel: +353 (0)52 26797
fax: +353 (0)52 27270
email: admin@galloglass.ie
programming manager: Jim Myers
programming policy: The performing base for
Galloglass Theatre Company, the Parochial Hall
Theatre, Clonmel is also available for use by
visiting companies.
terms: Rental
seats: 120
stage type: Flexible
stage dimensions: Height to grid 8.5m; width
7.5m; depth 7.5m
See also Subsidised Companies.

Pavilion Theatre

Marine Road, Dun Laoghaire,
Co. Dublin, Republic of Ireland
box office: + 353 (0)1 231 2929
tel: + 353 (0)1 231 2920
fax: + 353 (0)1 663 6328
email: boxoffice@paviliontheatre.ie
web: www.paviliontheatre.ie
theatre director: Polly O'Loughlin
technical manager: Matt Verso
programming policy: Pavilion Theatre aims to
promote a high quality year round artistic
programme including theatre, dance, music, opera,
comedy, puppetry and multi-media.
terms: Box office split, Guarantee, Rental,
Guarantee/spli
seats: 324 – 420
stage type: Proscenium arch/flexible
stage dimensions: Height to grid 5.8m; width
10.8m; depth 8.5m

The Playhouse

5-7 Artillery St, Derry BT48 6RG, Northern Ireland
tel: + 44 (0)28 7126 8027
fax: + 44 (0)28 7126 1884
programming manager: Jim Leckey
general manager: Niall McCaughan
programming policy: The Playhouse programmes
local, national and international professional,
amateur and community productions, encompassing
a wide range of styles from traditional to
experimental theatre, dance, music and comedy.
terms: Box office split, Guarantee, Rental,
Guarantee/split
seats: 200
stage type: Proscenium arch
stage dimensions: Height to grid 6.3m; width
7.31m; depth 7.31m

The Point

East Link Bridge, North Wall Quay,
Dublin 1, Republic of Ireland
box office: + 353 (0)1 836 3633
tel: + 353 (0)1 836 6777
fax: + 353 (0)1 836 6422
web: www.thepoint.ie
general manager: Cormac Rennick
theatre manager: Paddy Soper
programming policy: The Point provides the
facilities and flexibility to allow the staging of
the most complex productions from classical
pops to popular classics.
terms: Box office split, Guarantee, Rental,
Guarantee/split
Theatre rig
seats: 3,719
stage type: Flexible
stage dimensions: Height to grid 23.16m;
width 31.69m; depth 18.28m

Project Arts Centre

39 East Essex Street, Temple Bar,
Dublin 2, Republic of Ireland
tel: + 353 (0)1 881 9613/881 9614
fax: + 353 (0)1 679 2310
email: info@project.ie
web: www.project.ie
artistic director: Willie White
production manager: David Quinlan
programming policy: Project is a multi-
disciplinary contemporary arts centre and exists
in order to encourage emerging and established
artists in creating innovative work, and to
engage the public in a dynamic encounter with
this work.
terms: Box office split, Rental
space upstairs:
  seats: 180-250 **stage type:** Flexible
  stage dimensions: Height to grid 6.3m;
  width 14.6m; depth 18.65m
project cube:
  seats: 85 **stage type:** Flexible
  stage dimensions: Height to grid 4.5m;
  width 8.8m; depth 11.8m

Ramor Theatre

Virginia, Co. Cavan, Republic of Ireland
tel/fax: + 353 (0)49 854 7074
email: ramortheatre@cavancoco.ie
web: www.ramortheatre.com
theatre manager: Mary Hanley
technical manager: Steve Neale
programming policy: Open to professional dance, drama and music presentations, the venue is particularly interested in productions with an educational aspect.
terms: Box office split, Guarantee, Rental, Guarantee/split
seats: 200
stage type: Proscenium arch
stage dimensions: Height to grid 4.5m; width 6.4m; depth 6.6m

Riverbank Arts Centre

Main Street, Newbridge,
Co. Kildare, Republic of Ireland
tel: + 353 (0)45 433 480
fax: + 353 (0)45 432 490
email: artscentre@riverbank.ie
web: www.riverbank.ie
arts Centre manager: Denis Clifford
programming policy: Riverbank programmes small-scale theatre and dance with an emphasis on innovation, new writing and inter-disciplinary practice.
terms: Guarantee/split
seats: 150-200
stage type: Flexible
stage dimensions: Height to grid 5m; width 8m; depth 8m

Riverside Theatre

University of Ulster, Cromore Road,
Coleraine BT52 1SA, Northern Ireland
box office: + 44 (0)28 7032 3232
tel: + 44 (0)28 7032 4459
fax: + 44 (0)28 7032 4924
email: riversidetheatre@ulster.ac.uk
web: www.ulster.ac.uk/eventsr
artistic director: Andrea Montgomery
technical supervisor: David Coyle
programming policy: Riverside Theatre is a receiving house currently taking the first steps towards its own in-house producing programme. Special interests include accessible international work, relevant new translations, physical theatre and quirky, enjoyable re-interpretations of classic plays. It is particularly interested in premiering work and in receiving material that is not playing elsewhere in Northern Ireland, but will also actively participate with the four other regional theatres in the province to jointly schedule interesting material. It is currently establishing a monthly stand-up comedy night, foyer music night and foyer exhibitions with success.
terms: Box office split, Guarantee, Rental
seats: 270 – 360
stage type: Proscenium arch
stage dimensions: Height to grid 5.5m; width 9m; depth 6.8m

Roscommon Arts Centre

Circular Road, Roscommon, Republic of Ireland
box office: + 353 (0)90 662 5824
tel: + 353 (0)90 662 5993
email: roscartscentre@eircom.net, boxoffice@eircom.net
web: www.roscommonartscentre.ie
director: Jacinta Lynch
programming policy: Roscommon Arts Centre is a multi-disciplinary contemporary arts centre, including local, national and international events in visual art, theatre, music, dance. The Centre also conducts a number of educational programmes.
terms: Box office split, Guarantee, Rental, Hire, Guarantee/split
seats: 194
stage type: Flexible
stage dimensions: End-on: Height to grid 7m; width 11m; depth 8m

Royal Theatre

Castlebar, Co. Mayo, Republic of Ireland
tel: +353 (0)94 902 3111
fax: +353 (0)94 902 1919
email: patj@tfroyaltheatre.com
web: www.royaltheatre.ie
manager/owner: Pat Jennings
technical contact: Tim Ryan
programming policy: The Royal Theatre presents a broad range of local, national, international drama, dance, music and cabaret, particularly events that traditionally go to more densely populated centres.
terms: Box office split, Guarantee, Rental, Guarantee/split
seats: 300 – 1,600
stage type: Flexible
stage dimensions: Height to grid 6m; width 13.5m; depth 6.8m – 9m

Samuel Beckett Theatre

Trinity College, Dublin 2, Republic of Ireland
box office: + 353 (0)1 608 2461
tel: + 353 (0)1 608 1334
fax: + 353 (0)1 679 3488
email: fthackab@tcd.ie
web: www.tcd.ie/drama
general manager: Francis Thackaberry
technical manager: Michael Canney
programming policy: Hosts TCD School of Drama productions in University term time and is a touring venue for professional Irish and international theatre and dance companies for the rest of the year.
terms: Rental
seats: 208
stage type: Flexible
stage dimensions: Height to grid 7.5m; width 12.9m; depth 12.7m

Schoolyard Theatre & Arts Centre

Charleville, Co. Cork, Republic of Ireland
tel: + 353 (0)63 81844
fax: + 353 (0)63 81864
general manager: Kevin O'Shea
administrator: Bernadette Burhill
programming policy: The Schoolyard Theatre presents a broad range of high quality theatre.
terms: Box office split, Guarantee, Rental, Guarantee/split
seats: 102
stage type: Proscenium arch
stage dimensions: Height to grid 3.65m; width 7.31m; depth 5.79m

SFX City Theatre

23 Upper Sherrard Street,
Dublin 1, Republic of Ireland
box office: + 353 (0)1 855 4073
tel: + 353 (0)1 855 4090
fax: + 353 (0)1 855 4671
email: admin@sfx.ie
web: www.sfx.ie
artistic director: Michael Scott
technical director: Paul Hyland
programming policy: Home to The Machine, the SFX City Theatre aims to provide a platform for new and innovative local, national and international work.
terms: Box office split, Rental
seats: 600
stage type: Flexible
stage dimensions: Height to grid 10.66m; width 17.06m; depth 8.53m
See also Subsidised Drama Companies.

Siamsa Tíre Theatre

Town Park, Tralee, Co. Kerry, Republic of Ireland
tel: + 353 (0)66 712 3055
fax: + 353 (0)66 712 7276
email: siamsatire@eircom.net
web: www.siamsatire.com
artistic director: Oliver Hurley
general manager: Marianne Kennedy
programming policy: Siamsa Tíre presents a mixed programme of professional drama, amateur drama, ballet, contemporary dance and opera. The venue is also home to the National Folk Theatre.
terms: Box office split, Guarantee, Rental, Guarantee/split
seats: 355
stage type: Proscenium arch
stage dimensions: Height to grid 10.3m; width 10.5m; depth 11.2m
See also Subsidised Dance Companies.

SS Michael & John's Church and Buildings

15-19 Essex Street West, Dublin 8,
Republic of Ireland
tel: + 353 (0)1 677 2255
fax: + 353 (0)1 677 2525
email: info@templebar.ie
web: www.templebar.ie
enquiries: Zita Griffin
head of cultural development: Grainne Millar
programming policy: SS Michael & John's
consists of three spaces, the Banquet Hall, the
Black Box and the Exhibition Space, available
for performances, rehearsals, exhibitions and
commercial hire.
terms: Rental
banquet hall:
   seats: 220 **stage type:** Flexible
   stage dimensions: Width 13.3m; depth
   25.5m
black box:
   seats: 220 **stage type:** Flexible
   stage dimensions: Height to grid 5.5m;
   width 13.2; depth 12.1

St John's Theatre and Arts Centre

The Square, Listowel, Co. Kerry, Republic of Ireland
tel: + 353 (0)68 22566
fax: + 353 (0)68 23485
email: stjohnstheatre@eircom.net
web: www.stjohnstheatrelistowel.com
artistic director: Joe Murphy
programming policy: St John's presents 150
local, national and international productions
annually, ranging from theatre and dance to all
kinds of music including traditional, classical,
folk, world and popular.
terms: Box office split, Guarantee, Rental,
Guarantee/split
seats: 130
stage type: Proscenium arch
stage dimensions: Height to grid 5m; width
6m; depth 6m

St Michael's Theatre

South Street, New Ross,
Co. Wexford, Republic of Ireland
tel: + 353 (0)51 421 255
fax: + 353 (0)51 420 346
email: stmichaelsnewross@eircom.net
web: www.stmichaelsnewross.com
theatre director: Tomas Kavanagh
technician: David Ryan
programming policy: St Michael's Theatre has a
multi-disciplinary programming policy covering
all aspects of the arts. It has a 329-seat main
theatre, a 40-seat studio and an art gallery.
terms: Box office split, Rental
main auditorium:
   seats: 329
   stage type: Proscenium arch with apron
   stage dimensions: Height to grid 4.11m;
   width 8.07m; depth 6.09m
studio:
   seats: 40 **stage type:** Studio

Taibhdhearc na Gaillimhe

An tSráid Láir, Gaillimh, Republic of Ireland
box office: + 353 (0)91 563600
tel: + 353 (0)91 562024
fax: + 353 (0)91 563195
email: eolas@antaibhdhearc.com
web: www.antaibhdhearc.com
artistic director: Darach Mac Con Iomaire
manager: Aoife Ni Scolai
administrator: Bridget Bhreathnach
programming policy: Taibhdhearc na Gaillimhe
is the national Irish language theatre and
produces five in-house productions a year. The
venue is also available for touring productions
in any language.
terms: Rental
seats: 180
stage type: Proscenium arch with apron
stage dimensions: Height to grid 7.92m; width
7.39m; depth 8.07m

Theatre Royal

The Mall, Waterford, Republic of Ireland
box office: + 353 (0)51 874402
tel: + 353 (0)51 853626
fax: + 353 (0)51 856900
email: theatreroyal@eircom.net
web: www.theatreroyalwaterford.com
theatre manager: Appointment pending
technical director: Tony O'Regan
programming policy: The Theatre Royal is a Victorian-style theatre that acts as a receiving house for all types of production.
terms: Box office split, Guarantee, Rental, Guarantee/split
seats: 598
stage type: Proscenium arch
stage dimensions: Height to grid 11.12m; width 5.63m; depth 7.31m

Theatre Royal

High Street, Wexford, Republic of Ireland
box office: + 353 (0)53 22144
tel: + 353 (0)53 22400
fax: + 353 (0)53 24289
email: info@wexfordopera.com
web: www.wexfordopera.com
chief executive: Jerome Hynes
administrator: Phil Keeling
programming policy: Home of Wexford Festival Opera. Occasional receiving venue.
terms: Rental
seats: 550
stage type: Proscenium arch
stage dimensions: Height to grid 13m; width 6.75m; depth 5.2m

THEatre SPACE @ HENRY PLACE

Henry Place, Dublin 1, Republic of Ireland
tel: + 353 (0)1 872 9977
fax: + 353 (0)1 872 9402
email: theatrespace@eircom.net
programmer: Teresa O'Toole-Cahill
manager: Patrick Cahill
programming policy: THEatre Space's aim is to provide an approachable platform for emerging and established artists, and to encourage and promote Irish language and culture through the medium of theatre.
terms: Box office split, Rental
seats: 120
stage type: Flexible
stage dimensions: Height to grid 6m; width 12.6m; depth 8.5m

Tipperary Excel

Michael Street, Tipperary Town, Republic of Ireland
tel: + 353 (0)62 33466/(0)86 263 0608
email: bill.flynn@iol.ie
web: www.tipperary-excel.com
general manager: Bill Flynn
programming policy: Programmes a variety of amateur and professional productions.
terms: Box office split, Guarantee, Rental, Guarantee/split
seats: 380
stage type: Proscenium arch
stage dimensions: Height to grid 6.09m; width 8.53m; depth 7.92m

Tivoli Theatre

135-138 Francis Street, Dublin 8, Republic of Ireland
box office: + 353 (0)1 454 4472/(0)1 454 4473
tel: + 353 (0)1 454 6367/+ 353 (0)1 464 6369
fax: + 353 (0)1 453 3167
email: thetivoli@hotmail.com
managing director: Tony Byrne
general manager: Carol-Ann Byrne
programming policy: The Tivoli presents a varied programme of drama, dance, music and comedy events.
terms: Rental
main auditorium:
    seats: 446-560 **stage type:** Flexible
    stage dimensions: Height to grid 6.58m; width 18.46m; depth 12.19m
downstairs:
    seats: 300 (1,000 standing) **stage type:** Flexible
    stage dimensions: Not available

Town Hall Theatre

Courthouse Square, Galway, Republic of Ireland
box office: + 353 (0)91 569777
tel: + 353 (0)91 569755
fax: + 353 (0)91 569664
email: tht@galwaycity.ie
web: www.townhalltheatregalway.com
manager: Mike Diskin
technical manager: Peter Ashton
programming policy: Aims to be at the centre of the arts and entertainment life of Galway by presenting a broad range of professional theatre productions.
terms: Box office split, Guarantee, Rental, Guarantee/split
seats: 393
stage type: Proscenium arch
stage dimensions: Height to grid 5.4m; width 10.7m; depth 7.2m
See also the Black Box, Galway.

Triskel Arts Centre

Tobin Street, Cork, Republic of Ireland
tel: + 353 (0)21 427 2022
fax: + 353 (0)21 427 2592
email: info@triskelartscentre.com
artistic director: Penny Rae
marketing officer: Susan Kirby
programming policy: Triskel encourages and supports excellence, experimentation and innovation. Drama policy is currently being developed. Approaches from companies are welcomed.
terms: Box office split, Guarantee, Rental, Guarantee/split
seats: 90
stage type: End on
stage dimensions: Height to ceiling 3.8m; width 5.1m; depth 4.3m

Tuar Ard Arts Centre

Church Street, Moate,
Co. Westmeath, Republic of Ireland
tel: + 353 (0)90 648 2042
fax: + 353 (0)90 648 2044
email: tuarard@eircom.net
manager: Maura Farrell
technical contact: Tommy Mollen
programming policy: All types of drama, dance and music.
terms: Box office split, Guarantee, Rental, Guarantee/split
seats: 173
stage type: Proscenium arch
stage dimensions: Height to grid 4m; width 9.14m; depth 6.7m

University Concert Hall

Limerick, Republic of Ireland
tel: + 353 (0)61 331549
fax: + 353 (0)61 331585
web: www.uch.ie
director: Michael J. Murphy
technical manager: Gary Sciascia
programming policy: Multi-purpose venue, open to all art forms.
terms: Box office split, Guarantee, Rental, Guarantee/split
seats: 1,038
stage type: Concert platform
stage dimensions: Height to grid 9m; width 18m; depth 11m

Vicar Street

58-59 Thomas Street, Dublin 8, Republic of Ireland
box office: + 353 (0)870 534 4444
tel: + 353 (0)1 454 6650
fax: + 353 (0)1 454 6787
email: office@aikenpromotions.ie
web: www.vicarstreet.com
artistic contact: Bren Berry
technical contact: Gerry Brady
programming policy: Primarily a music venue but well-suited to comedy productions. Has also programmed some theatre.
terms: Rental
seats: 600
stage type: Proscenium arch
stage dimensions: Height to grid 5.48m; width 15.24m; depth 5.18m

The Village Arts Centre

The Square, Kilworth, Co. Cork, Republic of Ireland
tel: + 353 (0)25 24451
fax: + 353 (0)25 84463
email: liam.howard@avondhupress.ie
web: www.avondhupress.ie
chairman/administrator: Liam Howard
programming policy: To bring the work of professional, semi-professional and amateur actors, musicians and writers to the people of the local community.
terms: Box office split, Guarantee, Rental, Guarantee/split
seats: 100
stage type: End on
stage dimensions: Height to grid 4m; width 5.7m; depth 3.6m

Waterfront Hall, including the ntl Studio

2 Lanyon Place, Belfast BT1 3WH, Northern Ireland
box office: + 44 (0)28 9033 4455
tel: + 44 (0)28 9033 4400
email: magills@waterfront.co.uk
web: www.waterfront.co.uk
general manager: Tim Husbands
entertainments co-ordinator: Simon Magill
programming policy: The venue promotes a policy of partnerships with both home-based and visiting companies, including internationally renowned groups.
terms: Box office split, Guarantee, Rental, Guarantee/split
main auditorium:
  seats: 2197 **stage type:** Concert platform
  stage dimensions: Height to grid 22m; width 11m; depth 11m
ntl studio:
  seats: 380 **stage type:** Flexible
  stage dimensions: Height to grid 7m; width 14m; depth 6-10m

Watergate Theatre

Parliament Street, Kilkenny, Republic of Ireland
box office: + 353 (0)56 776 1674
tel: + 353 (0)56 775 1605
fax: + 353 (0)56 775 1780
email: watergateinfo@eircom.net
web: www.watergatekilkenny.com
theatre manager: Gerry Cody
technical manager: Arthur Drohan
programming policy: To promote and attract productions of quality theatre and dance from Ireland and abroad.
terms: Box office split, Guarantee, Rental, Guarantee/split
seats: 328
stage type: Proscenium arch
stage dimensions: Height to grid 12.5m; width 9.12m; depth 7.88m

West Cork Arts Centre

North Street, Skibbereen,
Co Cork, Republic of Ireland
tel: + 353 (0)28 22090
fax: + 353 (0)28 23237
email: westcorkarts@eircom.net
chairperson: Keran Brady
director: Ann Davoren
education and community co-ordinator: Justine Foster
programming policy: The centre has an extensive outreach programme incorporating dance, drama and youth theatre. It is also interested in developing a small-scale touring programme in its gallery space.
terms: Box office split
seats: 50 – 80
stage type: Flexible
stage dimensions: Height to grid 3.68m; width 4.72m; depth 2.43m

Wexford Arts Centre

Cornmarket, Wexford, Republic of Ireland
tel: + 353 (0)53 23764
fax: + 353 (0)53 24544
email: wexfordartscentre@eircom.net
web: www.wexfordartscentre.ie
artistic director: Denis Collins
publicity: Anne Comerford
programming policy: Wexford Arts Centre presents professional, semi-professional, amateur and community theatre by local and visiting groups. It receives touring product as well as producing its own shows and supporting local productions. It has a particular interest in minimal theatre.
terms: Box office split, Guarantee, Rental, Guarantee/split
seats: 122
stage type: End on
stage dimensions: Height to grid 3.5m; width 7.5m; depth 5m

Further details, plans, photographs and full technical specifications for the main venues on the Irish touring circuit will be available from the Arts Council's web: www.artscouncil.ie

irish festivals

*Declan Conlon in Kilkenny Arts Festival's production of The Book of Evidence,
by John Banville, adapted by Alan Gilsenan, 2002 © Ros Kavanagh*

Baboró – International Arts Festival for Children

The Black Box, Dyke Road, Galway, Republic of Ireland
tel: + 353 (0)91 509705/091 590706
fax: + 353 (0)91 562655
email: baboro@gaf.iol.ie, education@gaf.iol.ie
web: www.baboro.ie
executive director: Lali Morris
programming policy: Baboró is Ireland's leading arts festival devoted exclusively to children between the ages of three and twelve. Each year, the festival programmes the highest quality theatre, dance, music, puppetry from artists both national and international. Baboró also has an extensive outreach programme.
festival dates: Second week in October

Belfast Festival at Queen's

Festival House, 25 College Gardens, Belfast BT9 6BS, Northern Ireland
box office: + 44 (0)28 9097 2626
tel: + 44 (0)28 9097 2600
fax: + 44 (0)28 9097 2630
email: festival@qub.ac.uk
web: www.belfastfestival.com
director: Stella Hall
pr manager/programmer: Graeme Farrow
programming policy: Every year, the largest festival of its kind in Ireland brings the best of international art to Belfast and brings international attention to the city's dynamic arts practitioners. The beauty of the Festival lies in its bold and eclectic cultural mix. Visitors can experience the richness of Northern Irish culture alongside work from Lithuania, Japan, India, the US or Ghana in a range of venues across the city. The Festival covers the widest range of art forms including theatre, dance, classical music, literature, jazz, comedy, visual arts, folk music and popular music.
festival dates: Last week October/first week November

Boyle Arts Festival

Greatmeadow, Boyle, Co. Roscommon, Republic of Ireland
box office: + 353 (0)79 63085
tel: + 353 (0)79 62458
fax: + 353 (0)79 62894
chairperson: Rhona Feely
secretary: Michael Devine
programming policy: Boyle Arts Festival features both visual and performing arts. In the main exhibition, Ireland's leading artists and sculptors show their work in King House, complemented by exhibitions of local artists. The performing arts programme includes recitals by established and emerging performers, lectures, storytelling, drama, children's programmes and workshops.
festival dates: Eight days prior to August Bank Holiday weekend

Cathedral Quarter Arts Festival

20 North Street Arcade, Belfast BT1 1PB, Northern Ireland
tel: + 44 (0)28 9023 2403
fax: + 44 (0)28 9031 9884
email: info@cqaf.com
web: www.cqaf.com
festival director: Sean Kelly
administrator: Rosie McMichael
programming policy: The festival aims to promote contemporary new writing and has a strong fringe or alternative ethos. The festival has a particular interest in site-specific and promenade theatre works.
festival dates: Early May

Clifden Community Arts Week

Clifden, Co. Galway, Republic of Ireland
tel: + 353 (0)95 21644
email: artsweek@indigo.ie
director: Brendan Flynn
programming policy: A small, intimate, multi-disciplinary festival that includes theatre and dance in its programme.
festival dates: September

The Clonmel Junction Festival

Chamber of Commerce, 8 Sarsfield Street,
Clonmel, Co. Tipperary, Republic of Ireland
tel: + 353 (0)52 29339/(0)87 797 3639
email: dteevan@eircom.net
web: www.junctionfestival.com
festival director: David Teevan
programming policy: Nine days and nights of
the best of touring theatre and music from
America, Britain, and Ireland. Programme
includes children's theatre and comedy.
festival dates: July

Cootehill Arts Festival

61 Cavan Road, Cootehill,
Co. Cavan, Republic of Ireland
tel: + 353 (0)49 555 2241
chairperson: Anne Tully
programming policy: Events include exhibitions
of local and invited artists, craft shows, readings,
drama, classical music concerts, musical events
and workshops.
festival dates: October

Cork Arts Festival

Cork Institute of Technology, Bishopstown,
Cork, Republic of Ireland
box office: + 353 (0)21 432 6553
tel: + 353 (0)21 432 6445
fax: + 353 (0)21 432 6567
email: artsfest@cit.ie
web: www.cit.ie
arts officer: Una McCarthy
programming policy: To programme drama and
dance that will meet the needs of the student
body of Cork Institute of Technology.
festival dates: Second & third weeks of November

Cork Fringe Festival

c/o Granary Theatre, Mardyke,
Cork, Republic of Ireland
tel/fax: + 353 (0)21 490 4272
email: granary@ucc.ie
artistic director: Ali Robertson
administration assistant: Maeve Lewis
programming policy: The Cork Fringe Festival
presents a steadily expanding, artistically
adventurous programme of small to medium-
scale drama and dance from Ireland, the UK and
mainland Europe. The work is presented in a
number of venues across Cork city.
festival dates: Two weeks in September/October

Draiocht Children's Arts Festival

c/o Féile an Phobail, 473 Falls Road,
Belfast BT12 6AA, Co. Antrim, Northern Ireland
box office: + 44 (0)28 9020 9090
tel: + 44 (0)28 9031 3440
fax: + 44 (0)28 9031 9150
email: info@feilebelfast.com
web: www.feilebelfast.com
children's arts co-ordinator: Johnpaul Russell
programming policy: To showcase the top local,
national and international shows for children.
festival dates: March

Dublin Fringe Festival

12 East Essex Street, Dublin 2, Republic of Ireland
box office: 1850 374 643
tel: + 353 (0)1 679 2320
fax: + 353 (0)1 679 2790
email: info@fringefest.com
web: www.fringefest.com
festival director 2004: Vallejo Gantner
executive producer: Bea Kelleher
programming policy: Dublin Fringe Festival
programmes theatre, dance and performance art
from Irish and international companies. Specific
areas of focus are new Irish writing and work
not previously produced in Ireland, innovative
production style, physical theatre, and work
from young, recently formed companies.
festival dates: Last week in September to
second week in October

Dublin Theatre Festival

44 East Essex Street, Temple Bar,
Dublin 2, Republic of Ireland
tel: + 353 (0)1 677 8439
fax: + 353 (0)1 679 7709
email: info@dublintheatrefestival.com
web: www.dublintheatrefestival.com
director 2004: Fergus Linehan
commercial manager: Ross Keane
programming policy: The Dublin Theatre Festival
was founded in 1957 and has, with the exception of
two years, produced a season of international and
Irish theatre each autumn. Over the past four
decades, the Festival has become a crucial part of
Ireland's cultural landscape. It has played a dual
role as a window to world theatre, having presented
almost every great theatre artist of the late 20th
century, and as a champion of Irish writing on the
world stage. As well as inspiring local audiences,
the international programme has given Irish work a
fresh context and encouraged a shift in thinking
among Irish theatre artists. Programming
encapsulates large-scale progressive productions,
new plays, classics and work for children.
festival dates: Two weeks end September/early
October

Earagail Arts Festival

c/o Letterkenny Arts Centre, Oliver Plunkett Road,
Letterkenny, Co. Donegal, Republic of Ireland
box office: + 353 (0)74 912 0777
tel: + 353 (0)74 912 9186
fax: + 353 (0)74 912 3276
email: info@earagailartsfestival.ie
web: www.earagailartsfestival.ie
festival manager: Angela McLaughlin
programming policy: To programme the best of
Irish and international theatre, dance and art in
a wide range of venues and communities across
North Donegal. The Festival also commissions and
co-produces its own theatre and dance works.
festival dates: Second and third weeks in July

EarthQuake Festival of International Dance

Dance Northern Ireland, 15 Church Street,
Belfast BT1 1PG, Northern Ireland
tel: +44 (0)28 9024 9930
email: info@danceni.com
web: www.danceni.com
director: Vicki Maguire
project manager: Lisa May
programming policy: EarthQuake is a festival
aimed at bringing international dance to a wider
audience. The award-winning festival is unique
in that it includes all forms of dance and offers
a huge variety of turn-up-and-try dance
workshops free to the public in every dance
form imaginable. This year's visiting companies
included Zurich Ballet, Rhythm in Shoes from
Ohio and Dance Theatre of Harlem.
festival dates: April

Eigse Carlow Arts Festival

Foresters Hall, College Street,
Carlow, Republic of Ireland
tel: + 353 (0)59 914 0491
fax: + 353 (0)59 913 0065
email: eigsecarlo@eircom.net
web: www.eigsecarlow.ie
festival director: Averyl Dooher
programming policy: Eigse's programme includes
visual art, performance, theatre, dance, literature,
music and craft from Irish and international
artists. In the past two years, the festival has
commissioned new work in music and visual art,
and in 2004 this will be extended to include
performance and dance. Artists and companies in
these areas are invited to submit work for
consideration at any time, and the festival is
particularly keen to showcase the work of those
who are young and Irish.
festival dates: Ten days in June

Feile an Phobail

473 Falls Road, Belfast BT12 6AA, Northern Ireland
box office: + 44 (0)28 9028 4028
tel: + 44 (0)28 9031 3440
fax: + 44 (0)28 9031 9150
email: info@feilebelfast.com
web: www.feilebelfast.com
director: Carol Jackson
children's arts co-ordinator: Johnpaul Russell
programming policy: To showcase the top local,
national and international shows.
festival dates: August
See also Draíocht Children's Festival.

Galway Arts Festival

Black Box, Dyke Road, Galway, Republic of Ireland
tel: + 353 (0)91 509700
fax: + 353 (0)91 562655
email: info@gaf.iol.ie
web: www.galwayartsfestival.ie
festival director: Rose Parkinson
general manager: John Crumlish
programming policy: One of Ireland's largest
multi-disiplinary festivals. Participation is by
invitation. Companies are invited to submit
information at any time.
festival dates: Last fortnight in July

International Dance Festival Ireland

26 South Frederick Street,
Dublin 2, Republic of Ireland
tel: + 353 (0)1 679 0524
fax: + 353 (0)1 679 1685
email: info@dancefestivalireland.ie
web: www.dancefestivalireland.ie
artistic director: Catherine Nunes
general manager: Marina Rafter
programming policy: The first ever International
Dance Festival Ireland took place in May 2002,
with a programme including Merce Cunningham,
Michael Clark, Jerome Bel, Irish Modern Dance
Theatre, CoisCéim and Daghdha. The Festival's
artistic policy is to present the best of
international contemporary dance within a
festival context, to inspire and excite audiences
and artists through excellence and innovation, to
increase access to the art form and reflect its
diversity through a stimulating range of events,
to promote Ireland as an international focal
point for artistic exchange and collaboration.
The next Festival is May 2006.
festival dates: May

International Puppet Festival

c/o Lambert Puppet Theatre, Clifton Lane,
Monkstown, Co. Dublin, Republic of Ireland
tel: + 353 (0)1 280 0974/(0)1 280 1863
fax: + 353 (0)1 280 4772
email: festivalireland@lambertpuppettheatre.com
web: www.lambertpuppettheatre.com
festival director: Miriam Lambert
programming policy: To bring a wide range of
international puppeteers to an Irish audience with
an emphasis on innovation and artistic excellence.
festival dates: Second week in September

Kilkenny Arts Festival

9/10 Abbey Business Centre, Abbey Street,
Kilkenny, Republic of Ireland
box office: + 353 (0)56 775 2175 (opens July)
tel: + 353 (0)56 776 3663
fax: + 353 (0)56 775 1704
email: info@kilkennyarts.ie
web: www.kilkennyarts.ie
director: Claudia Woolgar
festival manager: Marion Gowran
programming policy: Kilkenny Arts Festival is
an international multi-arts festival, which takes
place annually over ten days in August in the
city and county of Kilkenny. The Festival is
continually developing new programming
strands. While continuing to present the very
best of established Irish and international
artists, the Festival invests in encouraging and
fostering new artistic talent. Theatre is a very
important part of the programme. Over the last
number of years the Festival has successfully
collaborated with some of Ireland's finest
theatre practitioners and is now committed to
producing its own work. It also engages with
leading street theatre companies.
festival dates: ten days early-mid August

Lisburn's Island Children's Arts Festival

Island Arts Centre, Lagan Valley Island
Lisburn, Co. Down BT27 4RC, Northern Ireland
tel: + 44 (0)28 9250 9509
fax: + 44 (0)28 9266 2679
email: manager.hhac@lisburn.gov.uk
arts manager: Siobhan McCormick
programming policy: This annual festival of
local work includes some visiting drama, dance
and street theatre productions, and usually runs
for the first two weeks of August.
festival dates: August

Murphy's Cat Laughs Comedy Festival

11 The Spires, Dean Street,
Kilkenny, Republic of Ireland
tel: +353 (0)56 776 3416
fax: +353 (0)56 776 3679
email: laughs@iol.ie
web: www.thecatlaughs.com
artistic director: Richard Cook
festival producer: Lynn Cahill
programming policy: Performance at the festival is
by invitation. Submissions can be made by sending
video/DVD of live stand-up to the festival director.
festival dates: June Bank Holiday weekend

Omagh Arts Festival

Omagh District Council, The Grange, Mountjoy Road
Omagh BT79 7BL, Co. Tyrone, Northern Ireland
box office: + 44 (0)28 8224 7831
tel: + 44 (0)28 8224 5321
fax: + 44 (0)28 8224 3888
email: jean.brennan@omagh.gov.uk
arts development officer: Jean Brennan
programming policy: The Omagh Arts Festival
programmes music, comedy, drama, literature,
storytelling, youth projects and art exhibitions.
festival dates: Three weeks in October

Opera Fringe Northern Ireland

Dublin Arts Centre, 2-6 Irish Street,
Downpatrick BT30 6BN, Northern Ireland
tel: + 44 (0)28 4461 5283
fax: + 44 (0)28 4461 6621
email: mail@downartscentre.com
web: www.operafringe.com
artistic director: Randall Shannon
festival director: Cathie McKimm
programming policy: Opera Fringe runs alongside
the main opera programme at Castleward each
June. The programme prioritises shorter alternative
opera performances and also has a short touring
programme into venues throughout the district
attempting to find new audiences for opera. There
is also a residency, workshops, free lunch-time
concerts, opera film and dinner night, exhibition,
talks and lectures.
festival dates: Mid-June

Pan Pan International Theatre Symposium

43 Upper George's Street, Dun Laoghaire,
Co. Dublin, Republic of Ireland
tel: + 353 (0)1 280 0544
fax: + 353 (0)1 230 0918
email: info@panpantheatre.com
web: www.panpantheatre.com
artistic directors: Gavin Quinn, Aedín Cosgrove
general manager: Aoife White
programming policy: The Pan Pan International
Theatre Symposium is a unique and dynamic
celebration of live performance, comprising talks,
workshops, demonstration performances and full
performances, presenting the extraordinary
variety of styles, approaches and viewpoints in
contemporary world theatre. It brings together
leading companies from all over the world with
very different theatrical traditions, giving
audiences an opportunity to see work never seen
in Ireland before. It also offers Irish theatre
practitioners the chance to see their work in the
context of contemporary world practice.
festival dates: Second week in January
(biennial – odd years)

Samhlaiocht Easter Arts Festival

The Boatyard, Blennerville,
Tralee, Co. Kerry, Republic of Ireland
tel: + 353 (0)66 712 9934
email: samhlaiocht@indigo.ie
web: www.samhlaiocht.com
artistic director: Maurice Galway
supervisor: Una Curran
programming policy: A community-based
programme celebrating the artistic and cultural
life of Co. Kerry. The four-day festival includes
exhibitions, performances and street theatre.
festival dates: Easter Weekend

Spraoi

The Studios, Carrickpherish,
Waterford, Republic of Ireland
tel: + 353 (0)51 841808
fax: + 353 (0)51 858023
email: info@spraoi.com
web: www.spraoi.com
director: T.V. Honan
programme director: Miriam Dunne
programming policy: An annual festival, held
over the first weekend in August. Spraoi takes
over the city centre of Waterford, transforming it
into a gigantic outdoor stage, featuring
international street theatre artists and companies,
and world music. Spraoi is committed to the
advancement of street theatre, and the production
and showcasing of the best national and
international theatre available in this diverse
discipline. The Spraoi Parade, regarded as the climax
of the festival, involves up to 300 costumed
performers, giant props and floats, lights and
special effects. Spraoi specialise in festival
organisation and production, street theatre and
spectacle. It is a full-time festival and
production company, employing seven people
full-time, and many more on a contract basis
throughout the year. The company also relies
heavily on the goodwill and support of a large
number of volunteers.
festival dates: First weekend in August
(30th July to 1st August 2004)

St Patrick's Festival

St Stephen's Green House, Earlsfort Terrace,
Dublin 2, Republic of Ireland
tel: + 353 (0)1 676 3205
fax: + 353 (0)1 676 3208
email: info@stpatricksday.ie
web: www.stpatricksday.ie
artistic director: Appointment pending
chief executive: Appointment pending
programming policy: An annual 5 day international
festival based around the national holiday. St
Patrick's Festival programmes a diverse range of arts
events as a celebration of Ireland and Irish people
around the world. It supports and develops street
theatre in Ireland by showcasing emerging talent
and promoting Irish street theatre and pageant
companies. The festival consolidates and develops
opportunities for young people to create and be
involved in street arts. St Patrick's Festival actively
seeks opportunities to co-commission projects.
Project ideas and proposals can be forwarded to the
Festival for the attention of the Artistic Director.
festival dates: Around 17th March

UnFringed

Belltable Arts Centre, 69 O'Connell Street,
Limerick, Republic of Ireland
box office: + 353 (0)61 319866
tel: + 353 (0)61 319709
fax: + 353 (0)61 418552
email: belltabl@iol.ie
web: www.belltable.ie
director: Peter McNamara
programming policy: To offer audiences of all
ages in the mid-West region an opportunity to see
the best of fringe theatre. The festival also
commissions work and engages in co-producing.
Since its debut in 1998, the programme has
extended to include award-winning shows from the
international stage, specially commissioned pieces,
workshops, talks and a children's programme.
festival dates: Last week in January and first
week in February.

Wainfest

Letterkenny Arts Centre, Central Library,
Oliver Plunkett Road, Letterkenny,
Co. Donegal, Republic of Ireland
tel: + 353 (0)74 912 9186
fax: + 353 (0)74 912 3276
email: lkarts@indigo.ie
web: www.donegalculture.com
director: John M. Cunningham
assistant director: Derek O'Connor
programming policy: Wainfest is an annual
children's arts festival featuring a broad
programme of literary, art and drama events
throughout County Donegal. Performances take
place in theatres, schools and other venues.
festival dates: Last week in October and first
week in November

Westport Arts Festival

Killeenacoff, Westport, Co. Mayo, Republic of Ireland
tel: + 353 (0)98 25078
email: info@westportartsfestival.com
web: www.westportartscentre.com
chairperson: Caroline Loftus
programming policy: Westport Arts Festival, now in its 28th year, has long since established itself on the West coast calendar as an exciting, diverse event. The festival is locally run by committed volunteers for the enjoyment of the local community as well as the thousands of tourists who visit the area. This year's programme will be run over a seven-day period starting 20 September and will be made up of a mix of daytime workshops, lectures and exhibitions which will complement the evening musical and theatrical programmes from some of Ireland's best-known artists.
festival dates: Last week in September

Wexford Festival Opera

Theatre Royal, High Street,
Wexford, Republic of Ireland
box office: + 353 (0)53 22144
tel: + 353 (0)53 22400
fax: + 353 (0)53 24289
email: info@wexfordopera.com
web: www.wexfordopera.com
artistic director: Luigi Ferrari
chief executive: Jerome Hynes
programming policy: For over 50 years, the Irish coastal town of Wexford has showcased this festival of rare opera, which boasts a reputation as international as its audience. The narrow, ancient Viking streets and tiny, atmospheric theatre set the scene for over 40 daytime events as well as 18 evening performances of three major productions. The productions are rehearsed and performed only in Wexford, with the Wexford company of artists, drawn from all over the world, participating in many of the events day and night.
festival dates: Late October/November

Woodford Bourne Cork Midsummer Festival

Festival House, O'Kellys Post Office, Grand Parade, Cork, Republic of Ireland
tel: + 353 (0)21 427 5874
fax: + 353 (0)21 427 5875
email: corkfestival@eircom.net
web: www.corkfestival.ie
artistic director: Ali Robertson
festival manager: Ciara Ní Shuilleabháin
programming policy: The Woodford Bourne Cork Midsummer Festival is Cork's only multi-disciplinary arts festival. It provides an annual platform for Cork artists and arts organisations in the fields of theatre, film, music, visual art, community art, literature, dance and family entertainment, and it provides Cork audiences with the chance to see a broad range of the best of local, national and international art of all kinds. We celebrate the new and the innovative alongside conventional work. We offer artists an opportunity to experiment with form, style and practice, while remaining true to the tenets of quality and accessibility. The festival is a curated festival and accepts submissions from any quarter.
festival dates: Twelve days around Midsummer's Day (21st June)

Young at Art

Room D105, Central Building, Stranmillis University, Belfast BT9 5DY, Northern Ireland
box office: + 44 (0)28 9038 4385
tel/fax: + 44 (0)28 9066 0515
email: admin@youngatart.co.uk
web: www.youngatart.co.uk
director: Ali FitzGibbon
audience development officer: Alice Jackson
programming policy: The festival programmes international quality contemporary work aimed at three to eighteen year olds. Cutting edge, inclusive, challenging and innovative work is selected.
festival dates: May Bank Holiday (Northern Ireland)

international festivals

Seán Kearns and Deirdre Molloy in Barabbas's production of
A Midsummer Night's Dream by Shakespeare 2004 © Pat Redmond

Asia

Hong Kong Arts Festival
12/F Hong Kong Arts Centre
2 Harbour Road, Wanchai
Hong Kong, China
tel: +852 2842 3555
fax: +852 2842 3722
email: afgen@hkaf.org
web: www.hk.artsfestival.org
executive director: Mr Kau Ng
dates: February/March

Singapore Arts Festival
c/o National Arts Council
140 Hill Street, MITA Building
#03-01, Singapore 179369
tel: +65 837 9712
fax: +65 837 3014
email: Goh_Ching_Lee@nac.gov.sg
web: www.nac.gov.sg
director: Ms Goh Ching-Lee
dates: May/June

Australia

Adelaide Festival of the Arts
PO Box 8116, Station Arcade
Adelaide, SA 5000, Australia
tel: +61 8 8216 4444
fax: +61 8 8216 4455
email: afa@adelaidefestival.net.au
web: www.adelaidefestival.org.au
artistic director: Brett Sheehy (2006)
dates: March (biennial)

Adelaide Fringe Festival
PO Box 3242, Rundle Mall
Adelaide, SA 5000, Australia
tel: +61 8 8100 2000
fax: +61 8 8100 2020
email: buzz@adelaidefringe.com.au
web: www.adelaidefringe.com.au
director: Karen Hadfield
dates: February/March
(biennial – even years)

Melbourne Festival
PO Box 10, Flinders Lane
Melbourne, VIC 8009, Australia
tel: +61 3 9662 4242
fax: +61 3 9663 4141
email: melfest@melbournefestival.com.au
web: www.melbournefestival.com.au
artistic director: Robyn Archer
(2004), Kristy Edmunds (2005/2006)
dates: October/November

New Zealand Festival
PO Box 10 113, The Terrace
Wellington, New Zealand
tel: +64 4 473 0149
fax: +64 4 471 1164
email: nzfestival@festival.co.nz
web: www.nzfestival.telecom.co.nz
artistic director: Carla van Zon
dates: February/March
(biennial - even years)

Perth International Arts Festival
UWA Festival Centre, 3 Crawley Ave.
Crawley WA 6009, Australia
tel: +61 8 6488 2000
fax: +61 8 6488 8555
email: festival@perthfestival.com.au
web: www.perthfestival.com.au
artistic director: Lindy Hume
dates: January/February

Sydney Festival
Festival Office, Level 2,
10 Hickson Road, The Rocks
NSW 2000, Sydney, Australia
tel: +61 2 8248 6500
fax: +61 2 8248 6599
email: mail@sydneyfestival.org.au
web: www.sydneyfestival.org.au
festival director: Brett Sheehy
(2005), Fergus Linehan (2006/2008)
dates: January

Ten Days on the Island
GPO Box 1403, Hobart, Tasmania 7001
tel: +61 3 6233 5700
fax: +61 3 6233 5830
email: info@tendaysontheisland.org
web: www.tendaysontheisland.org
artistic director: Robyn Archer
dates: March/April
(biennial - odd years)

Continental Europe

Barcelona Festival del Grec
Institut de Cultura
Ajuntament de Barcelona
La Rambla 99, 08002 Barcelona, Spain
email: grecicub@mail.bcn.es
web: www.bcn.es/grec25
director: Borja Sitja
dates: June-August

Bergen International Arts Festival
P.O. Box 183, Sentrum,
N5804 Bergen, Norway
tel: +47 55 210630
fax: +47 55 210640
email: henning.malsnes@fib.no
web: www.fib.no
director: Henning Målsnes
dates: May

Berliner Festspiele
Schaper Straße 24
10719 Berlin, Germany
tel: +49 30 2548 90
fax: +49 30 2548 9111
email: info@berlinerfestspiele.de
web: www.berlinerfestspiele.de
director: Prof. Joachim Sartorius
theatre & dance: Markus Luchsinger
dates: September

Celtic Festival
(Théâtres des Mondes Celtes)
Théâtre de Cornouaille
1 Esplanade François Mitterrand
29337 Quimper, Brittany, France
tel: +33 2 9855 9898
email: theatrecornouaille@
theatrequimper.asso.fr
web: www.theatrequimper.asso.fr
festival manager: Igor Gardes
dates: March

Euro-Scene Leipzig
Gottschedstraße16
D-04109 Leipzig, Germany
tel: +49 341 980 0284
fax: +49 341 980 4860
email: info@euro-scene.de
web: www.euro-scene.de
festival director: Ann-Elisabeth Wolff
dates: November

Festival d'Automne

156 rue de Rivoli, 75001 Paris, France
tel: +33 1 5345 1700
fax: +33 1 5345 1701
email: info@festival-automne.com
web: www.festival-automne.com
theatre & dance director: Marie Collin
dates: September-December

Festival d'Avignon

6 rue de Braque, 75003 Paris, France
tel: +33 1 4461 8484
fax: +33 1 4461 8523
email: art.festival@wanadoo.fr
web: www.festival-avignon.com
director: Thomas Ostermeier
dates: July

Festival International Montpellier Danse

Hôtel d'Assas, 6 rue Vieille Aiguillerie
34000 Montpellier, France
tel: +33 4 6760 8360
fax: +33 4 6760 8306
email: info@montpellierdanse.com
web: www.montpellierdanse.com
director general: Jean-Paul Montanari
dates: June/July

Festival Off d'Avignon

Avignon Public off 105, Bld Voltaire
75011 Paris, France
tel: +33 1 4805 0119
fax: +33 1 4805 4067
email: festoff@wanadoo.fr
web: www.avignon-off.org
director: Alain Léonard
dates: July

Florence Dance Festival

Florence Dance Cultural Centre,
Borgo Stella 23R,
50124 Florence, Italy
tel: +39 055 289276
fax: +39 055 265 4450
email: info@florencedance.org
web: www.florencedance.org
artistic directors: Marga Nativo,
Keith Ferrone
dates: July

Holland Festival

Kleine-Gartmanplantsoen 21,
1017 RP Amsterdam, The Netherlands
tel: +31 20 530 7110
fax: +31 20 530 7119
email: info@hollandfestival.nl
web: www.hollandfestival.nl
director: Ivo van Hove (2004),
Pierre Audi (2005)
dates: June

Im PulsTanz

formerly known as Tanzwochen Wien
Museumstraße 5/21
A-1070 Vienna, Austria
tel: +43 1 523 5558
fax: +43 1 523 16839
email: info@impulstanz.com
web: www.impulstanz.com
artistic director: Karl Regensburger
dates: July/August

Internationales Tanzfest Berlin – Tanz im August

TanzWerkstatt Berlin, Klosterstr. 68-70
10179 Berlin, Germany
tel: +49 30 2474 9756
fax: +49 30 2474 9757
email: twb@bkv.org
web: www.tanzfest.de
artistic directors: Ulrike Becker, André
Thériault (TanzWerkstatt Berlin), Nele
Hertling, Marion Ziemann (Hebbel-
Theater)
dates: August

KunstenFESTIVALdesArts

Handelskaai 18, Quai du Commerce
1000 Brussels, Belgium
tel: +32 2 219 0707
fax: +32 2 218 7453
email: info@kfda.be
web: www.kfda.be
artistic director: Frie Leysen
dates: May

Maifestspiele

Hessisches Staatstheater
Wiesbaden, Christian-Zais-Str. 3
D-65189 Wiesbaden, Germany
tel: +49 611 132 264
fax: +49 611 132 244
email: intendanz@staatstheater-
wiesbaden.de
web: www.hessisches-staatstheater.de
artistic director: Dr. Manfred Beilharz
dates: May

Prague Fringe Festival

Lumírova 27, 128 00 Prague 2
Czech Republic
tel: +420 602 549008/
+44 77 1953 1466
email: info@praguefringe.com
web: www.praguefringe.com
festival director: Steven Gove
dates: June

Roma Europa Festival

via XX Settembre, 3
00187 Rome, Italy
tel: +39 06 422 2961
fax: +39 06 4889 9238
email: festival@romaeuropa.net
web: www.romaeuropa.net
general/artistic manager:
Monique Veaute
dates: September-November

Springdance

PO Box 111, NL-3500 AC
Utrecht, The Netherlands
tel: +31 30 233 2032
fax: +31 30 231 9364
email: mail@springdance.nl
web: www.springdance.nl
artistic director: Simon Dove
dates: April (biennial - odd years)

Theater der Welt

Schloßstr. 48, 12165 Berlin, Germany
tel: +49 30 791 1777
fax: +49 30 791 1874
email: info@iti-germany.de
web: www.iti-germany.de
director: Dr. Manfred Beilharz
dates: June/July
(triennial - next festival 2005)

Verona Opera Festival

Piazza Bra 28, 37121 Verona, Italy
tel: +39 04 559 6517
web: www.arena.it
dates: June-August

Wagner Festival at Bayreuth

Bayreuther Festspiele
Festspielhügel 1-2
D-95445 Bayreuth, Germany
tel: +49 9217 8780
web: www.bayreuther-festspiele.de
director: Wolfgang Wagner
dates: July/August

Wiener Festwochen

Lehárgasse 11, 1060 Vienna, Austria
tel: +43 1 58922 0
fax: +43 1 58922 49
email: festwochen@festwochen.at
web: www.festwochen.at
artistic director: Luc Bondy
director drama & performing arts:
Marie Zimmermann
dates: May/June

Wiesbaden Biennale

New Plays From Europe
Hessisches Staatstheater
Wiesbaden, Christian-Zais-Str. 3
D-65189 Wiesbaden, Germany
tel: +49 611 132 264
fax: +49 611 132 244
email: biennale@staatstheater-
wiesbaden.de
web: www.hessisches-staatstheater.de
artistic director: Dr. Manfred Beilharz
dates: June

Zurich Theatre Spectacle

Zürcher Theater Spektakel
Stadthausquai 17, CH-8001 Zürich
tel: +41 1 216 3551
fax: +41 1 216 3574
email: info@theaterspektakel.ch
web: www.theaterspektakel.ch
director: Maria Magdalena
Schwaegermann
dates: August

Middle East

The Israel Festival

PO Box 4409, Jerusalem 91044, Israel
tel: +972 2 561 1438
fax: +972 2 566 9850
email: israel_f@zahav.net.il
web: www.israel-festival.org.il
artistic director: Ofira Henig
dates: May/June

DanceEuropa

Suzanne Dellal Centre for
Dance and Theatre
Neve-Tzedek, Tel Aviv, Israel
tel: +972 3 510 5656
email: info@suzannedellal.org.il
web: www.suzannedellal.org.il
dates: October/November

North America

American Dance Festival

PO Box 90772, Durham
NC 27708-0772
United States of America
tel: +1 919 684 6402
fax: +1 919 684 5459
email: adf@americandancefestival.org
web: www.adfinternational.org
directors: Charles Reinhart,
Stephanie Reinhart
dates: June/July

Canada Dance Festival

P. O. Box 1376, succursale B
Ottawa , Ontario K1P 5R4, Canada
tel: +1 613 947 7000
fax: +1 613 943 1399
email: cdffdc@nac-cna.ca
web: www.canadadance.ca
artistic producer: Brian H. Webb
dates: June (biennial - even years)

Festival de Théâtre des Amériques

C.P. 507, Succ. Desjardins
Montréal, Québéc H5B 1B6, Canada
tel: +1 514 842 0704
fax: +1 514 842 3795
email: info@fta.qc.ca
web: www.fta.qc.ca
director: Marie-Hélène Falcon
dates: May/June (biennial - odd years,
Théâtre du Monde - alternate years)

International Festival of Arts & Ideas New Haven

195 Church Street
12th Floor, New Haven CT 06510
Connecticut, United States of America
tel: +1 203 498 1212
fax: +1 203 498 2106
email: info@artidea.org
web: www.artidea.org
festival director: Mary Miller
dates: June

Jacob's Pillow Dance Festival

PO Box 287, Lee, MA 01238
United States of America
tel: +1 413 637 1322
fax: +1 413 243 4744
email: info@.jacobspillow.org
web: www.jacobspillow.org
executive director: Ella Baff
dates: June-August

Lincoln Center Festival

Lincoln Center, 70 Lincoln Center Plaza
New York, NY 10023-6583
United States of America
tel: +1 212 875 5030/5928
fax: +1 212 875 5027
email: webmaster@lincolncenter.org
web: www.lincolncenter.org
director: Nigel Redden
dates: July

Next Wave Festival

Brooklyn Academy of Music
30 Lafayette Avenue, Brooklyn
NY 11217, United States of America
tel: +1 718 636 4111
fax: +1 718 636 4179
email: info@bam.org
web: www.bam.org
executive producer: Joseph Melillo
dates: October-December

New York International Fringe Festival

The Present Company
520 Eighth Avenue, Suite 311
New York, NY 10018
United States of America
tel: +1 212 279 4488
fax: +1 212 279 4466
email: info@fringenyc.org
web: www.fringenyc.org
directors: Elena K. Holy, John Clancy
dates: August

Shaw Festival

Shaw Festival Theatre, Box 774, 10
Queen's Parade, Niagara on the Lake
Ontario L0S 1J0, Canada
tel: +1 905 468 2172
fax: +1 905 468 5438
email: info@shawfest.com
web: www.shawfest.com
artistic director: Jackie Maxwell
dates: April-October

Spoleto Festival

14 George Street, Charleston
South Carolina 29492
United States of America
tel: +1 843 722 2764
fax: +1 843 723 6383
email: info@spoletousa.org
web: www.spoletousa.org
general director: Nigel Redden
producer: Nunally Kersh
dates: May/June

Vancouver International Children's Festival

Canadian Institute of the Arts for Young Audiences
#402 - 873 Beatty Street
Vancouver, BC V6B 2M6, Canada
tel: +1 604 708 5655
fax: +1 604 708 5661
email: info@childrensfestival.ca
web: www.childrensfestival.ca
director: Lindy Sisson
dates: May

South America

Iberoamerican Theatre Festival of Bogota

web: www.festivaldeteatro.com.co
director: Fanny Mikey, Ramiro Osorio
dates: March/April

United Kingdom

Barbican International Theatre Event (BITE)

Barbican , Silk Street
London EC2Y 8DS, England
tel: +44 20 7382 7372
fax: +44 20 7382 7377
email: theatre@barbican.org.uk
web: www.barbican.org.uk/bite
head of theatre: Louise Jeffries
dates: Year round

Brighton Festival

12a Pavilion Buildings, Castle Square
Brighton BN1 1EE, England
tel: +44 1273 700747
fax: +44 1273 707505
email: info@brighton-festival.org.uk
web: www.brighton-festival.org.uk
chief executive: Nicholas Dodds
dates: May

Buxton Opera Festival

5 The Square, Buxton
Derbyshire, SK17 6AZ, England
tel: +44 1298 70395
fax: +44 1298 72289
email: info@buxtonopera.co.uk
web: www.buxtonfestival.co.uk
artistic director: Aidan Lang
dates: July

Cheltenham International Festival of Music

Town Hall, Imperial Square
Cheltenham GL50 1QA, England
tel: +44 1242 775862
fax: +44 1242 573902
email: toby.smith@cheltenham.gov.uk
web: www.cheltenhamfestivals.co.uk
artistic director: Michael Berkeley
dates: July

Dance Umbrella

20 Chancellor Street
London W6 9RN, England
tel: +44 20 8741 4040
fax: +44 20 8741 7902
email: mail@danceumbrella.co.uk
web: www.danceumbrella.co.uk
artistic director: Val Bourne
dates: October/November

Edinburgh Festival Fringe

Festival Fringe Office, 180 High Street
Edinburgh EH1 1QS, Scotland
tel: +44 131 226 0026
fax: +44 131 226 0039/0016
email: admin@edfringe.com
web: www.edfringe.com
director: Paul Gudgin
dates: August

Edinburgh International Festival

The Hub, Edinburgh Festival Centre
Castle Hill, Royal Mile
Edinburgh EH1 2NE, Scotland
tel: +44 131 473 2000
fax: +44 131 473 2003
email: eif@eif.co.uk
web: www.eif.co.uk
director: Brian McMaster
dates: August/September

Glyndebourne Opera Festival

Glyndebourne Productions Ltd
Glyndebourne, Lewes
East Sussex, BN8 5UU, England
tel: +44 1273 812321
fax: +44 1273 812783
email: info@glyndebourne.com
web: www.glyndebourne.com
general director: David Pickard
music director: Vladimir Jurowski
dates: May-August

Greenwich & Docklands International Festival

6 College Approach, Greenwich
London SE10 9HY, England
tel: +44 20 8305 1818
fax: +44 20 8305 1188
email: info@festival.org
web: www.festival.org
artistic director: Bradley Hemmings
dates: July

London International Festival of Theatre (LIFT)

19-20 Great Sutton Street
London EC1V 0DR, England
tel: +44 20 7490 3964
fax: +44 20 7490 3976
email: info@liftfest.org
web: www.liftfest.org
directors: Rose De Wend Fenton, Lucy Neal
dates: May/June & October

London International Mime Festival

35 Little Russell Street
London WC 1A 2HH, England
tel: +44 20 7637 5661
fax: +44 20 7323 1151
email: mimefest@easynet.co.uk
web: www.mimefest.co.uk
directors: Joseph Seelig, Helen Lannaghan
dates: January

international networks

Association of Performing Arts Presenters (USA)
1112 16th Street NW
Suite 400, Washington DC 20036
United States of America
tel: +1 202 833 2787
fax: +1 202 833 1543
email: kspellman@artspresenters.org
web: www.artspresenters.org
consultant & conference specialist: Karen Spellman

CINARS International Market for the Performing Arts
3575, St Laurent boulevard, suite 216,
Montréal H2X 2T7, Canada
tel: +1 514 842 5866
fax: +1 514 843 3168
email: arts@cinars.org
web: www.cinars.org
ceo: Alain Paré

European Festivals Association
Château de Coppet, Case Postale 26
CH-1296 Coppet, Switzerland
tel: +41 22 738 8673
fax: +41 22 738 4275
email: info@euro-festival.net
web: www.euro-festival.net
secretary general: Tamás Klenjánszky

European Theatre Convention
c/o Kononklijke Vlaamse
Schouwburg, Rue Delaunoy 58
1080 Brussels, Belgium
tel: +32 2 412 7040
fax: +32 2 412 7068
email: cte@skynet.be
web: www.etc-centre.org
general secretary: Patricia Canellis

Informal European Theatre Meeting (IETM)
Sainctelettessquare 19
1000 Brussels, Belgium
tel: +32 2 201 0915
fax: +32 2 203 0226
email: ietm@ietm.org
web: www.ietm.org
network co-ordinator: Mary Ann De Vlieg

International Amateur Theatre Association (AITA/IATA)
IATA Secretariat, Vene 6
10123 Tallinn, Estonia
tel: +372 6 418 405
fax: +372 6 418 406
email: secretariat@aitaiata.org
web: www.aitaiata.org
administrator: Kaja Põld
irish office: IATA/AITA Irish Centre
email: iatairl@eircom.net
administrator: Mary Pears

International Association for Theatre for Children & Young People (ASSITEJ)
ASSITEJ International, Box 6033,
S – 121 06, Johanneshov, Sweden
tel: + 46 8659 8633
fax: + 46 8658901
email: sec.gen@assitej.org
secretary general: Niclas Malmcrona
irish representative: Lali Morris,
Baboro International Arts Festival
for Children, Galway
tel: +353 (0)91 509705
email: baboro@gaf.iol.ie
uk representative: Jeremy Turner,
Cwni Theatr Arad Goch,
Aberystwyth, Wales
tel: +44 1970 617998
email: jeremy@aradgoch.org

International Association of Theatre Critics
Association Internationale des
Critiques de Théâtre (AICT)
Avenue Elmwood 54
Outremont, Québec H2V 2E4, Canada
tel: +1 514 278 5764
fax: +1 514 278 5521
email: vais@ca.inter.net
web: www.aict-iatc.org
secretary general: Michel Vais

International Dance Council
Conseil International de la Danse
UNESCO, 1 Rue Miollis
75732 Paris cedex 15, France
tel: +33 1 4568 4953
fax: +33 1 4568 4931
email: cid@unesco.org
web: www.unesco.org/ngo/cid
secretary general: Nicole Luc-Maréchal

International Festivals & Events Association Europe (IFEA)
P.O. Box 270, 2000 AG Haarlem
The Netherlands
tel: +31 23 534 8482
fax: +31 23 551 9170
email: office-ifea@planet.nl
web: www.ifeaeurope.com
chairman: Paul van Gessel

International Society for the Performing Arts (ISPA)
17 Purdy Avenue, P.O. Box 909, Rye
NY 10580, United States of America
tel: +1 914 921 1550
fax: +1 914 921 1593
email: info@ispa.org
web: www.ispa.org
board chair: Graham Sheffield
ceo: Johann Zietsman

International Theatre Institute (ITI)
UNESCO, 1 Rue Miollis
75732 Paris Cedex 15, France
tel: +33 1 4568 2650
fax: +33 1 4566 5040
email: iti@unesco.org
web: www.iti-worldwide.org
president: Dr. Manfred Beilharz
secretary general: Andre-Louis Perinetti
irish centre: c/o Steve Wilmer
Samuel Beckett Centre
Trinity College, Dublin 2
tel: 01 608 1441
fax: 01 679 3488
email: swilmer@tcd.ie
web: www.tcd.ie/drama

World Dance Alliance – Europe
Erkrather Straße 30
40233 Düsseldorf, Germany
tel: +49 211 172 7010
fax: +49 211 172 7017
email: tanzhausnrw@t-online.de
executive director: Bertram Müller

funding bodies

Eanna McLiam and Emily Nagle in Passion Machine's production of
Diarmuid and Grainne by Paul Mercier, 2001 © Derek Speirs

The Arts Council/An Chomhairle Ealaíon

70 Merrion Square, Dublin 2, Republic of Ireland
tel: +353 (0)1 618 0200
callsave: 1850 392 492
fax: +353 (0)1 676 1302
email: info@artscouncil.ie
web: www.artscouncil.ie

director: Appointment pending
arts policy director: Séamus Crimmins
arts programme director: John O'Kane

arts programme managers
festivals and events: Andrea Corbett
production companies: Maria Johnston
resource and service organisations: Claire Doyle
venues: Liz Culloty

artform specialists
theatre specialist: Enid Reid Whyte
opera specialist: James Conway
dance specialist: Finola Cronin

The Arts Council is the state development agency for the arts in Ireland and is the primary source of support for individual artists and arts organisations. Its funds come from the Department of Arts, Sport and Tourism. Its role is to provide advice to government on artistic matters; to advise, assist and support individuals and arts organisations and a wide range of governmental and non-governmental bodies on art matters; and to provide financial assistance and other forms of support to individuals and organisations, for artistic purposes.

funds: The Arts Council supports theatre companies and venues throughout the country and provides awards and bursaries for the development of individual artists (and managers) working within the theatre and dance sector *(see Supports for Artists entry in Scholarships and Bursaries section)*. Eligible areas for support include professional drama, dance, opera and mime, theatre and dance in education, youth theatre, youth and community dance, puppetry and circus arts. Areas not eligible include amateur drama groups, charity events, variety artistes and shows and cabaret. Currently, Arts Council funding to organisations can be divided into Revenue and Minor Capital grants.

revenue funding: Revenue grants to arts organisations account for c. 72% of the Council's total annual

expenditure (2004). The Council's grant support to arts organisations is delivered through four sub-programmes, which operate on a cross-disciplinary basis: Resource and Service Organisations/Production Companies/Venues/Festivals and Events. Therefore, in common with other artforms, organisations involved with theatre, dance and opera are now considered for funding within the context of the four sub-programmes, each with its own budget. Organisations in receipt of one-year funding are those that operate all year-round and implement artistic and financial policy agreed in partnership with the Arts Council.

capital funding: Normally, the Arts Council allocates a dedicated fund for minor capital purposes annually. Typically, minor capital grants have been provided to contribute towards the cost of purchases of essential equipment, together with repairs and refurbishment of existing buildings (amounts up to €50,000). No minor capital grants were offered in 2003. However, it is expected that the Arts Council will publish details of a 2004 Minor Capital Funding Scheme in the summer.

other funding: The Council also operates a number of schemes including Projects and Commissions. Project Awards are considered for individual projects that encourage innovation and experimentation. Commissioning Awards are considered for the creation of new performance works. In theatre and dance these may be awarded to writers, choreographers, composers, and devisors. The criteria and closing dates for these applications vary and further information can be obtained on the Council's website or in the Supports for Artists folder, available from the Arts Council. *(Please see Supports for Artists entry in the Scholarships and Bursaries section for other award information)*.

application procedures: Applications for revenue funding are considered once a year, in the autumn of the year prior to the funding year. The Arts Council publishes details of its revenue funding scheme in July/August in the national press and by direct communication with organisations with whom it has an existing funding relationship. Application forms must be requested from the Arts Council directly, as they are individually tagged, and can be submitted either by using a specially designed on-line application process or by post.

Arts Council of Northern Ireland

MacNeice House, 77 Malone Road,
Belfast BT9 6AQ, Northern Ireland
tel: +44 (0)28 9038 5200
fax: +44 (0)28 9066 1715
email: info@artscouncil-ni.org
web: www.artscouncil-ni.org
director, arts development department: Philip Hammond
drama and dance officer: Gilly Campbell
assistant drama and dance officer: Maria O'Kane

The Arts Council of Northern Ireland is the statutory body through which public funding for the arts in Northern Ireland is channelled. The Arts Council is funded by grant-in-aid by the Department of Culture, Arts and Leisure (DCAL) and has responsibility for distributing Lottery funds to the arts in Northern Ireland. Its principal functions are: to develop and improve the knowledge, appreciation and practice of the arts; to increase public access to, and participation, in the arts; to advise DCAL and other government departments, district councils and other bodies on matters relating to the arts.

support is available to organisations and individuals through three major programmes: Annual Support for Organisations Programme (ASOP), Lottery programmes, and the Support for the Individual Artist Programme (SIAP). Full details and application forms available on the website or from the Arts Council directly.

The British Council

22-24 Lower Mount Street, Dublin 4, Republic of Ireland
tel: +353 (0)1 676 4088
fax: +353 (0)1 676 6945
email: Madeline.Boughton@ie.britishcouncil.org
web: www.britishcouncil.org/ireland
director: Tony Reilly
arts officer: Madeleine Boughton

The British Council in Ireland, in partnership with individuals, institutions and organisations, supports the relationship between Ireland and the UK through developing projects in arts, science and society. In the interests of mutual benefit to both Ireland and the UK, the organisation seeks to present and develop work that breaks new ground and reaches new and diverse audiences. Aspects of the British Council's current arts plan (2003-2005) include: showcasing and sharing the best of contemporary cutting edge work; projects

which cross over arts and society; sharing models of best practice in the UK; and joint projects which have a North/South component.

funds: The British Council is not a funding agency and grants are not provided simply on the basis of an arts event or project having a UK component. The organisation is moving towards medium to longterm project development, working with Irish partners, and where the British Council can add value, including financial resources.

application procedure: No formal application form exists. Project ideas for development can be discussed with or emailed to the Arts Officer. The financial year for the British Council is April to March.

The British Council in Northern Ireland

Norwich Union House, 7 Fountain Street,
Belfast BT1 5EG, Northern Ireland
tel: +44 (0)28 9024 8220
fax: +44 (0)28 9023 7592
email: colette.norwood@britishcouncil.org
web: www.britishcouncil.org/nireland
arts manager: Colette Norwood

The British Council in Northern Ireland seeks to present a realistic and balanced image of Northern Ireland overseas in partnership with bodies working primarily in the cultural sector, civil society, human rights and gender issues.

funds: Contributes to Northern Irish companies touring abroad (including Republic of Ireland). Will also assist with foreign practitioners visiting Northern Ireland. Application Procedure: No formal procedure exists. Applications outlining project details are accepted all year round.

Community Relations Council

6 Murray Street, Belfast BT1 6DN, Northern Ireland
tel: +44 (0)28 9022 7500
fax: +44 (0)28 9022 7551
email: info@community-relations.org.uk
web: www.community-relations.org.uk
information officer: Ray Mullan

The Community Relations Council aims to support and advise projects which encourage a positive awareness of difference and diversity both between communities and within communities in Northern Ireland.

funds: The Council administers various grant schemes in pursuit of the above aims and arts-based projects may be eligible.

application procedure: Application forms, criteria and further information are available from the above address or the CRC website.

Cultural Co-operation And Touring / Comhoibriú Cultúrtha agus Turais CCAT@ Temple Bar Properties

12 East Essex Street, Temple Bar, Dublin 2, Republic of Ireland
tel: +353 (0)1 677 2255
fax: +353 (0)1 677 2525
email: ccat@templebar.ie
web: www.ccat.ie
contact: Zita Griffin

CCAT @ Aberystwyth Arts Centre & Temple Bar is an Interreg IIIa programme designed to develop relationships between cultural practitioners on both sides of the Irish sea and to raise the profile of the arts of Wales and Ireland both at home and internationally. CCAT will provide financial support and networking events for the development of arts organisations, from all disciplines, touring in the Interreg regions of Ireland and Wales.
funds: 'Go see' awards are also available to develop relationships between practitioners and presenters. CCAT @ Aberystwyth Arts Centre & Temple Bar is part-funded by Ireland Wales INTERREG programme. It is an initiative of the Theatre Shop and Aberystwyth Arts Centre and is managed in Ireland by Temple Bar Properties.

Cultural Relations Committee of Ireland/Comhar Cultúra Éireann

Department of Arts, Sport and Tourism, Frederick Buildings, South Frederick Street, Dublin 2, Republic of Ireland
tel: +353 (0)1 631 3956
fax: +353 (0)1 679 9261
email: crc@dast.gov.ie
web: www.arts-sport-tourism.gov.ie
higher executive officer: Maura O'Connor

The Cultural Relations Committee (CRC) is a voluntary, non-statutory body, established in 1949 which advises on the distribution of financial grants from the allocation for cultural relations abroad made to the Department of Arts, Sport and Tourism. Its members, who are appointed for a three-year period by the Minister, draw on a wide range of expertise and experience in cultural matters.

funds: The CRC allocates grants in support of Irish cultural activity of excellence in other countries. In deciding on which events to assist the Committee considers their potential to promote tourism and investment from abroad. Particular attention is given to events staged in countries where awareness of Irish cultural and artistic achievement may not have kept pace with political or economic ties. Please check Department of Arts, Sport and Tourism website for any changes in policy around funding of Irish Arts abroad *(www.arts-sport-tourism.gov.ie)*.

application procedure: Application forms, including details of eligibility and criteria for grant aid, are available on request from the address above.

European Union

Republic of Ireland Office:
European Commission Representation in Ireland:
18 Dawson Street, Dublin 2, Republic of Ireland
tel: +353 (0)1 634 1111
fax: +353 (0)1 634 1112
email: eu-ie-info-request@cec.eu.int
web: www.euireland.ie
contact: Information Department

European Parliament Office in Ireland:
43 Molesworth Street, Dublin 2, Republic of Ireland
tel: +353 (0)1 605 7900
fax: +353 (0)1 605 7999
email: epdublin@europarl.eu.int
web: www.europarl.ie

European Commission Office in Northern Ireland:
9-15 Bedford Street, Belfast BT2 7EG, Northern I reland
tel: +44 (0)28 9024 0708
fax: +44 (0)28 9053 0113
email: karen.morrison@cec.eu.int
web: www.cec.org.uk/ni/index
contact: Information Department

European Cultural Contact Point Ireland:
The Arts Council/An Chomhairle Ealaíon,
70 Merrion Square, Dublin 2, Republic of Ireland
tel: +353 (0)1 618 0234/0202
email: catherine@artscouncil.ie
web: www.artscouncil.ie
contact: Charlotte Mangan, Catherine Boothman

European Cultural Portal
European Commission, Cultural Unit pages and
Culture 2000 information
European Cultural Contact Point Partnersearch Database

Culture 2000 is the name of a framework programme for supporting culture at a European level, administered by the Cultural Unit in the DG for Education and Culture in the European Commission. The programme is supervised from year to year by the Culture 2000 Management Committee, which is made up of representatives of the cultural ministries of the EU member and economically associated states. The overall Culture 2000 budget for the original duration of five years was €167 million, but this was increased slightly due to the extension of the programme until the end of 2006, and the inclusion of accession countries to the EU.

funds: The main purpose of Culture 2000 is to promote transnational cooperation in the field of culture, which is taken to include both cultural heritage and contemporary arts practice. This means that project proposals must be presented by partnerships of organisations from various European states. Those eligible to participate are the 25 European Union member states, 3 economically associated states (Norway, Iceland and Lichtenstein), and 2 applicant states to the EU, Romania and Bulgaria.

Applications are invited on the basis of a Call for Proposals published annually by the European Commission. The Call for Proposals contains specified minimum and maximum costs for projects, effectively categorising all projects into two groups.

The first is largely aimed at encouraging 'experiment and innovation', and is for projects lasting about one year and involving partners from a minimum of three eligible European states. These types of projects must cost between €100,000 and €300,000, and it is possible to request 50% of the eligible costs.

The second scale is for projects between partners from at least five eligible European states who have entered into a multi-annual cooperative agreement, recognised by the legal system of one of the states involved. They can cost a maximum of €500,000 per year, and it is possible to request up to 60% of the eligible costs.

Small translation grants are also available to publishers wishing to publish a minimum of four and a maximum of 10 titles in translation in the field of contemporary European literature and European humanities. These grants cover the translators' fees.

application procedure: The European Commission publishes an application form at the same time as it releases the Call for Proposals each year. They are only published electronically, and are also available from the European Cultural Contact Points (CCPs), which also provide advice and technical assistance with the application process. The web address for the Cultural Unit in DG Education and Culture in the European Commission is: **www.europa.eu.int/comm/culture/index_en.html** Networks and associations within which to build project partnerships: European network for dance and theatre professionals, information providers, other resource and funding organisations

European network of arts organisations for children and young people Les Rencontres network of European cities and regions for culture Res Artis, International Association of Residential Arts Centres

Goethe-Institut Inter Nationes Dublin
37 Merrion Square, Dublin 2, Republic of Ireland
tel: +353 (0)1 661 1155
fax: +353 (0)1 661 1358
email: goethe@iol.ie
web: www.goethe.de/dublin
director: Dr. Matthias Müller-Wieferig
programme manager: Barbara Ebert

The Goethe-Institut is a worldwide organisation promoting German language and culture and developing international cultural co-operation. The Dublin branch was established in 1962. It organises cultural events (music, theatre, film, literature, exhibitions), German language courses and runs a library and information service. A calendar of events is issued bi-monthly. The Institut offers an annual scholarship to professional actors, directors and stage designers to participate in a seminar during the Berlin Theatre Festival (every May). Further details from Barbara Ebert.

The Ireland Funds

5 Foster Place, Dublin 2, Republic of Ireland
tel: +353 (0)1 662 7878
fax: +353 (0)1 662 7879
email: grants@ifdublin.iol.ie
web: www.irlfunds.org
project officer: Gillian Wynne

Founded in 1976 by Dr A.J.F. O'Reilly and a number of key American businessmen, The Ireland Funds are described as 'a confederation of concern, connecting people around the world with Ireland, North and South'. The Ireland Funds are non-political and non-sectarian with most monies secured from private sources. The funds assist groups in Ireland 'whose initiatives serve the people of Ireland directly.'

funds: The funds identify arts and culture as one of their four funding areas. They wish to support excellence and innovation in arts activities within communities, especially projects that make the arts more accessible to the wider community. In particular, The Ireland Funds focus on arts applied in settings of socio-economic disadvantage; arts applied in educational or health settings and arts promoting tolerance and reconciliation.

application procedure: The Funds allocate awards once each year. Application packs, including full details of dates, rules and procedures, are available from the above address.

At time of going to print, these funds are under review. Please contact the Ireland Funds for the latest information.

Local Authorities & District Councils

Most local authorities, North and South, employ Arts Officers who administer budgets of varying size and significance. Application procedures for these funds vary from authority to authority.
See also Arts Officers and Scholarships and Bursaries.

Trusts and Foundations

Various private trusts and foundations, including many based in Britain, fund artistic activities in Ireland. Examples of these trusts include the Esme Mitchell Trust, the Carnegie United Kingdom Trust, the Northern Ireland Voluntary Trust and the Foundation for Sports and the Arts.

Údarás Na Gaeltachta

Na Forbacha, Gaillimh, Eireann
tel: +353 (0)91 503100
fax: +353 (0)91 503101
email: eolas@udaras.ie
web: www.ealain.ie
feidhmeannach forbartha ealaíon: Micheal Ó Fearraigh

Údarás na Gaeltachta is the development agency for the Gaeltacht region, which covers extensive parts of counties Donegal, Mayo, Galway, Kerry, Cork, Meath, and Waterford. Údarás promotes the socio-economic development of the Gaeltacht so as to facilitate and promote the preservation of Irish as the principal language of the region.

funds: Projects in manufacturing, internationally-traded services and natural resources are the priority for assistance from Údarás na Gaeltachta, however, the agency has recently appointed a number of Arts Officers who have limited budgets to support cultural projects delivered through the Irish language.

application procedure: Applications forms, containing full application details, are available from all Údarás local offices on request.

For contact information, see Arts Officers or log on to the website.

Calypso's production of Five Kinds of Silence by Shelagh Stephenson © Tom Lawlor

Amateur Drama Council of Ireland

Ballymote Road, Tubbercurry,
Co Sligo, Republic of Ireland
tel: + 353 (0)71 918 6517
fax: + 353 (0)71 918 5239
email: brendan.mcgowan@cgold.ie
web: www.adci.ie
honourable secretary: Brendan
McGowan
An organisation that co-ordinates
the full-length competitive drama
circuit and organises the annual
Confined All-Ireland Drama Finals
and the RTE Open All-Ireland Drama
Finals in April and May each year.

Arts in Business

53 Malone Road, Belfast BT9 6RY,
Northern Ireland
tel: +44 (0)28 9066 4736
fax: +44 (0)28 9066 4500
email: kevin.o'connor@aandb.org.uk
web: www.aandb.org.uk
contact: Kevin O'Connor
The aim of Arts in Business is to help
build communities by developing
creative partnerships between business
and the arts in Northern Ireland.

Arts Marketing Association

7a Clifton Court, Clifton Road,
Cambridge CB1 7BN, England
tel: +44 (0)1223 578078
fax: +44 (0)1223 578079
email: info@a-m-a.co.uk
web: www.a-m-a.co.uk
director: Pam Henderson
The Arts Marketing Association is
the professional development body
for the arts marketing industry, with
over 1300 members across the UK.

Association of Drama Adjudicators

Edenmore, Courtown Harbour, Gorey
Co Wexford, Republic of Ireland
tel: + 353 (0)55 25124
secretary: Dolores Deacon
The Association of Drama
Adjudicators is a regulatory body
that oversees drama adjudicators
to ensure high standards.

Association of Irish Festival Events (AOIFE)

AOIFE Administration Office,
The Enterprise & Technology Centre,
Creagh, Ballinasloe, Co. Galway,
Republic of Ireland
tel: +353 (0)909 643779
email: info@aoifeonline.com
web: www.aoifeonline.com
contact: Nicole Mulholland
AOIFE, the Association of Irish
Festivals and Events, aims to
support festival organisers to make
festivals in Ireland entertaining,
safe and financially sustainable.
Services include training, the
provision of information and
networking opportunities and a
group insurance scheme.

Association of Professional Dancers in Ireland

Space 28, North Lotts,
Dublin 1, Republic of Ireland
tel: + 353 (0)1 873 0288
fax: + 353 (0)1 873 4573
email: prodance@iol.ie
web: www.prodanceireland.com
managing director: Emma R.
Corcoran
The APDI is a national resource
organisation for professional
dancers, choreographers, dance
teachers and dance students.

Association of Ulster Drama Festivals

31 Shorelands, Greenisland,
Carrickfergus BT38 8FB,
Co. Antrim, Northern Ireland
email: AWR@enterprise.net
irvine@cmgsolicitors.com
web: www.audf.org.uk
secretary: Alan Marshall
The Association of Ulster Drama
Festivals aims to encourage amateur
drama through the holding of
festivals, promotion of co-operation
and co-ordination between festivals
and the fostering of relations with
similar organisations in Northern
Ireland and other regions.

Business2Arts

44 East Essex Street, Temple Bar,
Dublin 2, Republic of Ireland
tel: + 353 (0)1 672 5336
fax: + 353 (0)1 672 5373
email: info@business2arts.ie
web: www.business2arts.ie
chief executive: Siobhan Broughan
training programmes: Julie T. Brady
Business2Arts promotes creative
partnerships between business and
the arts. We provide training in
business skills for arts
organisations as well as advice for
business members on potential arts
sponsorship opportunities.
Business2Arts is a non-profit
organisation funded by business
members. In addition, we operate
an Arts Affiliate membership
scheme, organise the annual Arts
Sponsor of the Year Awards and
produce publications relating to
arts sponsorship.
See also Awards & Competitions.

Community Arts Forum (CAF)

15 Church Street, Belfast BT1 1PG,
Northern Ireland
tel: +44 (0)28 9024 2910
fax: +44 (0)28 9031 2264
email: admin@caf.ie
web: www.caf.ie
administrator: Kate Muldoon
information officer: Chris Ball
CAF is an umbrella body for
community arts in Northern Ireland.
Its primary aim is to create access
to the arts for more people. It also
incorporates the Community Theatre
Association of Belfast, a support
organisation for community theatre
groups in Belfast.

Contemporary Music Centre

19 Fishamble Street, Temple Bar,
Dublin 8, Republic of Ireland
tel: + 353 (0)1 673 1922
fax: + 353 (0)1 648 9100
email: info@cmc.ie
web: www.cmc.ie
information officer: Jonathon Grimes
The Contemporary Music Centre is
Ireland's national archive and
resource centre for new music,
supporting the work of composers
throughout the Republic and
Northern Ireland. The Centre is
used, nationally and internationally,
by performers, composers,
promoters and members of the
public interested in finding out
more about music in Ireland. Its
library and sound archive, open to
the public free of charge, contain
the only comprehensive collection
in existence of music by Irish
composers. The Contemporary Music
Centre engages in an ongoing
programme of development work to
promote new Irish music at home
and abroad, and is a member of the
Forum for Music in Ireland and the
International Association of Music
Information Centres (IAMIC).

CREATE

previously **Creative Activity For
Everyone - CAFE**
10-11 Earl Street South, Dublin 8,
Republic of Ireland
tel: + 353 (0)1 473 6600
fax: + 353 (0)1 473 6599
email: info@artsincontext.com
web: www.communityartsireland.com
executive director: Wes Wilkie
CREATE supports arts development
and practice in Ireland.

Dance Northern Ireland

15 Church Street, Belfast BT1 1PG,
Northern Ireland
tel: +44 (0)28 9024 9930
fax: +44 (0)28 9024 9930
email: vicki@danceni.com
web: www.danceni.com
development officer: Victoria Maguire
Dance Northern Ireland's principal
aim is to promote and support all
forms of dance in Northern Ireland.
See also Irish Festivals.

Department of Arts, Sport and Tourism

23 Kildare Street, Dublin 2,
Republic of Ireland
tel: + 353 (0)1 631 3800
fax: + 353 (0)1 661 1201
email: pressoffice@dast.gov.ie
web: www.gov.ie/arts-sport-tourism
press officer: Nigel Daly
The Department's mission is to
contribute to the economic, social
and cultural progress of Irish society
and the enrichment of its quality of
life through promoting sustainable
tourism; encouraging excellence in
sporting and artistic achievement;
facilitating greater access to sport
and the arts; and preservation of our
cultural inheritance.

Drama League of Ireland (DLI)

Carmichael House, North Brunswick
Street, Dublin 7, Republic of Ireland
tel: + 353 (0)1 874 9084
fax: + 353 (0)1 873 5737
email: dli@eircom.net
web: www.dli.ie
project officer: Dara Carolan
The DLI is the resource organisation
for amateur drama practitioners.
Evening classes on acting and
directing are conducted Spring and
Autumn in Carmichael House. Services
include provision of workshops,
libraries, insurance, annual summer
and winter schools, and a quarterly
magazine. The DLI are also Irish
agents for amateur performing rights
of Samuel French Ltd, Josef
Weinberger Plays, and others.

Institute for Choreography and Dance (ICD)

Firkin Crane, Shandon, Cork,
Republic of Ireland
tel: + 353 (0)21 450 7487
fax: + 353 (0)21 450 1124
email: info@instchordance.com
web: www.instchordance.com
artistic director: Mary Brady
development director: Mowbray Bates
The Institute for Choreography and
Dance is a unique model for
stimulating choreographic practice
and dance research as a means of
dance development. ICD provides
space for interchange between
choreographers to examine issues,
work methodologies and goals
particular to each, in a positive,
challenging and practice-centred
environment. Achieved through four
interconnecting sites: Residencies –
Resource based, Choreographic
Fellowship Award, Choreographer in
residence, Writer in Residence;
Performances/Presentations – Work
in progress, International season
(spring/summer), Co-presentations
of Irish-based companies (Cork and
festivals), Fora for Debate and
Training – Choreographic Encounter
forums, OPID: Older People in Dance
– accredited dance/health training
initiative, Colloquia/seminars to
discuss issues and disseminate
models of practice. Documentation/
Publications – Choreographic
Encounters (annual journal),
Writing Dancing Righting Dance:
Articulations on a Choreographic
Practice, Dancing on the Edge of
Europe: Irish Choreographers in
Conversation.
See also Venues.

Ireland Literature Exchange (ILE)

19 Parnell Square, Dublin 1,
Republic of Ireland
tel: + 353 (0)1 872 7900
fax: + 353 (0)1 872 7875
email: info@irelandliterature.com
web: www.irelandliterature.com
director: Sinéad Mac Aodha
ILE provides funds to allow
publishers to translate the literature
of Ireland from both Irish and
English into other languages.

Irish Actors Equity Group

9th Floor, Liberty Hall,
Dublin 1, Republic of Ireland
tel: + 353 (0)1 858 6403
fax: + 353 (0)1 874 3691
email: equity@siptu.ie
web: www.irishactorsequity.ie
group secretary: Jane Boushell
Irish Actors Equity Group is the
only performers' trade union for
stage, screen, radio, television and
cabaret in Ireland.

Irish Playwrights and Screenwriters Guild

The Writers Centre, 19 Parnell Square,
Dublin 1, Republic of Ireland
tel: + 353 (0)1 492 3808
mobile: +353 (0)86 837 1203
email: david.kavanagh@script.ie
web: www.script.ie
chairman: Sean Moffatt
The Guild is the representative body
for writers in Ireland for the stage
and screen. It is a member of the
International Affiliation of Writers
Guilds, the European Writers
Congress, the Federation of
Scriptwriters in Europe; nominates
two members of the National
Theatre; has a joint membership
agreement with the Writers Guild of
Great Britain; an agreement with
the Authors Licensing and Collecting
Society and is affiliated to SIPTU.
See also Awards and Competitions.

Irish Theatre Archive

c/o Dublin City Library & Archive,
138-142 Pearse Street,
Dublin 2, Republic of Ireland
tel: + 353 (0)1 674 4800/4999
fax: + 353 (0)1 674 4881
email: cityarchives@dublincity.ie
web: www.dublincity.ie
honorary archivist: Mary Clark
The archive collects memorabilia
relating to the history of theatre
in Ireland, curates exhibitions,
provides research facilities and
organises occasional lectures.

Irish Music Rights Organisation

Copyright House, Pembroke Row,
Lower Baggot Street, Dublin 2,
Republic of Ireland
tel: + 353 (0)1 661 4844
fax: + 353 (0)1 661 3789
email: info@imro.ie
web: www.imro.ie
chief executive: Adrian Gaffney
Ireland's National Association of
Songwriters, Composers and
Publishers. IMRO collects royalties
from theatre companies using
copyrighted music.

Irish Writers Centre

19 Parnell Square, Dublin 1,
Republic of Ireland
tel: + 353 (0)1 872 1302
fax: + 353 (0)1 872 6282
email: info@writerscentre.ie
web: www.writerscentre.ie
director: Cathal McCabe
The IWC was founded in 1991 in
order to foster writing and an
audience for literature in Ireland.
The Centre aims to assist writers in
pursuing their work, to organise
and promote a programme of
literary activities, to cultivate an
interest in contemporary Irish
literature and to promote cultural
exchange between Ireland and
other countries.

LD Dance Trust

Shawbrook, Legan,
Co. Longford, Republic of Ireland
tel: + 353 (0)44 57570
fax: + 353 (0)44 57895
email: shawbrook@tinet.ie
directors: Anica Louw, Philip Dawson
LD Dance is a facility-based
resource organisation. Shawbrook
is a centre for dance education and
promotion of dance and dance
theatre in Ireland. It is also a
retreat facilty for the creation of
dance pieces. LD Dance creates
opportunities for Irish students to
develop their training and
performance skills. Its major aim is
to provide experiential learning
and performing opportunities.

National Association for Youth Drama

34 Upper Gardiner Street,
Dublin 1, Republic of Ireland
tel: + 353 (0)1 878 1301
fax: + 353 (0)1 878 1302
email: info@nayd.ie
web: www.youthdrama.ie
national director: Orlaith McBride
**publications and information
officer:** Fíona Ní Chinnéide
The National Association for Youth
Drama is the umbrella organisation
for youth drama and youth theatre
in Ireland. NAYD advocates a way
of working through drama with
young people which emphasises
personal and social development
equally with the attainment of
artistic excellence. There are over
75 youth theatres in Ireland.

Northern Amateur Theatre Association

49 Beverly Gardens, Bangor,
Co. Down BT20 4NQ,
Northern Ireland
tel: +44 (0)28 9145 5819
chairman: Tony Coghlan
The Northern Amateur Theatre Association provides education and training for the amateur theatre movement in Northern Ireland and organises a Summer School each year.

Theatre Forum

First Floor, 67 Middle Abbey Street,
Dublin 1, Republic of Ireland
tel: + 353 (0)1 874 6582/6584
fax: + 353 (0)1 872 8509
email: theatreforum@ireland.com
web: www.theatreforumireland.com
contact: Tania Banotti
Theatre Forum is the membership body for the professional performing arts in the Republic of Ireland. Membership is open to producing theatre companies and venues of every scale, as well as festivals, arts centres, TIE, YPT, dance and opera companies and individuals. Its mission is to support, represent and develop the environment in which the performing arts are made in Ireland, through advocacy, information exchange, organisational development and training.

Theatrical Management Association

32 Rose Street, Covent Garden,
London, WC2E 9ET, England
tel: +44 (0)20 7557 6706
fax: +44 (0)20 7557 6799
email: enquiries@solttma.co.uk
web: www.tmauk.org
principal officer: Kathleen Hamilton
The Theatrical Management Association provides a professional support network for the performing arts industry in the UK.

Theatre Producers Group (NI)

Unit 20 Drumgoon Estate,
Maguiresbridge, Co. Fermanagh
BT94 4QX, Northern Ireland
tel: + 44 (0)28 6772 3766
email: bez@bryonyflanagan.freeserve.co.uk
web: www.theatreproducersgroup.com
administrative officer: Bryony Flanagan
chair: Jan Branch
vice chair: Paul McEneaney
The TPG was formed in 1988 with the following aims: to raise the profile of professional and semi-professional live theatre in Northern Ireland; act upon issues of common concern; lobbying and advocacy on behalf of the theatre sector; liaise with funding bodies and decision makers; encourage new companies; provide a base for sharing information and provide training for professionals and new professionals working in theatre in Northern Ireland.

Theatre Shop

7 South Great George's Street,
Dublin 2, Republic of Ireland
tel: + 353 (0)1 670 4906
fax: + 353 (0)1 670 4908
co-producers: Siobhán Bourke, Jane Daly
irish playography director: Caroline Williams
administrator/editor, irish theatre handbook: Paula Shields
Theatre Shop, founded in 1994, exists to promote Irish theatre, dance and opera companies, plays, playwrights and theatre artists in an international and all-island context. Theatre Shop is committed to the strategic development of Irish theatre through international collaboration, networking, promotion, touring, research, publication, web development and debate. The organisation operates through its annual October conference and through promotion of Irish theatre and dance at key events abroad. In 2003 two major internet databases, The Irish Playography and Irish Theatre Handbook On Line were launched, creating a critical base on which to resource Irish theatre in years ahead. Theatre Shop is currently building on the success of these years, broadening the scope of its activity leading to a re-positioning and re-branding of the organisation in 2005. Theatre Shop aims to play a key role in the long-term strategic development of Irish theatre in an international context.

Tyrone Guthrie Centre

Annaghmakerrig, Newbliss,
Co. Monaghan, Republic of Ireland
tel: + 353 (0)47 54003
fax: + 353 (0)47 54380
email: thetgc@indigo.ie
web: www.tyroneguthrie.ie
director: Sheila Pratschke
The Tyrone Guthrie Centre was established in 1981 as a flagship North/South project providing a workplace retreat for practitioners in all art forms. Facilities include studios, darkroom and music room with grand piano.

Ulster Association of Youth Drama

Island Arts Centre, Lagan Valley Island,
Lisburn BT27 4RL, Northern Ireland
tel: +44 (0)28 9250 9520
fax: +44 (0)28 9250 9535
email: uayd@ukonline.co.uk
administrator: Naomi Conway
UAYD is a membership-led organisation, set up to support, develop and promote youth theatre and drama in Northern Ireland.

70 Merrion Square,   70 Cearnóg Mhuirfean,   **t** +353 1 6180200   **e** info@artscouncil.ie
Dublin 2, Ireland   Baile Átha Cliath 2, Éire   **f** +353 1 6761302   **w** www.artscouncil.ie
    Callsave 1850 392492

The Arts Council is the Irish government agency for developing the arts
An Chomhairle Ealaíon – foras forbartha na n-ealaíon á tacú ag Rialtas Éireann

Eoin Lynch in Storytellers' production of Rashomon by Ivor Benjamin, 2004

Republic of Ireland Local Authority Arts Officers

Carlow County Council
Athy Road, Carlow, Republic of Ireland
tel: + 353 (0)59 913 6237
fax: + 353 (0)59 914 1503
email: art@carlowcoco.ie
web: www.carlow.ie
contact: Caoimhín Corrigan

Cavan County Council
Arts Office, 17 Farnham St., Cavan, Republic of Ireland
tel: + 353 (0)49 437 2099
fax: + 353 (0)49 436 2127
email: artsoffice@cavancoco.ie
contact: Catriona O'Reilly

Clare County Council
Arts Office, County Library Headquarters, Mill Road, Ennis, Co. Clare, Republic of Ireland
tel: + 353 (0)65 684 6267
fax: + 353 (0)65 684 2462
email: siobhan.mulcahy@clarelibrary.ie
web: www.clarelibrary.ie
contact: Siobhán Mulcahy

Cork City Council
City Hall, Cork, Republic of Ireland
tel: + 353 (0)21 492 4298
fax: + 353 (0)21 431 9957
email: arts@corkcity.ie
web: www.corkcity.ie
contact: Liz Meaney

Cork County Council
Arts Office, Cork County Library, County Hall, Cork, Republic of Ireland
tel: + 353 (0)21 434 6210
fax: + 353 (0)21 434 7122
email: corkcountyarts@eircom.net
web: www.corkcoco.com
contact: Ian McDonagh

Donegal County Council
Donegal County Library, Rosemount, Letterkenny, Co. Donegal, Republic of Ireland
tel: + 353 (0)74 912 1968
fax: + 353 (0)74 912 1740
email: traolach@donegalcoco.ie
web: www.donegalculture.com
contact: Traolach O'Fionnáin

Drogheda Borough Council
Fair Street, Drogheda, Co. Louth, Republic of Ireland
tel: + 353 (0)41 987 6165
fax: + 353 (0)41 983 9306
email: rosemary.collier@droghedaboro.ie
web: www.createlouth.ie
contact: Rosemary Collier

Dublin City Council
Arts Office, Environment and Cultural Department, Dublin City Council, 10 Cornmarket, Dublin 8, Republic of Ireland
tel: + 353 (0)1 671 3639
fax: + 353 (0)1 675 9816
email: arts@dubc.iol.ie
web: www.dublincity.ie
contact: Jack Gilligan

Dundalk Town Council
Town Hall, Dundalk, Co. Louth, Republic of Ireland
tel: + 353 (0)42 939 6437
fax: + 353 (0)42 935 1539
email: dundarts@eircom.net
contact: Marie Gray

Dun Laoghaire-Rathdown County Council
County Hall, Marine Road, Dun Laoghaire, Co. Dublin, Republic of Ireland
tel: + 353 (0)1 205 4749
fax: + 353 (0)1 205 4736
email: arts@dlrcoco.ie
web: www.dlrcoco.ie/arts
contact: Sarah Searson

Fingal County Council
County Hall, Swords, Co. Dublin, Republic of Ireland
tel: + 353 (0)1 890 5099
fax: + 353 (0)1 890 4323
email: fingalartsoffice@eircom.net
web: www.fingalarts.ie
contact: Rory O'Byrne

Galway City Council
City Arts Office, City Hall, College Road, Galway, Republic of Ireland
tel: + 353 (0)91 536546
fax: + 353 (0)91 567493
email: jharrold@galwaycity.ie
web: www.galwaycity.ie
contact: James C. Harrold

Galway County Council
County Arts Office, Prospect Hill, Galway, Republic of Ireland
tel: + 353 (0)91 746877/75
fax: + 353 (0)91 779082
email: artsoffice@galwaycoco.ie
web: www.galway.ie
contact: Marilyn Gaughan

Kerry County Council
Aras an Chontae, Rathass, Tralee, Co. Kerry, Republic of Ireland
tel: + 353 (0)66 712 1111
fax: + 353 (0)66 718 3613
email: kkennell@kerrycoco.ie
web: www.kerrycoco.ie
contact: Kate Kennelly

Kildare County Council
Kildare County Library & Arts Service, Riverbank Arts Centre, Newbridge, Co. Kildare, Republic of Ireland
tel: + 353 (0)45 448318/448328
fax: + 353 (0)45 432490
email: lrussell@kildarecoco.ie
web: www.kildare.ie
contact: Lucina Russell

Kilkenny County Council

County Hall, John Street,
Kilkenny, Republic of Ireland
tel: + 353 (0)56 779 4137/36
email: mary.butler@kilkennycoco.ie
web: www.kilkennycoco.ie
contact: Mary Butler

Laois County Council

Arts Office, Aras an Chontae,
Portlaoise, Co. Laois,
Republic of Ireland
tel: + 353 (0)502 74344
fax: + 353 (0)502 74382
email: artsoff@laoiscoco.ie
web: www.laoiscoco.ie
contact: Muireann Ní Chonaill

Leitrim County Council

Arts Office, Aras an Chontae,
Park Lane House, Carrick-on-Shannon,
Co. Leitrim, Republic of Ireland
tel: + 353 (0)71 962 0005
fax: + 353 (0)71 962 1982
email: artoff@leitrimcoco.ie
web: www.leitrimcoco.ie
contact: Terre Duffy

Limerick City Council

City Hall, Merchant's Quay,
Limerick, Republic of Ireland
tel: + 353 (0)61 407421
fax: + 353 (0)61 418345
email: artsoff@limerickcity.ie
web: www.limerickcity.ie
contact: Sheila Deegan

Limerick County Council

County Hall, Dooradoyle, Limerick,
Republic of Ireland
tel: + 353 (0)61 496498
fax: + 353 (0)61 496009
email: arts@limerickcoco.ie
web: www.limerickcoco.ie
contact: Joan MacKernan

Longford County Council

County Library and Arts Service,
Town Centre, Longford,
Republic of Ireland
tel: + 353 (0)43 40729
fax: + 353 (0)43 48576
email: fkennedy@longfordcoco.ie
web: www.longfordlibrary.ie
contact: Fergus Kennedy

Louth County Council

County Hall, Millennium Centre,
Dundalk, Co. Louth,
Republic of Ireland
tel: + 353 (0)42 933 5457
fax: + 353 (0)42 933 4549
email: brian.harten@louthcoco.ie
web: www.louthcoco.ie
contact: Brian Harten

Mayo County Council

Aras an Chontae, Castlebar,
Co. Mayo, Republic of Ireland
tel: + 353 (0)94 904 7560
fax: + 353 (0)94 902 8188
email: artsstaf@mayococo.ie
web: www.mayococo.ie
contact: Anne McCarthy

Meath County Council

Arts Office, Dunshaughlin Library,
Main Street, Dunshaughlin,
Co. Meath, Republic of Ireland
tel: + 353 (0)1 824 0000
fax: + 353 (0)1 824 0233
email: artsoffice@meathcoco.ie
web: www.meath.ie
contact: Denis Boyle (acting)

Monaghan County Council

Monaghan Arts Office,
The Market House, Monaghan,
Republic of Ireland
tel: + 353 (0)47 71114
fax: + 353 (0)47 71113
email: info@monaghanartsoffice.org
web: www.monaghanartsoffice.org
contact: Somhairle MacConghail

Offaly County Council

Aras an Chontae, Charleville Road,
Tullamore, Co. Offaly,
Republic of Ireland
tel: + 353 (0)506 46800
fax: + 353 (0)506 46868
email: artsoff@offalycoco.ie
web: www.offaly.ie
contact: Sally O'Leary

Roscommon County Council

Roscommon County Arts Office,
Library Buildings, Abbey Street,
Roscommon, Republic of Ireland
tel: + 353 (0)90 663 7285
fax: + 353 (0)90 663 7101
email: artsoffice@roscommoncoco.ie
contact: Philip Delamere

Sligo County Council

Arts Office, Market Yard,
Sligo, Republic of Ireland
tel: + 353 (0)71 914 0985
fax: + 353 (0)71 914 0990
email: arts@sligococo.ie
web: www.sligococo.ie
contact: Mary McAuliffe

South Dublin County Council

County Hall, Tallaght, Dublin 24,
Republic of Ireland
tel: + 353 (0)1 414 9270
fax: + 353 (0)1 414 9111
email: artsofficer@sdublincoco.ie
web: www. sdublincoco.ie
contact: Orla Scannell

Tipperary North Riding County Council

The Courthouse, Nenagh,
Co. Tipperary, Republic of Ireland
tel: + 353 (0)67 44860/52
fax: + 353 (0)67 31478
email: artsoffice@northtippcoco.ie
contact: Melanie Scott

Tipperary South Riding County Council

Arts Facilitator, Friar St., Cashel, Co. Tipperary, Republic of Ireland
tel: + 353 (0)62 64700
email: annryan@southtippcoco.ie
contact: Ann Ryan

Waterford City Council

City Hall, Waterford, Republic of Ireland
tel: + 353 (0)51 309983
fax: + 353(0)51 844709
email: arts@waterfordcity.ie
web: www.waterfordcity.ie
contact: Conor Nolan

Waterford County Council

Civic Offices, Davitt's Quay, Dungarvan, Co. Waterford, Republic of Ireland
tel: + 353 (0)58 41416
fax: + 353 (0)58 42911
email: morgan@waterfordcoco.ie
web: www.waterfordcoco.ie
contact: Margaret Organ

Wexford County Council

County Hall, Wexford, Republic of Ireland
tel: + 353 (0)53 76369
fax: + 353 (0)53 43532
email: arts@wexfordcoco.ie
web: www.wexford.ie
contact: Rosaleen Molloy

Wicklow County Council

Arts Office, St Manntan's House, Kilmantin Hill, Wicklow Town, Republic of Ireland
tel: + 353 (0)404 20155
fax: + 353 (0)404 66057
email: SRedmond@wicklowcoco.ie
web: www.wicklow.ie
contact: Sinead Redmond

Northern Ireland Local Authority Arts Officers & Arts Development Officers

Antrim Borough Council

Clotworthy Arts Centre, Antrim Castle Gardens, Randalstown Road, Antrim BT41 4LH, Northern Ireland
tel: +44 (0)28 9442 8000
fax: +44 (0)28 9446 0360
email: clotworthyarts@antrim.gov.uk
web: www.antrim.gov.uk
contact: Cathy McNally
Philip Magennis

Ards Borough Council

Ards Arts Centre, Town Hall, Conway Square, Newtownards, Co. Down BT23 4DB, Northern Ireland
tel: +44 (0)28 9181 0803
fax: +44 (0)28 9182 3131
email: arts@ards-council.gov.uk
web: www.arts@ards-council.gov.uk
contact: Eilis O'Baoill

Armagh City & District Council

The Market Place Theatre & Arts Centre, Market Street, Armagh BT61 7AT, Northern Ireland
tel: +44 (0)28 3752 1820
fax: +44 (0)28 3752 1822
email: admin@marketplacearmagh.com
web: www.marketplacearmagh.com
contact: Jill Holmes

Ballymena Borough Council

Ballymena Showgrounds, Warden St., Ballymena, Co. Antrim BT43 7OR, Northern Ireland
tel: +44 (0)28 2563 9853
fax: +44 (0)28 2563 8549
email: rosalind.lowry@ballymena.gov.uk
web: www.ballymena.gov.uk
contact: Rosalind Lowry

Ballymoney Borough Council

Riada House, 14 Charles Street, Ballymoney, Co. Antrim BT53 6DZ, Northern Ireland
tel: +44 (0)28 2766 0229
fax: +44 (0)28 2766 7659
email: margaret.edgar@ballymoney.gov.uk
web: www.ballymoney.gov.uk
contact: Margaret Edgar

Banbridge District Council

Civic Building, Downshire Road, Banbridge, Co. Down BT32 3JY, Northern Ireland
tel: +44 (0)28 4066 0600
fax: +44 (0)28 4066 0601
email: leah.duncan@banbridge.gov.uk
web: www.banbridge.gov.uk
contact: Leah Duncan

Belfast City Council

The Cecil Ward Building, 4-10 Linenhall Street, Belfast BT2 8BP, Northern Ireland
tel: +44 (0)28 9027 0227
fax: +44 (0)28 9027 0325
email: otoolec@belfastcity.gov.uk
web: www.belfastcity.gov.uk/arts
contact: Christine O'Toole
See also Awards & Competitions

Carrickfergus Borough Council

Heritage Plaza, Antrim Street, Carrickfergus, Co. Antrim BT38 7DG, Northern Ireland
tel: +44 (0)28 9336 6666
fax: +44 (0)28 9335 0350
email: jmccormick.marina@carrickfergus.org
web: www.carrickfergus.org
contact: John McCormick

Castlereagh Borough Council

Civic and Administrative Offices,
Bradford Court, Upper Galwally,
Castlereagh, Co. Down BT8 6RB,
Northern Ireland
tel: +44 (0)28 9049 4500
fax: +44 (0)28 9049 4555
email: emilywalsh@castlereagh.gov.uk
web: www.castlereagh.gov.uk
contact: Emily Walsh

Coleraine Borough Council

185 Coleraine Road, Portstewart,
Coleraine BT52 1EY,
Northern Ireland
tel: +44 (0)28 7083 1400
fax: +44 (0)28 7083 1432
email: info@flowerfield.org
web: www.colerainebc.gov.uk
contact: Malcolm Murchison

Cookstown District Council

Council Offices, Burn Road,
Cookstown, Co. Tyrone BT80 8DT,
Northern Ireland
tel: +44 (0)28 8676 2205
fax: +44 (0)28 8676 4360
email: linda.mcgarvey@cookstown.gov.uk
web: www.cookstown.gov.uk
contact: Linda McGarvey

Craigavon Borough Council

Pinebank House Arts Centre,
Tullygally Road, Craigavon,
Co. Armagh BT65 5BY,
Northern Ireland
tel: +44 (0)28 3834 1618
fax: +44 (0)28 3834 2402
email: emma.wilson@craigavon.gov.uk
web: www.craigavon.gov.uk
contact: Emma Wilson

Derry City Council

98 Strand Road, Derry BT48 7NN,
Northern Ireland
tel: +44 (0)28 7136 5151
fax: +44 (0)28 7126 4858
email: orchard.gallery@derrycity.gov.uk
web: www.derrycity.gov.uk
contact: Brendan McMenamin

Down District Council

Down Civic Arts Centre,
2-6 Irish Street, Downpatrick,
Co. Down BT30 6BN, Northern Ireland
tel: +44 (0)28 4461 5283
fax: +44 (0)28 4461 6621
email: mail@downartscentre.com
web: www.downartscentre.com
contact: Cathie McKimm

Dungannon & South Tyrone Borough Council

Dungannon Enterprise Centre,
Unit T11, 2 Coalisland Road,
Dungannon, Co. Tyrone BT71 6JT,
Northern Ireland
tel: +44 (0)28 8775 3626
fax: +44 (0)28 8775 3789
email: ddas@talk21.com
web: www.dungannon.gov.uk
contact: Aine Dolan

Fermanagh District Council

Town Hall, Enniskillen,
Co. Fermanagh BT74 7BA,
Northern Ireland
tel: +44 (0)28 6632 5050
fax: +44 (0)28 6632 2024
email: geraldine.oreilly@
fermanagh.gov.uk
web: www.fermanagh.gov.uk
contact: Geraldine O'Reilly

Larne Borough Council

Smiley Buildings, Victoria Road,
Larne, Co. Antrim BT40 1RU,
Northern Ireland
tel: +44 (0)28 2827 2313
fax: +44 (0)28 2826 0660
email: francish@larne.gov.uk
web: www.larne.gov.uk
contact: Herbie Francis

Limavady Borough Council

7 Connell Street, Limavady,
Co. Londonderry BT49 0HA,
Northern Ireland
tel: +44 (0)28 7776 0304
fax: +44 (0)28 7772 2010
email: stephen.bell@limavady.gov.uk
contact: Stephen Bell

Lisburn Borough Council

Island Arts Centre,
Lagan Valley Island,
Lisburn, Co. Antrim BT27 4RL,
Northern Ireland
tel: +44 (0)28 9250 950 9
fax: +44 (0)28 9250 9510
email: siobhan.mccormick@
iac.lisburn.gov.uk
web: www.lisburn.gov.uk
contact: Siobhan Stewart

Magherafelt District Council

50 Ballyronan Road, Magherafelt,
BT45 6EN, Northern Ireland
tel: +44 (0)28 7939 7979
fax: +44 (0)28 7939 7980
email: mgbrowne@magherafelt.gov.uk
web: www.magherafelt.gov.uk
contact: Michael Browne

Moyle District Council

Sheskburn House, 7 Mary Street,
Ballycastle, Co. Antrim BT54 6QH,
Northern Ireland
tel: +44 (0)28 2076 2225
fax: +44 (0)28 2076 2515
email: arts@moyle-council.org
web: www.moyle-council.org
contact: Pauline Russell

Newry & Mourne District Council

The Sean Hollywood Arts Centre,
1a Bank Parade, Newry, Co. Down,
BT35 5HP, Northern Ireland
tel: +44 (0)28 3031 3180
fax: +44 (0)28 3026 6839
email: mark.hughes@newry
andmourne.gov.uk
web: www.newryandmourne.gov.uk
contact: Mark Hughes

Newtownabbey Borough Council

Mossley Mill, Newtownabbey,
Co. Antrim BT36 5QA,
Northern Ireland
tel: +44 (0)28 9034 0063
fax: +44 (0)28 9034 0062
email: ccole@newtownabbey.gov.uk
web: www.newtownabbey.gov.uk
contact: Cathy Cole

North Down Borough Council

Town Hall, The Castle, Bangor,
Co. Down BT20 4BT, Northern
Ireland
tel: +44 (0)28 9127 8032
fax: +44 (0)28 9127 0371
email: arts.officer@northdown.gov.uk
web: www.northdown.gov.uk
contact: Gail Prentice

Omagh District Council

The Grange, Mountjoy Road,
Omagh, Co. Tyrone BT79 7BL,
Northern Ireland
tel: +44 (0)28 8224 5321
fax: +44 (0)28 8224 3888
email: jean.brennan@omagh.gov.uk
web: www.omagh.gov.uk
contact: Jean Brennan

Strabane District Council

47 Derry Road, Strabane, Co. Tyrone
BT82 8DY, Northern Ireland
tel: +44 (0)28 7138 2204
fax: +44 (0)28 7138 1348
email: lkyle@strabanedc.com
web: www.strabanedc.com
contact: Lorrie Kyle

University Arts Officers

Cork Institute of Technology

Rossa Avenue, Bishopstown,
Cork, Republic of Ireland
tel: + 353 (0)21 432 6566
fax: + 353 (0)21 432 6567
email: artsfest@cit.ie
web: www.cit.ie
contact: Úna McCarthy

Magee College

Cultural Development Dept,
Northland Road, Derry BT48 7JL,
Northern Ireland
tel: +44 (0)28 7137 5679
fax: +44 (0)28 7137 5487
email: ke.bond@ulst.ac.uk
web: www.ulst.ac.uk/culture
contact: Kate Bond

National University of Ireland

Bank of Ireland Theatre,
Galway, Republic of Ireland
tel: + 353 (0)91 512062
fax: + 353 (0)91 512534
email: fionnuala.gallagher@
nuigalway.ie
web: www.nuigalway.ie/arts_office
contact: Fionnuala Gallagher

University of Limerick

Arts Office, Dromroe Village Centre,
University of Limerick, Limerick,
Republic of Ireland
tel: + 353 (0)61 202130
fax: + 353 (0)61 330316
email: patricia.moriarty@ul.ie
web: www.ul.ie
contact: Patricia Moriarty

University of Ulster

Cultural Development Office,
Room F129, Cromore Road,
Coleraine BT52 1SA, Northern Ireland
tel: +44 (0)28 7032 4683
fax: +44 (0)28 7032 4160
email: j.mackle@ulster.ac.uk
web: www.ulst.ac.uk/culture
contact: Janet Mackle

Údarás na Gaeltachta Arts Officers

Údarás na Gaeltachta

Baile Mhic Íre, Maigh Chromtha,
Co. Chorcaí, Éire
tel: + 353 (0)66 915 0100
(0)26 45946
fax: + 353 (0)66 915 0101
email: e.depaor@udaras.ie
web: www.ealain.ie
contact: Eibhlín de Paor

Údarás na Gaeltachta

Ealaín na Gaeltachta, Na Forbacha,
Co. na Gaillimhe, Éire
tel: + 353 (0)91 503197
fax: + 353 (0)91 503101
email: ealain@udaras.ie
web: www.ealain.ie
contact: Majella Ní Chríocháin

Údarás na Gaeltachta

Doirí Beaga, Leitir Ceanainn,
Tír Chonaill, Éire
tel: + 353 (0)74 956 0100
fax: + 353 (0)74 956 0101
email: m.fearraigh@udaras.ie
web: www.udaras.ie
contact: Mícheál í Fearraigh

Area Partnership/Leader Initiative Arts Officers

Dublin Inner City Partnership

16 Upper Ormond Quay, Dublin 7,
Republic of Ireland
tel: + 353 (0)1 872 1321
fax: + 353 (0)1 872 1330
email: info@artsresource.net
contact: Emer Coveney

County Sligo Leader Partnership Co. Ltd

Sligo Development Centre,
Cleveragh Road, Sligo,
Republic of Ireland
tel: + 353 (0)71 914 1138
fax: + 353 (0)71 914 1162
email: info@sligoleader.com
contact: Anna Spearman

South Kerry Development Partnership Ltd

Sun Hill, Killorglin, Co. Kerry,
Republic of Ireland
tel: + 353 (0)66 976 1615
fax: + 353 (0)66 976 2059
email: sobrien@skdp.net
web: www.southkerry.ie
contact: Sarah O'Brien

scholarships and bursaries

Patrick O'Kane and Michelle Fairley in Prime Cut's production
of Ashes To Ashes by Harold Pinter © Chris Hill

Arts Council/An Chomhairle Ealaíon

70 Merrion Square, Dublin 2, Republic of Ireland
tel: +353 (0)1 618 0235
callsave: 1850 392492
fax: +353 (0)1 676 1302
email: artistsservices@artscouncil.ie
web: www.artscouncil.ie
artists' services manager: Paul Johnson
artists' services officer: Sian Cunningham

The Arts Council offers financial supports to individual artists (including dance, theatre and music practitioners), and groups of artists through a number of bursaries, awards and schemes. The Council embraces the principle of equal access to public funds, and assesses all applications regardless of gender, race or disability in a fair and unbiased manner. As demand for Arts Council support grows, the Council employs a three-tier assessment process; applications are short-listed by artform by specialists/external assessors, assessed by peer panels, whose recommendations become decisions once ratified by Council. As demand for grant aid always exceeds funds available, not all good and eligible applications may be funded.

A core objective of the Arts Council is to encourage and assist arts practice. To achieve this objective, the Council offers a suite of Artists' Bursaries, which aim to assist individual artists in the development of their practice; Artists' Awards (commissions, projects and residencies), which aim to assist artists and organisations in the creation of new work, and Artists' Schemes, which aim to assist artists and organisations in the production and dissemination of work, and seeks to respond to the needs of artists and to provide a flexible instrument for the Council to encourage innovation, research and artistic experiment.

As part of the Arts Council's on-going development as an agency for developing arts practices, this new awards system was piloted in 2001 and 2002 and is due for completion during 2004. Features of the new awards programmes, contained in the Supports for Artists folder available from the Council, include broader eligibility criteria, new art form combinations, and greater flexibility for new arts practices and artists working together. The Arts Council is moving towards a system of general awards open to artists working in all disciplines, and away from an earlier system where awards were linked to particular art forms.

general awards

travel and mobility award: by facilitating travel, the aim is to improve the professional development, formation and networking opportunities of artists and people working professionally in the arts. It supports a short period (up to six months) of travel outside Ireland. It is not intended to fund study periods or courses abroad. Artists, performers, arts administrators and managers, arts practitioners and technical personnel working in the arts can apply. Award range: up to €5,000 may be awarded (average award €1,000). Applications (on-going) should be made no later than six weeks before date of departure. For current information, please consult the Arts Council website: www.artscouncil.ie

professional development and training strand 1: This annual award (one closing date) facilitates artists and performers to achieve the highest standards through further professional development and formation. Specifically, it assists any development activity that enhances artistic and creative practice and contributes to career development. Presently undergoing internal executive review – Strand 1 is directed at artists and performers (dance, theatre, music practitioners) wishing to pursue formal postgraduate or equivalent studies abroad, which commence in the autumn. Award range: up €12,000 may be awarded (average award €4,000). Applications for this award must be submitted by the closing date; for current information, please consult the Arts Council website: www.artscouncil.ie

professional development and training strand 2: Strand 2 is directed at artists and performers wishing to take up short courses, mentoring or internships opportunities that may arise during the year. There are a number of closing dates per year, and applications must be made at least six to eight weeks in advance of the opportunity commencing. All practising creative and performing artists and technical personnel working in any context or any art form are eligible to apply. Applicants may only be in receipt of one award per year. Award range: up to €12,000 may be awarded (average award €2,000); for current information, please consult the Arts Council website: www.artscouncil.ie

bursaries: the primary aim is to allow artists to pursue ideas and fulfil their artistic potential. The award allows artists buy the time, space and freedom to concentrate on a specific body of work, particularly through releasing them from their usual commitments. It is open to practising creative artists working in any context or any art form. Undergoing internal review, it is current Arts Council policy that mid-career practitioners have priority in these awards. Award range: Up to €12,000. One closing date per year; for current information, please consult the Arts Council website: www.artscouncil.ie

residency schemes: The Arts Council operates a number of residency schemes, which encourage direct contact between professional artists and different community/host groups and organisations, which aim to offer an artist the opportunity to work on a specific project or programme and/or develop his/her own practice in a new environment or specific location outside of their normal workplace. Undergoing internal review, please consult Residencies, Banff residency, Artist-in-the-Community Scheme (Create), and residency schemes run in conjunction with Department of Justice, Equality and Law Reform, Irish Writers' Centre, and Poetry Ireland; for current information, please consult the Arts Council website: www.artscouncil.ie

commissions: The aim is to foster the creation of new work through commissioning. Specifically, the Commissions award intends to build artistic networks and artistic relationships between artists and commissioners by encouraging new types of commissioners, and promoting greater diversity in the opportunities available to artists. It is open to all artists, organisations and other individuals working in the arts. Undergoing internal review, it is important to note that this award is specifically concerned with commissioning fees (with the Arts Council contributing up to 75% of the overall artist fees). Award range: €1,000 to €10,000; for current information, please consult the Arts Council website: www.artscouncil.ie

projects: The Projects scheme aims to assist artists in the devising, exploration and implementation of creative ideas in any art form or combination of art forms. The emphasis is on the creation of new work, experimentation and innovation. Specifically, this scheme offers once-off funding for the development and/or production phases of artistic projects that may last up to five years. Undergoing internal review, Projects is open to all artists, organisations and other individuals working within a contemporary arts context. Award range: up to €25,000; for current information, please consult the Arts Council website: www.artscouncil.ie

drama awards

international directing mentoring scheme: Introduced in 2003, this award is intended to address training deficits in theatre direction and to build levels of craft in mid-career artists. It is anticipated that this mentoring will offer wider knowledge of international

practice to directors; enable organisations they work with to realise better productions, and to improve significantly the efficient use of human and physical resources. Specifically, it assists the formalisation of a mentoring relationship between an Irish director and a director from abroad who also teaches or has taught directing at third level. There will be two to four awards made in any one year. Award range: up to €15,000 may be awarded. Note: very specialised criteria must be met to qualify for this award. Please take careful note of the criteria that are detailed in the Supports for Artists folder which can also be downloaded from www.artscouncil.ie

application procedures: please consult the Supports for Artists folder for specific application forms, and detailed information on all artists' bursaries, artists' awards and artists' schemes or download Supports for Artists sheets from www.artscouncil.ie

completed applications should be sent by post to: The Arts Council, 70 Merrion Square, Dublin 2, with the name of the award clearly marked to the envelope. Supports for Artists' folders are updated each year are available from late autumn onwards (for use in the year ahead).

Arts Council of Northern Ireland

MacNeice House, 77 Malone Road,
Belfast BT9 6AQ, Northern Ireland
tel: +44 (0)28 9038 5200
fax: +44 (0)28 9066 1715
email: info@artscouncil-ni.org
web: www.artscouncil-ni.org
director, arts development department: Philip Hammond
drama and dance officer: Gilly Campbell
assistant drama and dance officer: Maria O'Kane

The Arts Council of Northern Ireland has developed a special programme of new schemes for the individual artist. Full details of the following awards available through the Support for the Individual Artist Programme (SIAP) are on the ACNI website.

general arts awards: For specific projects, specialised research, personal artistic development and certain materials/equipment.

major individual award: To create the circumstances in which established artists can develop individually with a view to attempting extended or ambitious work.

artists in the community: For community groups or organisations to have an artist in residence for up to six months.

artists in education: For artists to undertake programmes that will establish innovative learning situations of the highest quality.

arts & disability: To celebrate work of quality and innovation by disabled artists throughout Ireland.

young artists award: Awards for young, exceptionally talented people who have finished their academic studies leading to specific qualifications.

the milton violin award: The loan of a fine violin by the distinguished Neapolitan violin maker Joseph Gagliano to an outstanding young violinist from Northern Ireland wishing to pursue or continue professional training.

arts & artists abroad: To contribute towards touring costs of performance, exhibition and presentation of Northern Irish works abroad and in the other regions of the UK.

arts & disability networking abroad: To contribute towards touring costs of performance, exhibition and presentation of Northern Irish arts abroad and towards networking costs, in connection with arts and disability.

travel awards: For artists to travel outside Ireland in advancement of their skills and expertise, or the furtherance of their career.

international artists' profile: Specialist advice and support in creating international marketing material for individual artists' profiling.

international residency awards scheme: Banff; Skidmore Jazz Studentship; British School at Rome; MacDowell Colony; Self-arranged International Residencies.

Bank of Ireland Millennium Scholars Trust

National College of Ireland, Mayor Street, IFSC, Dublin 1, Republic of Ireland
tel: +353 (0)1 406 0500
fax: +353 (0)1 497 2200
email: boischolars@ncirl.ie
web: www.ncirl.ie / www.boi.ie
contact: Eileen Punch

award: €12.5 million, which will provide 60 third-level scholarships each year of the first decade of the new millennium. Individual awards of up to €6,300 per year, to a maximum of €38,000 for the course duration, will be made.

open to: The Creative/Performing Arts category of the Trust identifies candidates with exceptional ability in the arts who face significant obstacles to developing their potential through further study or training. Scholarships are awarded to candidates at three levels: Foundation [within the Education application category only]; Degree/Initial Professional Training; Advanced Studies/Specialised Professional Training.

application details: A nominating body must propose candidates and provide a personal reference. Candidates must also complete an application form. A

list of registered Nominating Bodies, including organisations in the Arts field, is available from the Trust office. Organisations wishing to act as nominating bodies should contact the Trust Office for an applicat ion form.

closing date: April 1st (Creative/Performing Arts Category)

Foreign Embassy Bursaries

Many Embassies offer bursaries to Irish post-graduate students to undertake accredited post-graduate courses (including dance and theatre courses) in their respective countries. Application procedures vary and information is available from individual embassies. Examples of these bursaries include the Chevening Scholarship Awards administered by the British Council *(see also Funding Bodies)* and the Fulbright Scholarships administered by the American Embassy.

Local Authority Bursaries

Many local authorities, North and South, operate bursaries and awards for individual artists that are open to artists born, or residing in, the local authority's geographic area. Details of these schemes vary and are available from individual Arts Officers.

Tyrone Guthrie Centre Regional Bursary Scheme

Tyrone Guthrie Centre, Annaghmakerrig, Newbliss, Co. Monaghan, Republic of Ireland
tel: + 353 (0)47 54003
fax: + 353 (0)47 54380
email: thetgc@indigo.ie
web: www.tyroneguthrie.ie
director: Sheila Pratschke

award: A two-week stay at the Tyrone Guthrie Centre, Annaghmakerrig.

open to: Artists born or resident in 30 different local authorities, North and South.

application details: Individual Arts Officers in association with Annaghmakerrig administer the bursaries. Application details and deadlines vary and are available from local Arts Officers.
See also Arts Officers and Support Organisations.

Kelly Campbell in The Abbey's production of The Burial at Thebes from Sophocles'
Antigone, adapted by Seamus Heaney © Tom Lawlor

Non Submission Awards

Belfast Arts Awards

c/o Culture and Arts Unit, Belfast City Council,
The Cecil Ward Building, 4-10 Linenhall Street,
Belfast BT2 8BP, Northern Ireland
tel: +44 (0)28 9027 0227
fax: +44 (0)28 9027 0325
email: otoolec@belfastcity.gov.uk
web: www.belfastcity.gov.uk/arts
contact: Christine O'Toole
For the current format of the awards, please contact
Arts Development Officer Christine O'Toole.

ESB Dublin Fringe Festival Awards

12 East Essex Street, Dublin 2, Republic of Ireland
Admin: +353 (0)1 679 2320 /677 8511
Box Office: 1850 374 643
fax: +353 (0)1 679 2790
email: info@fringefest.com
web: www.fringefest.com
festival director: Vallejo Gantner
executive producer: Bea Kelleher
programme manager & co-ordinator: Maedhbh McCullagh
open to: All official entrants in the festival.
categories: Best Irish Production, Best International
Production, Best Irish Male Performance, Best Irish
Female Performance, and Special Award for Innovation.
selection procedure: A panel of ten independent theatre
practitioners selects the winners.
presentation/announcement of awards: The awards
are announced on the last night of the festival.

The Irish Times/ESB Irish Theatre Awards

Promotions Department, The Irish Times,
10-16 D'Olier Street, Dublin 2, Republic of Ireland
tel: +353 (0)1 675 8709
fax: +353 (0)1 679 2789
email: theatreawards@irish-times.ie
web: www.ireland.com
contact: Claire Mullin
categories: Best Actor, Best Actress, Best Actor in a
Supporting Role, Best Actress in a Supporting Role,
Best Director, Best Designer: Set, Best Designer:
Costumes, Best Designer: Lighting, Best Production,
Best New Play, Opera of the Year, Special Tribute
Award. Opera productions will also be eligible for
nomination in the Design categories.
selection procedure: Judges attend all plays
performed by professional theatre companies in the
Republic of Ireland and Northern Ireland within each
calendar year. A short-list of four nominations per
category is then established. Those selected for the
shortlist are announced in January in the Irish Times.
presentation/announcement of awards: The awards are
presented every February at a gala Prize-giving ceremony
in Dublin.

Submission Awards

Allianz Business2Arts Sponsor of the Year Awards

44 East Essex Street, Temple Bar,
Dublin 2, Republic of Ireland
tel: +353 (0)1 672 5336
fax: +353 (0)1 672 5373
email: info@business2arts.ie
web: www.business2arts.ie
chief executive: Siobhan Broughan
training officer: Julie T. Brady
contact: appointment pending
awards: Open to any nominated arts organisation and
is awarded for the most effective and imaginative
collaboration with a business. Business sponsors can
also be nominated for the following six awards.
categories: Best Business/Arts Collaboration by a Small
Business, Best Business/Arts Collaboration for the First
Time, Best Business/Arts Sponsorship in Kind, Best
Business/Arts Collaboration in the Community, Best
Business/Arts Collaboration Enhancing Corporate Identity,
Best Business/Arts Collaboration with Continuity
open to: All businesses, large and small, engaging in
imaginative and effective sponsorship of the arts. The
judges look for collaboration and creativity in business
and arts partnerships.
application procedure: Nomination forms available
from the Business2Arts Office.
closing date: Last Friday in March.

Guinness Living Dublin Awards

Dublin Chamber of Commerce, 7 Clare Street,
Dublin 2, Republic of Ireland
tel: +353 (0)1 644 7228
fax: +353 (0)1 676 6043
email: Ciara@dubchamber.ie
web: www.dubchamber.ie
awards co-ordinator: Ciara Duncan
award: €25,000 prize fund divided between projects
that improve the quality of life in our communities.
open to: The awards have identified five categories, one
of which is Culture & Tourism.
application procedure: Application forms available
from the above address.
closing date: July.

Playwriting Awards

Corcadorca Playwright Award
Corcadorca Theatre Company, 11/12 Marlboro Street,
Cork, Republic of Ireland
tel: + 353 (0)21 427 8326
fax: + 353 (0)21 427 8326
email: corcadorcatheatre@eircom.net
web: www.corcadorca.com
artistic director: Pat Kiernan
company manager: Dyane Hanrahan
competition details: Biennial award for an original
full-length play which has not been published,
produced or performed before the submission date.
prize: €2,000 cash, a commissioned sculpture and a
professional production or workshopping of the script.
application procedure: Full application details and
criteria available from the company on request
closing date: 31 January

Eamon Keane Full Length Play Award
Writers Week, 24 The Square, Listowel,
Co. Kerry, Republic of Ireland
tel: + 353 (0)68 21074
fax: + 353 (0)68 22893
email: writersweek@eircom.net
web: www.writersweek.ie
contact: The Administrator
competition details: Full-length plays award
prize: €1,000
application procedure: Advance information brochure
available on request
entry fee: €20
closing date: 1st March

Ireland Funds Annual Literary Award
5 Foster Place, Dublin 2, Republic of Ireland
tel: + 353 (0)1 662 7878
fax: + 353 (0)1 662 7879
email: info@irelandfunds.ie
web: www.irlfunds.org
competition details: An annual award for outstanding
work presented by the American Ireland Fund.
prize: €25,000
application procedure: Non-submission award

Oireachtas Literary Awards
c/o Stiúrthóir an Oireachtas, 6 Sráid Fhearchair,
Baile Átha Cliath 2
tel: +353 (0)1 475 3857
fax: +353 (0)1 475 8767
email: eolas@antoireachtas.ie
web: www.antoireachtas.ie
contact: Liam Ó Maolaodha
competition details: Playwriting awards include: Full-
Length Play Award; One Act Play Award (sponsored by
Údarás na Gaeltachta).

prizes: €600 each
application procedure: Competition programme and
application form available on request
entry fee: €15 per play
closing date: 1st July

O.Z. Whitehead Play Competition
c/o Society of Irish Playwrights and Screenwriters Guild
The Writers Centre, 19 Parnell Square,
Dublin 1, Republic of Ireland
tel: + 353 (0)1 492 3808/ (0)86 837 1203
web: www.script.ie
email: david.kavanagh@script.ie
contact: David Kavanagh
competition details: Competition under review.

P.J. O'Connor Awards
c/o Radio Centre, RTE, Donnybrook,
Dublin 4, Republic of Ireland
tel: +353 (0)1 208 3111
web: www.rte.ie/radio1/events/pjawards/
contact: Daniel Reardon
competition details: 30-minute radio drama award
Prizes: €3,000 (winner), €2,000 (runner up), €1,000
(second runner up), writing workshops for writers
showing promise. The three winning plays will be
professionally produced for transmission.
application procedure: Entry form and full details
available on request
closing date: February [2004]

Stewart Parker Trust Playwriting Bursaries
Stewart Parker Trust, Institute of Irish Studies
Queens University, Belfast BT7 1NN, Northern Ireland
tel: +44 (0)28 9033 5137
fax: +44 (0)28 9043 9238
email: jfairleigh@eircom.net
contact: John Fairleigh
competition details: Open to new playwrights in receipt
of their first professional production in each calendar year.
prizes: Stewart Parker New Playwright Bursary
(stg£7,500); BBC Radio Drama Award (stg£1,000 plus
an invitation to submit a play for production); BBC
Radio Drama Award in the Irish Language (stg£1,000
plus an invitation to submit a play for production).
application procedure: A non-submission award.
Professional theatre companies are invited to submit
nominations.
closing date: End of calendar year

CONFIDENCE & CREATIVITY

2 YEAR FULL TIME INTENSIVE ACTOR TRAINING PROGRAMME

1 YEAR PART TIME PERFORMANCE COURSE

1 YEAR PART TIME FOUNDATION COURSE

PART TIME ADULT NIGHT COURSES
INTRO TO DRAMA, PAGE TO STAGE, ACTING FOR CAMERA, CREATIVE WRITING, EASTER COURSES, SUMMER COURSES, VOICE WEEKENDS .

CHILDREN'S CLASSES AGE 6–19
(STARTING AGES VARY ACCORDING TO LOCATION)

THE GAIETY SCHOOL OF ACTING

Studios for Hire in Temple Bar

TEMPLE BAR
SUTTON PARK SCHOOL
BRAY
CORK
KILLARNEY
KENMARE

FOR MORE INFORMATION
01 679 9277   Lo Call 1890 258 358   Fax: 01 679 9568
www.gaietyschool.com

DIRECTOR: PATRICK SUTTON   CHAIRMAN: JOE DOWLING

Fabulous Beast's production of Giselle by Michael Keegan-Dolan © Michael Keegan-Dolan

The Actors' Studio

Focus Theatre, 6 Pembroke Place,
off Pembroke Street, Dublin 2
office: 12 Fade Street,
Dublin 2, Republic of Ireland
tel: +353 (0)1 671 2417
email: focustheatre@eircom.net
artistic director: Joe Devlin
administrator: Alastar Mac Aongusa
head of studio: Tim McDonnell
course: Weekly workshops in
Stanislavski process
entry procedure: By application
contact: Joe Devlin/Alastar Mac
Aongusa

Belfast Institute of Further and Higher Education (BIFHE)

Department of Creative and Health
Studies, Tower Street, Belfast BT5
4FH, Northern Ireland
tel: +44 (0)28 9026 5221
fax: +44 (0)28 9045 7612
email: chsadmissions@
belfastinstitute.ac.uk
web: www.belfastinstitute.ac.uk

course: Two-year National Diploma
in Performing Arts – Acting
accreditation: EDEXCEL
entry procedure: By application,
workshop and interview
contact: Malcolm Smith

course: Two-year National Diploma
in Performing Arts – Dance
accreditation: EDEXCEL
entry procedure: By application,
workshop and interview
contact: Malcolm Smith

course: Two-year Higher National
Diploma in Performing Arts – Theatre
Studies
accreditation: EDEXCEL
entry procedure: By application,
workshop and interview
contact: Malcolm Smith

Bray Senior College

Novara Road, Bray, Co. Wicklow,
Republic of Ireland
tel: +353 (0)1 282 9668
course: Post-Leaving Certificate in
Performing Arts - Theatre, and
Dance
accreditation: NCVA - Level 2
entry procedure: application/interview
contact: Mary Kelly-Borgatta

Coláiste Dhulaigh

Baryscourt Road, Coolock, Dublin 17,
Republic of Ireland
tel: +353 (0)1 847 4399
fax: +353 (0)1 847 4294
email: info@cdc.cdvec.ie
web: www.coláistedhulaigh.ie

course: Two-year Post-Leaving
Certificate in Theatre Studies
accreditation: NCVA, LAMDA,
Guildhall, BTEC (HND)
entry procedure: By audition and
interview
contact: Gill Matthews, Darragh Collins

Coláiste Stiofáin Naofa

Tramore Road, Cork, Republic of Ireland
tel: +353 (0)21 496 1020
fax: +353 (0)21 496 1320
email: info@csn.ie
web: www.csn.ie

course: Two-year Post-Leaving
Certificate in Performing Arts - Dance
accreditation: NCVA – Level 2
entry procedure: By interview and
audition
contact: Alan Foley

course: One/two-year Post-Leaving
Certificate in Performing Arts –
Theatre Performance
accreditation: NCVA – Level 2
entry procedure: By interview and
audition
contact: Marion Wyatt

course: One/two-year Post-Leaving
Certificate in Performing Arts –
Theatre Production
accreditation: NCVA – Level 2
entry procedure: By interview
contact: Marion Wyatt

course: One/two-year Post-Leaving
Certificate in Performing Arts –
Theatre Wardrobe, Set Design and
Construction
accreditation: NCVA – Level 2
entry procedure: By interview
contact: Marion Wyatt

College of Dance

Knox Hall, Monkstown Road,
Monkstown, Co. Dublin,
Republic of Ireland
tel/fax: +353 (0)1 230 4115
email: college.dance@ntlworld.ie
course: Two-year foundation course
in Professional Dance Training
entry procedure: By audition
contact: Joanna Banks

Dublin Institute of Technology

Conservatory of Music & Drama,
Rathmines Road, Dublin 6,
Republic of Ireland
tel: +353 (0)1 402 3515/7815
fax: +353 (0)1 402 3512
email: peter.mcdermott@dit.ie
conservatory@dit.ie
web: www.dit.ie

course: Three-year Diploma in
Speech and Drama [under review]
accreditation: Dublin Institute of
Technology
entry procedure: By CAO application,
audition and interview
contact: Peter McDermott

Dundalk Institute of Technology

Dublin Road, Dundalk,
Co. Louth, Republic of Ireland
tel: +353 (0)42 937 0200/0496
fax: +353 (0)42 933 0944
email: mark.fearon@dkit.ie
web: www.dkit.ie

course: Three/four-year Diploma/
BA in Applied Cultural Studies
accreditation: HETAC
entry procedure: By CAO/CAS
application
dept. of humanities: Mark Fearon

Gaiety School of Acting

Sycamore Street, Temple Bar,
Dublin 2, Republic of Ireland
tel: +353 (0)1 679 9277
fax: +353 (0)1 679 9568
email: info@gaietyschool.com
web: www.gaietyschool.com

course: Two-year full time Intensive
Actor Training Programme
entry procedure: By audition
contact: Patrick Sutton

course: One-year part-time
Performance course
entry procedure: By audition
contact: Patrick Sutton

course: One-year part-time
Foundation course
entry procedure: By interview
contact: Patrick Sutton

course: One-year part-time
Introduction to Drama course
entry procedure: By interview
contact: Patrick Sutton

Inchicore College of Further Education

Emmet Road, Dublin 8,
Republic of Ireland
tel: +353 (0)1 453 5358/3330
fax: +353 (0)1 454 5494
email: enquiries@inchicore.cdvec.ie
web: www.iol.ie/~inchvec/

course: Two-year Post-Leaving
Certificate in Costume, Wardrobe
and Construction
accreditation: NCVA
entry procedure: By interview and
portfolio assessment
contact: Leonore McDonagh

course: Two-year Post-Leaving
Certificate in Dance
accreditation: FETAC, Royal
Academy of Dancing (optional),
Imperial Society of Teachers of
Dancing (optional)
entry procedure: By interview and
audition
contact: Marian Lennon

course: One-year Post-Leaving
Certificate in Directing
accreditation: NCVA
entry procedure: By interview
contact: Roisin Flood

course: Two-year Post-Leaving
Certificate in Set Design and
Construction
accreditation: NCVA
entry procedure: By application
and interview
contact: Ann Myler

course: Two-year Post-Leaving
Certificate in Stage Management
accreditation: NCVA
entry procedure: By application
and interview
contact: Colm O'Driscoll

course: Two-year Post-Leaving
Certificate in Theatre Sound and
Lighting
accreditation: NCVA
entry procedure: By interview
contact: Colm O'Driscoll

course: Two-year Post-Leaving
Certificate in Acting
accreditation: NCVA, Guildhall
School of Music and Drama
entry procedure: By interview and
audition
contact: Roisin Flood

Institute for Choreography and Dance (ICD)

Firkin Crane, Shandon, Cork,
Republic of Ireland
tel: + 353 (0)21 450 7487
fax: + 353 (0)21 450 1124
email: info@instchordance.com
web: www.instchordance.com
artistic director: Mary Brady
development director:
Mowbray Bates

The Institute for Choreography and
Dance is a unique model for
stimulating choreographic practice
and dance research as a means of
dance development. ICD provides
space for interchange between
choreographers to examine issues,

work methodologies and goals
particular to each, in a positive,
challenging and practice-centred
environment.

course: OPID: Older People in
Dance – accredited dance/health
training initiative.
accreditation: FETAC – Level 2
entry procedure: application/interview
contact: Mowbray Bates

Kinsale Further Education College

Bandon Road, Kinsale,
Co. Cork, Republic of Ireland
tel: +353 (0)21 477 2275
fax: +353 (0)21 477 2446
email: kinsalefurthered@eircom.net

course: One/Two-year Post-Leaving
Certificate in Theatre Performance
accreditation: NCVA – Level 2
entry procedure: application/interview
contact: Belinda Wild

Liberties College (Bull Alley)

Bull Alley Street, Off Patrick Street,
Dublin 8, Republic of Ireland
tel: +353 (0)1 454 0044
fax: +353 (0)1 454 9686
email: info@liberties.cdvec.ie
web: www.libertiescollege.ie

course: Two-year Post-Leaving
Certificate in Performance:
Foundation/Development
accreditation: FETAC Award, NCVA
entry procedure: By audition and
interview
contact: Neville Style, Brian Daly
course: Two-year Post-Leaving
Certificate in Performance:
Advanced/Professional
accreditation: CDVEC Certificate
entry procedure: By audition and
interview
contact: Neville Style, Brian Daly

course: One-year Post-Leaving
Certificate Foundation Course in
Puppetry
accreditation: FETAC Award, CDVEC
Certificate
entry procedure: By application
contact: Eunan Robbins

Marino College CDVEC

Connolly House,
171 North Strand Road,
Dublin 1, Republic of Ireland
tel: +353 (0)1 855 7116
fax: +353 (0)1 855 4064
email: info@marino.cdvec.ie
web: www.marinocollege.com

course: One-year Post-Leaving
Certificate in Theatre Performance
accreditation: FETAC Award – Level 2
entry procedure: By application
and interview
contact: Roisin Lonergan

National University of Ireland, Cork

Cork, Republic of Ireland
tel: +353 (0)21 490 2664/2241
fax: +353 (0)21 490 3288
email: admissionsoffice@ucc.ie
web: www.ucc.ie

course: BA in Drama and Theatre
accreditation: NUI
entry procedure: By CAO
application, interview and workshop
course co-ordinator: Ger FitzGibbon,
Department of English

course: MA in Drama and Theatre
accreditation: NUI
entry procedure: By application,
interview and workshop
course co-ordinator: Ger FitzGibbon,
Department of English
email: g.fitzgibbon@ucc.ie

National University of Ireland, Dublin

Belfield, Dublin 4, Republic of Ireland
tel: +353 (0)1 706 7777; +353
(0)1 716 8625 (Arts Management)
email: Elizabeth.Varley@ucd.ie
web: www.ucd.ie
course: MA in Cultural Policy and
Arts Administration
accreditation: National University
of Ireland, Dublin
entry procedure: By application
and interview
contact: Elizabeth Varley

National University of Ireland, Galway

Newcastle, Galway, Republic of Ireland
tel: +353 (0)91 524411
fax: +353 (0)91 750436
email: admissions@mis.nuigalway.ie
web: www.mis.nuigalway.ie

course: One-year MA in Drama and
Theatre Studies
accreditation: NUI
entry procedure: By application
contact: Adrian Frazier
tel: +353 (0)91 512120

course: One-year Higher Diploma
in Arts Administration
accreditation: NUI
entry procedure: By application
contact: Joe Mahon
tel: +353 (0)91 524411 ext. 2574

Queen's University Belfast

University Road, Belfast BT7 1NN,
Northern Ireland
tel: +44 (0)28 9033 5231
fax: +44 (0)28 9032 4549
email: admissions@qub.ac.uk
web: www.qub.ac.uk/lla/drama/about.htm
course: Three-year BA in Drama
accreditation: Queen's University
Belfast
entry procedure: By UCAS application
contact: David Grant
email: d.grant@qub.ac.uk

course: Two-Year Part-Time MA in
Drama (delivered at Monaghan
Education Centre).
contact: Monaghan Education Centre,
Seamus McDermott
tel: +353 (0)47 74000

Sallynoggin College of Further Education

Pearse Road, Sallynoggin,
Co. Dublin, Republic of Ireland
tel: +353 (0)1 285 2997/2985
fax: +353 (0)1 284 8437
email: reception@scfe.ie
web: www.scs.dife.ie

course: Two-year Post-Leaving
Certificate in Dance

accreditation: Royal Academy of
Dancing (RAD), Imperial Society of
Teachers of Dance (ISTD)
entry procedure: By audition
contact: Deirdre O'Neill

School of Drama TCD

Samuel Beckett Centre, Trinity
College, Dublin 2, Republic of Ireland
tel: +353 (0)1 608 2266/1239
fax: +353 (0)1 679 3488
email: amulligan@tcd.ie
web: www.tcd.ie/drama

course: Three-year BA Degree in
Acting Studies
accreditation: TCD
entry procedure: By audition
administrator: Ann Mulligan

course: Four-year Hons BA Degree
in Drama and Theatre Studies
accreditation: TCD
entry procedure: By application,
workshop and interview
administrator: Ann Mulligan

course: One year M. Phil in Irish
Theatre & Film
accreditation: TCD
entry procedure: By application
contact: Graduate Admissions
email: gradinfo@tcd.ie

UCD Drama Studies Centre

Carysfort Avenue, Blackrock,
Co. Dublin, Republic of Ireland
tel: +353 (0)1 716 8049 (am only)
fax: +353 (0)1 716 8048
email: drama.studies@ucd.ie
web: www.ucd.ie/dramastd

course: MA in Modern Drama Studies
/Higher Diploma in Drama Studies
accreditation: National University
of Ireland, Dublin
course director: Joseph Long
entry procedure: by application
contact: Hilary Gow

University of Limerick

Irish World Music Centre, Plassey,
Limerick, Republic of Ireland
tel: +353 (0)61 202700
web: www.ul.ie/~iwmc

course: One-year full-time MA in
Dance Performance
accreditation: University of Limerick
entry procedure: By application,
interview and audition
course directors: Mary Nunan,
Catherine Foley
tel: +353 (0)61 213464 / 202922
fax: +353 (0)61 202589
email: mary.nunan@ul.ie

course: One-year full-time MA in
Irish Traditional Dance Performance
accreditation: University of Limerick
entry procedure: By application,
interview and audition
course director: Dr Catherine Foley
tel: +353 (0)61 202922
fax: +353 (0)61 202589
email: catherine.e.foley@ul.ie

course: One-year full-time MA in
Ethnochoreology
accreditation: University of Limerick
entry procedure: By application,
interview and audition
course director: Dr Catherine Foley
tel: +353 (0)61 202922
fax: +353 (0)61 202589
email: catherine.e.foley@ul.ie

University of Ulster

Cromore Road, Coleraine BT52 1SA,
Northern Ireland
tel: +44 (0)28 7034 4141
email: online@ulst.ac.uk
web: www.ulst.ac.uk

course: Certificate in Community
Drama
accreditation: University of Ulster
entry procedure: By application
contact: John Deeney, Coleraine
Campus
tel: +44 (0)28 7032 4852

course: BA Hons Drama
accreditation: University of Ulster
entry procedure: By UCAS

application, interview and workshop
contact: John Deeney, Coleraine
Campus
tel: +44 (0)28 7032 4852

course: BA Hons Dance
From October 2004, details to be
announced

course: Postgraduate Certificate/
Postgraduate Diploma/MA Cultural
Management
accreditation: University of Ulster
entry procedure: By application
contact: John Thompson
tel: +44 (0)28 9036 8949/8039
email: je.thompson@ulster.ac.uk

Major British Drama and Dance Schools

Bristol Old Vic Theatre School

2 Downside Road, Clifton,
Bristol BS8 2XF, England
tel: +44 117 973 3535
fax: +44 117 923 9371
email: enquiries@oldvic.drama.ac.uk
web: www.oldvic.drama.ac.uk
principal: Christopher Denys
scholarships available: Yes

Central School of Ballet

10 Herbal Hill, Clerkenwell Road,
London EC1R 5EJ, England
tel: +44 20 7837 6332
fax: +44 20 7833 5571
email: central@centralschoolof
ballet.fsnet.co.uk
web: www.centralschoolofballet.co.uk
registrar: Alison Kennedy
scholarships available: Yes

Central School of Speech and Drama

Embassy Theatre, 64 Eton Avenue,
London NW3 3HY, England
tel: +44 20 7722 8183
fax: +44 20 7722 4132
email: enquiries@cssd.ac.uk
web: www.cssd.ac.uk
principal: Prof. Gary Crossley
scholarships available: Yes

City University, Department of Arts Policy & Management

Level 7, Frobisher Crescent, Barbican,
London EC2Y 8HB, England
tel: +44 20 7477 8751
fax: +44 20 7477 8887
email: u.k.richards@city.ac.uk
web: www.city.uk/artspol
contact: Ursula Richards
scholarships available: Yes

East 15 Acting School

Corbett Theatre, Rectory Lane,
Loughton, Essex IG10 3RY, England
tel: +44 20 8508 5983
fax: +44 20 8508 7521
email: east15.acting@ukonline.co.uk
contact: Linda Humphries
scholarships available: Yes

English National Ballet School

Carlyle Building, Hortensia Road,
London SW10 0QS, England
tel: +44 20 7376 7076
fax: +44 20 7376 3404
email: info@enbschool.org.uk
web: www.enbschool.org.uk
contact: Laura Lavender
scholarships available: Yes

Guildford School of Acting (GSA)

Millmead Terrace, Guildford,
Surrey GU2 4YT, England
tel: +44 1483 560 701
fax: +44 1483 535 431
email: enquiries@gsa.drama.ac.uk
web: www.gsa.drama.ac.uk
principal: Gordon McDougall
scholarships available: Yes

Guildhall School of Music and Drama

Silk Street, Barbican,
London EC2Y 8DT, England
tel: +44 20 7628 2571
fax: +44 20 7256 9439
email: registry@gsmd.ac.uk
web: www.gsmd.ac.uk
registrar: Richard Gerrom
scholarships available: Yes

Laban Centre London

Laurie Grove, New Cross,
London SE14 6NH, England
tel: +44 20 8692 4070
fax: +44 20 8694 8749
email: info@laban.co.uk
web: www.laban.co.uk
contact: Dr Marion North
scholarships available: Yes

Liverpool Institute for Performing Arts

Mount Street, Liverpool L1 9HF, England
tel: +44 151 330 3000
fax: +44 151 330 3131
email: admissions@lipa.ac.uk
web: www.lipa.ac.uk
contact: Mark Featherstone-Witty
scholarships available: Yes

London Academy of Music and Dramatic Art (LAMDA)

Tower House, 226 Cromwell Road,
London SW5 0SR, England
tel: +44 20 7373 9883
fax: +44 20 7370 4739
email: enquiries@lamda.org.uk
web: www.lamda.org.uk
contact: Admissions
scholarships available: Yes

London Contemporary Dance School

16 Flaxman Terrace,
London WC1H 9AT, England
tel: +44 20 7387 0152
fax: +44 20 7383 4851
email: lcds@theplace.org.uk
web: www.theplace.org.uk
contact: Alison Ashford
scholarships available: Dance and Drama Awards

Northern Ballet School

The Dance House, 10 Oxford Road,
Manchester M1 5QA, England
tel: +44 161 237 1406
fax: +44 161 237 1408
email: nbsadm@aol.com
web: www.dancehouse.fsnet.co.uk
principal: Patricia McDonald
scholarships available: Yes

Rambert School

Brunel University, 300 St Margarets
Road, Twickenham, Middlesex
TW1 1PT, England
tel: +44 20 8891 0121
fax: +44 20 8891 8270
email: admissions@brunel.ac.uk
web: www.brunel.ac.uk
contact: Ross McKim
scholarships available: No

Royal Academy of Dramatic Art (RADA)

62-64 Gower Street, London
WC1E 6ED, England
tel: +44 20 7636 7076
fax: +44 20 7323 3865
email: enquiries@rada.ac.uk
web: www.rada.org.uk
principal: Nicholas Barter
scholarships available:
Scholarship fund being established

Royal Scottish Academy of Music and Drama

100 Renfrew Street,
Glasgow G2 3DB, Scotland
tel: +44 141 332 4101
fax: +44 141 332 8901
email: registry@rsamd.ac.uk
web: www.rsamd.ac.uk
registrar: Ewen Heiney
scholarships available: Yes

Royal Welsh College of Music and Drama

Castle Grounds, Cathays Park
Cardiff CF10 3ER, Wales
tel: +44 29 2039 1327
fax: +44 29 2039 1304
email: drama.admissions@rwcmd.ac.uk
web: www.rwcmd.ac.uk
contact: Louise Moggridge
scholarships available: Yes

youth theatre groups

Fiona O'Shaughnessy and Lalor Roddy in Bedrock's production of Blasted by Sarah Kane, 2001 © R

Activate Youth Theatre

Graffiti Theatre Company,
2 Church Street, Shandon, Cork
tel: +353 (0)21 439 7111
email: graffiti@eircom.net
contact: Geraldine O'Neill

Amharclann Na Nóg (AnnÓg)

Dún Chaoin, Trá Lí, Co. Chiarraí
tel: +353 (0)66 915 6305
email: bfeasa@iol.ie
contact: Áine Moynihan

Blanchardstown Youth Theatre

26 Johns Street South,
Pimlico, Dublin 8
tel: +353 (0)87 203 3151
contact: Nuala Smith/Jennifer Cummins

Boomerang Youth Theatre Company

CBS, Sullivans Quay, Cork
tel: +353 (0)21 431 6826
email: info@boomerang-theatre.com
web: www.boomerang-theatre.com
contact: Trish Edelstein

Brewery Lane Youth Theatre

Pill Road, Carrick-on-Suir, Co. Tipperary
tel: +353 (0)51 640312
contact: Tom Nealon

Cabinteely Youth Theatre

74 Granitefield, Dun Laoghaire,
Co.Dublin
tel: +353 (0)1 285 6842
email: fifil@eircom.net
contact: Fiona Lester

Carlow County Youth Theatre

Carlow Arts Office, Carlow County
Council, Athy Road, Carlow
tel: +353 (0)59 917 0300
email: drama@carlowcoco.ie
contact: Noeline Kavanagh

Castleblaney Youth Theatre

2 Rosevale, Castleblaney, Co. Monaghan
tel: +353 (0)42 974 9114
contact: Joan McArdle

Cavan County Youth Drama

The Arts Office, Cavan County
Council, Cavan
tel: +353 (0)49 437 1799
contact: Chris O'Brien

Celbridge Youth Drama

27 Turret Road, Palmerstown,
Dublin 20
tel: +353 (0)1 626 4351
contact: Margaret Cosgrove

Clondalkin Youth Theatre

11 Woodford Downs, Clondalkin,
Dublin 22
tel: +353 (0)1 459 2875
contact: Peter Harrison

Cloud Shadows MYTC

Shanakill Family Resource Centre,
Shanakill, Moyvalley, Tralee, Co. Kerry
tel: +353 (0)66 712 7831
contact: Jackie Landers

Cork School of Music Youth Theatre Group

School of Music Union Quay, Cork
tel: +353 (0)21 427 0076
contact: Trina Scott/Regina Crowley

Crooked Mice Drama Group

Crooked House Theatre Company,
Riverbank Arts Centre,
Newbridge, Co. Kildare
tel: +353 (0)45 433480 ext 209
contact: Anna Swords-Murphy

Cryptic Youth Drama

67 Dublin Street, Balbriggan,
Co. Dublin
tel: +353 (0)1 841 5135
contact: Geraldine O'Neill/Brian Quinn

Droichead Youth Theatre

Droichead Arts Centre, Stockwell
Street, Drogheda, Co. Louth
tel: +353 (0)41 983 3946
contact: Thomas Heeney
web: www24.brinkster.com/youththeatre

Dublin Youth Theatre

23 Upper Gardiner Street, Dublin 1
tel: +353 (0)1 874 3687
email: dyt@iol.ie
contact: Maria Schweppe

Dundalk Youth Theatre Company

Arts Office, Town Hall, Dundalk,
Co. Louth
tel: +353 (0)42 933 2276
contact: Denis Darcy

Eureka Youth Theatre

Loreto Secondary School,
Spawell Road, Co. Wexford
tel: +353 (0)53 42783
contact: Gerri Roche

Galway Youth Theatre

Galway Arts Centre,
47 Dominick Street, Galway
tel: +353 (0)91 566313
email: gyt@eircom.ie
web: www.galwayartscentre.ie/gyt.htm
contact: Sonja Brodie

Holy Faith Youth Theatre

45 Ardmore Drive, Artane, Dublin 5
tel: +353 (0)1 847 6967
contact: Imelda Noone

Kildare Youth Theatre

Crooked House Theatre Company,
Riverbank Arts Centre,
Newbridge, Co. Kildare
tel: +353 (0)45 448309
email: crookedhouse@riverbank.ie
web: www.crookedhouse.ie
contact: Peter Hussey

Kilkenny Youth Theatre
Good Shepherd Centre,
Church Lane, Kilkenny.
tel: +353 (0)56 7751266
fax: +353 (0)56 7770495
email: barnstorm@eircom.net
web: www.barnstorm.ie
contact: Philip Hardy

Killarney Youth Theatre
Muckross Drive, Killarney, Co. Kerry
tel: +353 (0)64 33478
contact: Liz Ryan

Limerick County Youth Theatre
County Arts Office,
Limerick County Council,
78/84 O'Connell Street, Limerick
tel: +353 (0)61 318477
contact: Joan MacKernan

Limerick Youth Theatre
Belltable Arts Centre
69 O'Connell Street, Limerick
tel: +353 (0)61 311100
contact: Bridget Wallace

Lucan Youth Dance/Drama Group
58 Sarsfield Park, Lucan, Co. Dublin
tel: +353 (0)87 973 2230
contact: Helen Farmer

Mayo Youth Theatre
Arts Office, Mayo County Council,
Castlebar, Co. Mayo
tel: +353 (0)94 902 4444 ext 577
contact: Sean Walsh

Moate Youth Theatre
Moate Performing Arts Centre,
Ballymore Road, Moate, Co. Westmeath
tel: +353 (0)90 648 1435
contact: Nuala McDermott

Monaghan Youth Theatre
Dawson Street, Monaghan,
Co. Monaghan
tel: +353 (0)47 71844
contact: Gerry Farrelly

Mountmellick Youth Theatre
3 Moyne Cottages,
Durrow, Co. Laois
tel: +353 (0)502 36909
contact: Helen Cullen

National Youth Theatre for the Deaf (NYTD)
43 Upper Georges Street,
Dun Laoghaire, Co. Dublin
tel: +353 (0)1 280 0544
web: www.nytd.connect.ie
contact: Aoife White

Neilstown Youth Theatre
Ronanstown Youth Service,
Neilstown Road, Dublin 22
tel: +353 (0)1 457 0363
contact: John O'Hara

North Tipperary Youth Drama
34 Beechwood Lawns,
Thurles, Co. Tipperary
contact: Jim Woodlock

Physically Phishy
Weighmasters House,
2 Church Street, Shandon, Cork
tel: +353 (0)21 439 7111
contact: Geraldine O'Neill

Portlaoise Youth Theatre
c/o Laois County Council, County
Hall, Portlaoise, Co. Laois
tel: +353 (0)86 864 0228
contact: Paul O'Neill

Rainbow Factory
Youth Action Northern Ireland,
Glenmachen Park, Belfast BT4 2PJ
tel: +44 (0)28 9076 0067
contact: Brian Draine

Rathdowney Youth Theatre
c/o Laois County Council, County
Hall, Portlaoise, Co. Laois
tel: +353 (0)1 832 4330
contact: Peter Kelly

Roscommon County Youth Theatre
County Arts Office, County Library,
Roscommon
tel: +353 (0)90 663 7285/
(0)1 429 9609
contact: Philip Delamere
Catherine Simon

Roundabout Youth Theatre
Central Youth Facility,
Ballymun, Dublin 9
tel: +353 (0)1 862 5049
contact: Louise Lowe

Rush Junior Drama
Millbank Theatre,
Chapel Green, Rush, Co. Dublin
tel: +353 (0)1 843 7475
contact: Celeste Jones

Shadow Box Youth Theatre
21 Ledwidge Crescent, Bray, Co. Wicklow
tel: +353 (0)1 276 5091
contact: Frieda Hand/Gemma Gallagher

Shake the Spear-e Theatre Co
De Vesci Estate, The Gardener's
House, Abbeyleix, Co. Laois
contact: Cabrini Cahill

Sligo County Youth Theatre
Lower Quay Street, Sligo
tel: +353 (0)71 913 8489
contact: Bernadette Meehan

Stage Craft Youth Theatre
9 Davitt Avenue, Clonmel, Co. Tipperary
tel: +353 (0)87 947 6968
email: stage_craft@hotmail.com
contact: Shane Dempsey

Strange Snow Youth Theatre

38 Irishtown, Clonmel, Co. Tipperary
tel: +353 (0)87 659 7929
contact: Anne O'Gorman

Tallaght Youth Theatre

Tallaght Youth Service, Main Road,
Tallaght, Dublin 24
tel: +353 (0)1 451 6400
email: tys@foroige.iol.ie
contact: Joseph Cully

Tramps & Poets Youth Theatre

Tinahely Courthouse Centre,
Tinahely, Co. Wicklow
tel: +353 (0)402 38529
contact: Margaret Gallagher

Waterford Youth Drama

15 Broad Street, Waterford
tel: +353 (0)51 879377/879374
email: wyd@indigo.ie
web: http://indigo.ie/~wyd
contact: Maria Cullen

Wexford Youth Theatre

c/o The Arts Dept, Wexford County
Council, Spawell Road, Wexford
tel: +353 (0)53 65000 ext. 369
email: info@barecheektheatre.com
web: www.wexford.ie/Arts/index.htm
contact: Tony McCleane-Fay,
Monika McCleane

Youghal Youtheatre

32 Sarsfield Terrace, Youghal, Co. Cork
tel: +353 (0)24 92556
contact: Sinead O'Brien

Young Dramateers

50 Tara Court, Balbriggan, Co. Dublin
tel: +353 (0)1 841 3685
contact: Phyllis Monaghan

Youth Theatre Tipperary

Annacarty, Tipperary Town, Co. Tipperary
tel: +353 (0)62 71555
email: youththeatretipperary@hotmail.com
contact: Paul Maher

Youthopia Theatre Company

12 Selskar Rise, Skerries, Co. Dublin
tel: +353 (0)1 849 0903
email: youthopia@eircom.net
contact: Paddy Langton

publications

Declan Conlon in Lyric Theatre's production of *True West* by Sam Shepard, 2004 © Chris Hill Photographic

Periodicals

ArtsProfessional

PO Box 957, Cottenham
Cambridge CB4 8AB, England
tel: + 44 (0)1954 250600
fax: + 44 (0)1954 252600
email: editors@artsprofessional.co.uk
web: www.artsprofessional.co.uk
contact: Damian Hebron,
Elizabeth Hill
frequency: Fortnightly
cost: Annual subscription from
stg£30, fees on application
An arts management magazine for
professionals working within
professional arts organisations and
the cultural sector.

Choreographic
Encounters Vol. 1

*For contact information see Support
Organisations*
Edited by Mary Brady, Institute of
Choreography and Dance
frequency: an annual journal
isbn: 0953839419
price: €15 (Ireland)/€19
(internationally)
This inaugural volume features
contributions from choreographers,
dance artists, dance writers and
scholars who have had research
links with icd in recent years.

Drama League
of Ireland Magazine

*For contact information see Support
Organisations*
editor: Karen Carleton
cost: Free to members
frequency: Quarterly
Newsletter of the Drama League
focusing on the non-professional
theatre sector in Ireland. Its
contents include feature articles,
interviews, festival news, local and
international new and library
acquisitions.

Footnotes

The Dance Collective
*For contact information see Support
Organisations*
cost: Free to members of The Dance
Collective
frequency: Monthly
Monthly news from the Dance
Collective Northern Ireland
promoting and supporting all forms
of dance in Northern Ireland.

Intermission

National Association for Youth Drama
*For contact information see Support
Organisations*
contact: Fíona Ní Chinnéide
cost: Free to members, membership
from €6
frequency: Monthly
Youth theatre news and events
from around the country, including
training opportunities, workshops,
youth theatre productions, and
international festivals and events.

Irish Youth Theatre Handbook

National Association for Youth Drama
*For contact information see Support
Organisations*
contact: Fiona Dowling
cost: €13 (+ postage)
Information on all aspects of youth
theatre practice, including guidelines
on welfare, artistic programming,
administration and funding – a
wealth of useful advice for
experienced youth theatre leaders
and newcomers to youth theatre.
Includes a comprehensive directory.

Irish Theatre Magazine

*For contact information see Media
Lists*
contact: Karen Fricker/Maura O'Keeffe
cost: €6 per issue, or annual
subscription from €32 to €45
frequency: Quarterly
A publication for and about Irish
theatre, combining reviews,
columns, and feature articles. The
magazine provides a platform for
serious theatre criticism in Ireland.

Irish Writers Centre News

*For contact information see Support
Organisations*
contact: Ian Oliver
cost: €10
frequency: Bi-monthly
Covers news of competitions, literary
events and readings at the Centre,
around Dublin and nationwide. It
also features news from the Irish
Playwrights and Screenwriters' Guild
and the Irish Writers' Union.

Prodance News

Association of Professional Dancers
in Ireland
*For contact information see Support
Organisations*
cost: Free to members,
subscriptions for non-members
from €18 - €35
frequency: Monthly
Newsletter of the Association of
Professional Dancers in Ireland.
Provides information on what is
happening nation-wide for dancers,
choreographers, dance teachers,
students of dance, artists of other
disciplines and all those interested
in dance and dance theatre.

Youth Drama Ireland

National Association for Youth Drama
*For contact information see Support
Organisations*
contact: Fíona Ní Chinnéide
cost: None
frequency: Annual
Youth Drama Ireland is an NAYD
publication that focuses on youth
drama/theatre and aims to
disseminate information, to
encourage good practice and
debate, to publish practical and
theoretical articles and to promote
writing on the topic of youth
drama/theatre in a national and
international context.

Reference Books

casting:

Spotlight Actors and Actresses
publisher: The Spotlight
tel: (+) 44 20 7437 7631
email: info@spotlightcd.com
web: www.spotlightcd.com
most recent edition: 2004
rrp: stg£75 per set of 5
isbn: None
(also available as Spotlight Interactive)
Spotlight also has a Video Casting
Studio - it means you can cast to/
from London without having to fly
over! We get actors in to our studio
who can do a live audition via
video link to casting directors in
Dublin - or vice versa.
email: laura.albery@spotlightcd.com

directories:

British Performing Arts Yearbook
publisher: Rhinegold Publishing Ltd
tel: (+) 44 (0) 1832 270 333
email: booksales@rhinegold.co.uk
web: www.rhinegold.co.uk
most recent edition: 2003/04
rrp: stg£30.95
isbn: 1904226604

Contacts
A Contact Listings for UK Stage,
Television and Radio
publisher: The Spotlight
tel: (+) 44 20 7437 7631
email: info@spotlightcd.com
web: www.spotlightcd.com
editor: Kate Poynton
most recent edition: 2004
rrp: stg£10.99
isbn: 0053921042

MOD
Music, Opera, Dance and Drama in
Asia, the Pacific and North America
editor: Wiebke Morgan
publisher: Alain Charles Arts
Publishing Ltd
tel: (+) 44 20 7834 7676
email: yearbooks@alaincharles.com
most recent edition: 2004
rrp: stg£57.00
isbn: 0954416538

Performing Arts Yearbook for Europe (PAYE)
editor: Wiebke Morgan
publisher: Alain Charles Arts
Publishing Ltd
tel: (+) 44 20 7834 7676
email: yearbooks@alaincharles.com
most recent edition: 2004
rrp: stg£70.00
isbn: 095441652X

www.irishplayography.com
tel: + 353 (0)1 670 4906
email: playography@theatreshop.ie
web: www.irishplayography.com
director: Caroline Williams
An on-line searchable catalogue of
all new Irish plays produced
professionally since 1975 including
information on scripts and rights
availability.

www.irishtheatreonline.com
tel: + 353 (0)1 670 4906
email: handbook@theatreshop.ie
web: www.irishtheatre.com
editor: Paula Shields
The Irish Theatre Handbook on-line:
information on all theatre, dance
and opera companies, festivals and
venues in Ireland. North and South

finance:

Employers Guide to PAYE
publisher: Revenue Commissioners
tel: 1890 30 67 06
web: www.revenue.ie
most recent edition: 1994
rrp: Free
isbn: None

fundraising:

Funding for Voluntary Action
publisher: The Community
Foundation for Northern Ireland
tel: (+) 44 (0) 28 9024 5927
email: info@communityfoundationni.org
web: www.communityfoundationni.org
most recent edition: 2003
rrp: Free
isbn: None

Funding Handbook
publisher: CAFE (Ireland)
*For contact information see Support
Organisations*
most recent edition: 2000
rrp: £15
isbn: 1869895061

management:

Care, Diligence and Skill:
A Handbook for the Governing
Bodies of Arts Organisations
authors: Graham Berry, Paul Pia
publisher: Scottish Arts Council
tel: (+) 44 131 226 6051
email: help.desk@scottisharts.org.uk
web: www.sac.org.uk
most recent edition: 2002
rrp: stg£5.00
isbn: 1851191054

Guide to Labour Law
publisher: Department of
Enterprise Trade and Employment
tel: (+) 353 1 631 2121
email: webmaster@entemp.ie
web: www.entemp.ie
most recent edition: 2003
rrp: Free
isbn: None

Planning an Arts Building Project
editor: Alan Tweedie
publisher: The Arts Council/An
Chomhairle Ealaíon
*For contact information see Funding
Bodies*
most recent edition: 1996
rrp: £4
isbn: 0906627753

the theatre shop

presents

www.irishplayography.com

an on-line searchable catalogue of all new Irish plays produced professionally since 1975 including information on script and rights availability

www.irishtheatreonline.com

The Irish Theatre Handbook on-line: information on all theatre, dance and opera companies, festivals and venues in Ireland, North and South

THE THEATRE SHOP 7 SOUTH GREAT GEORGE'S STREET, DUBLIN 2, IRELAND
TEL: ·353 1 6704906 **FAX:** ·353 1 6704908
email: admin@theatreshop.ie **website:** www.theatreshop.ie

Barry McGovern in Island Theatre Company's production of Faith Healer by Brian Friel, 2001 © Arthur Gough

newspapers:

The Belfast Telegraph
124-144 Royal Avenue
Belfast BT1 1EB, Northern Ireland
tel: + 44 (0)28 9026 4000
fax: + 44 (0)28 9055 4517
email: njohnston@belfasttelegraph.co.uk
web: www.belfasttelegraph.co.uk
arts editor: Neil Johnston
theatre critic: Grania McFadden
opera critic: John Graydon

The Evening Herald
90 Middle Abbey Street
Dublin 1, Republic of Ireland
tel: + 353 (0)1 705 5333
fax: + 353 (0)1 705 5378
email: mhaugh@unison.independent.ie
web: www.unison.ie
arts editor: Maurice Haugh
theatre critic: Luke Clancy
dance critic: Don Smyth

The Irish Examiner
PO Box 21, Academy Street
Cork, Republic of Ireland
tel: + 353 (0)21 427 2722
fax: + 353 (0)21 427 5477
email: arts@examiner.ie
web: www.irishexaminer.com
arts editor: Declan Hassett
Opera: Michael Dungan

The Irish Independent
90 Middle Abbey Street
Dublin 1, Republic of Ireland
tel: + 353 (0)1 705 5333
fax: + 353 (0)1 705 5792
email: jspain@unison.independent.ie
web: www.unison.ie
arts editor: John Spain
theatre critic: Bruce Arnold
opera critic: Pat O'Kelly
dance critic: Sophie Gorman

The Irish News
113 Donegal Street, Belfast BT1 2GE
Northern Ireland
tel: + 44 (0)28 9033 7548
fax: + 44 (0)28 9033 7505
email: j.braniff@irishnews.com
web: www.irishnews.com
arts editor: Joanna Braniff

The Irish Times
13 D'Olier Street, Dublin 2
Republic of Ireland
tel: + 353 (0)1 679 2022
fax: + 353 (0)1 677 9181
email: arts@irish-times.ie
web: www.ireland.com
arts editor: Deirdre Falvey
theatre critic: Fintan O'Toole
opera critic: Arminta Wallace
dance critic: Michael Seaver
*See also Awards & Competitions &
Scholarships & Bursaries*

The Newsletter
Boucher Crescent, Belfast BT12 6QY
Northern Ireland
tel: + 44 (0)28 9068 0000
fax: + 44 (0)28 9066 4412
email: newsletter@newsletter.co.uk
arts correspondent: Jeff Magill
c/o Entertainment Section

The Sunday Business Post
80 Harcourt Street, Dublin 2
Republic of Ireland
tel: + 353 (0)1 602 6000
fax: + 353 (0)1 679 6283
email: jennifer@sbpost.ie
web: www.thepost.ie
features editor: Fiona Ness
opera: Dick O'Riordan

The Sunday Independent
90 Middle Abbey Street
Dublin 1, Republic of Ireland
tel: + 353 (0)1 705 5333
fax: + 353 (0)1 705 5779
email: mkeane@unison.independent.ie
web: www.unison.ie
arts editor: Madeleine Keane
theatre critic: Emer O'Kelly
opera: Gus Smith

Sunday Life
124-144 Royal Avenue
Belfast BT1 1EB, Northern Ireland
tel: + 44 (0)28 9026 4311
fax: + 44 (0)28 9055 4507
email: sbell@belfasttelegraph.co.uk
web: www.sundaylife.co.uk
magazine editor: Stephanie Bell
theatre critic: Jane Coyle

The Sunday Times
4th Floor, Bishop's Square
Redmond Hill, Dublin 2
Republic of Ireland
tel: + 353 (0)1 479 2424
fax: + 353 (0)1 479 2428
email: culture.ireland@sunday-times.ie
web: www.sunday-times.ie
culture ireland editor: Michael Ross
theatre critic: Karina Buckley
opera/dance critic: Kate Butler

The Sunday Tribune
15 Lower Baggot Street
Dublin 2, Republic of Ireland
tel: + 353 (0)1 631 4300
fax: + 353 (0)1 631 4390
email: imag@tribune.ie
web: www.tribune.ie
arts editor: Lise Hand
theatre critic: Rachel Andrews
opera critic: Ian Fox
dance critic: Seona Mac Reamoinn

magazines:

Cara Magazine
Smurfit Publications Ltd.
2 Clanwilliam Court, Lower Mount
Street, Dublin 2, Republic of Ireland
tel: + 353 (0)1 662 3158
fax: + 353 (0)1 661 9757
editor: Paul Whitington
email: pwhitington@smurfit-comms.ie
web: www.ivenus.com

The Event Guide
D&K Media Ltd., Regus House
Harcourt Road, Dublin 2
Republic of Ireland
tel: + 353 (0)1 477 3933
fax: + 353 (0)1 235 2204
email: info@eventguide.ie
web: www.eventguide.ie
editor: Kieran Owens
theatre critic: Trish Murphy

Gay Community News
Unit 2, Scarlet Row, West Essex Street
Dublin 8, Republic of Ireland
tel: + 353 (0)1 671 0939
fax: + 353 (0)1 671 3549
email: info@gcn.ie
web: www.gcn.ie
arts editor: Rachel Armstrong

Hot Press
13 Trinity Street, Dublin 2
Republic of Ireland
tel: + 353 (0)1 241 1500
fax: + 353 (0)1 241 1538
email: info@hotpress.ie
web: www.hotpress.com
theatre listings: Sinead Ní Mhórdha

Image
22 Crofton Road, Dun Laoghaire
Co. Dublin, Republic of Ireland
tel: + 353 (0)1 280 8415
fax: + 353 (0)1 280 8309
email: smcdonnell@image.ie
web: www.image.ie
editor: Sarah McDonnell

Irish Theatre Magazine
44 East Essex Street
Dublin 2, Republic of Ireland
tel: + 353 (0)1 677 8439
fax: + 353 (0)1 679 7709
email: info@irishtheatremagazine.com
web: www.irishtheatremagazine.com
editor: Karen Fricker
See also Periodicals

Ireland's Issues
30 Gardiner Place
Dublin 1, Republic of Ireland
tel: + 353 (0)1 873 5137
fax: + 353 (0)1 873 5143
email: issuesmag@iolfree.ie
editor: Seán Kavanagh

IT Magazine
2 Clanwilliam Court, Lower Mount
Street, Dublin 2, Republic of Ireland
tel: + 353 (0)1 662 3158
fax: + 353 (0)1 661 9757
email: celliott@smurfit-comms.ie
web: www.ivenus.com
editor: Jennifer Stevens

RTÉ Guide
RTÉ, Donnybrook, Dublin 4
Republic of Ireland
tel: + 353 (0)1 208 2162
fax: + 353 (0)1 208 3085
email: donal.odonoghue@rte.ie
web: www.rte.ie
arts editor: Donal O'Donoghue

television & radio:

Aertel
RTÉ, Donnybrook, Dublin 4
Republic of Ireland
tel: + 353 (0)1 208 3398
fax: + 353 (0)1 208 3094
email: aertel@rte.ie
web: www.rte.ie
listings: Ann Marie Griffin

Artszone
RTÉ Lyric FM, Cornmarket Square
Limerick, Republic of Ireland
tel: + 353 (0)61 207 300
fax: + 353 (0)61 207 390
email: arts.lyricfm@rte.ie
web: www.rte.ie/lyricfm
producer: Olga Buckley

Arts Extra
BBC Radio Ulster, Broadcasting
House, Ormeau Avenue
Belfast BT2 8HQ, Northern Ireland
tel: + 44 (0)28 9033 8000
fax: + 44 (0)28 9033 8805
email: arts.extra@bbc.co.uk
web: www.bbc.co.uk/ni
producer: Regina McMahon

BBC Northern Ireland
Broadcasting House, Ormeau Avenue,
Belfast BT2 8HQ, Northern Ireland
tel: + 44 (0)28 9033 8000
fax: + 44 (0)28 9033 8806
email: maggie.taggart@bbc.co.uk
web: www.bbc.co.uk/ni
arts and education
correspondent: Maggie Taggart

Rattlebag
RTÉ Radio 1, Donnybrook
Dublin 4, Republic of Ireland
tel: + 353 (0)1 208 2412
fax: + 353 (0)1 208 3304
email: rattle@rte.ie
web: www.rte.ie
series producer: Kevin Reynolds
presenter: Myles Dungan

Television & Radio News
RTÉ, Donnybrook, Dublin 4
Republic of Ireland
tel: + 353 (0)1 208 3111
fax: + 353 (0)1 208 3086
email: newsdesk@rte.ie
web: www.rte.ie
arts and media correspondent:
Jennifer Smith

TV3
Westgate Business Park, Ballymount
Dublin 24, Republic of Ireland
tel: + 353 (0)1 419 3333
fax: + 353 (0)1 419 3322
email: lorraine.keane@tv3.ie
web: www.tv3.ie
entertainment correspondent:
Lorraine Keane

UTV
Havelock House, Ormeau Road
Belfast BT7 1EB, Northern Ireland
tel: + 44 (0)28 9032 8122
fax: + 44 (0)28 9023 8381
email: jjohnston@utvplc.com
web: www.utvlive.com
contact: Jeanie Johnston

The View
RTÉ, Donnybrook, Dublin 4
Republic of Ireland
tel: + 353 (0)1 208 2698
fax: + 353 (0)1 208 2220
email: theview@rte.ie
web: www.rte.ie
producer: Stephen Plunkett

british broadsheets:

Daily Telegraph
1 Canada Square, Canary Wharf
London E14 5DT, England
tel: + 44 (0)20 7538 5000
fax: + 44 (0)20 7538 7650
web: www.telegraph.co.uk
arts editor: Sarah Crompton
theatre critic: Charles Spencer
dance critic: Ismene Brown
opera critic: Rupert Christiansen

The Evening Standard
Northcliffe House, 2 Derry Street
London W8 5TT, England
tel: + 44 (0)20 7938 6000
fax: + 44 (0)20 7937 2648
web: www.thisislondon.com
arts editor: Fiona Hughes
theatre critic: Nicholas de Jongh
dance critic: Sarah Frater
opera critic: Fiona Maddocks

The Financial Times

1 Southwark Bridge
London SE1 9HL, England
tel: + 44 (0)20 7873 3000
fax: + 44 (0)20 7873 3929
email: peter.aspin@ft.com
web: www.ft.com
arts editor: Lorna Dolan
theatre critic: Martin Holye
opera: Richard Fairman
dance: Clement Crisp

The Guardian

119 Farringdon Road
London ECIR 3ER, England
tel: + 44 (0)20 7278 2332
fax: + 44 (0)20 7713 4366
email: charlie.english@guardian.co.uk
web: www.guardian.co.uk
arts editor: Charlie English
chief theatre critic: Michael Billington
dance critic: Bill Harpe
opera: Tim Ashley

The Independent

Independent House, 191 Marsh Wall
London E14 9RS, England
tel: + 44 (0)20 7005 2000
fax: + 44 (0)20 7005 2999
email: arts@independent.co.uk
web: www.independent.co.uk
arts editor: Ian Erving
chief theatre critic: Paul Taylor
opera: Jan Smaczny

The Independent on Sunday

Independent House, 191 Marsh Wall
London E14 9RS, England
tel: + 44 (0)20 7005 2000
fax: + 44 (0)20 7005 2999
email: m.field@independent.co.uk
web: www.independent.co.uk
culture editor: Marcus Field
chief theatre critic: Kate Bassett
opera: Marcus Field

The Observer

119 Farringdon Road
London ECIR 3ER, England
tel: + 44 (0)20 7278 2332
fax: + 44 (0)20 7713 4250
email: jane.ferguson@observer.co.uk
web: www.observer.co.uk
arts editor: Jane Ferguson
review editor: Louise France
theatre critic: Susannah Clapp
dance critic: Jann Parry
opera critic: Anthony Holden

PA Listings

*(Provide listings information to
British broadsheets)*
Queen's Buildings, 8 - 10 Royal Avenue
Belfast BT1 1DB, Northern Ireland
tel: + 44 (0)28 9024 6169
fax: + 44 (0)28 9024 6163
email: philip.allely@pa.press.net
contact: Phil Allely

Sunday Telegraph

1 Canada Square, Canary Wharf
London E14 5DT, England
tel: + 44 (0)20 7538 5000
fax: + 44 (0)20 7538 7872
email: starts@telegraph.co.uk
web: www.telegraph.co.uk
arts editor: Lucy Tuck
chief theatre critic: John Gross
opera: Michael Kennedy
dance: Louise Levene

The Times

News International, 1 Pennington
Street, London E98 1TT, England
tel: + 44 (0)20 7782 5000
fax: + 44 (0)20 7782 5748
email: arts@thetimes.co.uk
web: www.thetimes.co.uk
arts editor: Sarah Vine
chief theatre critic: Benedict
Nightingale
opera critic: Robert Thicknesse
dance critic: Debra Craine

internet sites:

Dublin Live

Irish Times New Media Division
4th Floor, Ballast House, Aston Quay
Dublin 2, Republic of Ireland
tel: + 353 1 472 7100
fax: + 353 1 472 7117
email: eocaollai@irish-times.com
web: www.ireland.com
content manager: Eannai Ó Collai

Entertainment Ireland

Fusio Ltd. 26 Great Strand Street
Dublin 1, Republic of Ireland
tel: + 353 1 809 0000
fax: + 353 809 0005
email: elaine@entertainment.ie
web: www.entertainmentireland.ie
content manager: Julian Douglas
theatre critic: Elaine Reilly

The Event Guide

For contact details see Magazines

iVenus.com

Smurfit Communications
2 Clanwilliam Court, Lower Mount
Street, Dublin 2, Republic of Ireland
tel: + 353 1 240 5300
fax: + 353 1 661 9757
email: brendam@smurfit-comms.ie
web: www.ivenus.com
contact: Brenda McCormick

WOW!

South Block, The Malthouse
Grand Canal Quay, Dublin 2
Republic of Ireland
tel: + 353 1 670 8975
fax: + 353 1 670 8968
email: maria.shannon@98fm.ie
web: www.wow.ie
content manager: Maria Shannon
chief theatre critic: Susan Conley

Olwen Fouere in Operating Theatre's production of Chair by Olwen Fouere, Roger Doyle and Johnny Hanrahan, 2001 © Amelia Stein

Actors Agencies/Agents:

The Agency
47 Adelaide Road, Dublin 2
Republic of Ireland
tel: +353 (0)1 661 8535
fax: +353 (0)1 676 0052
email: info@tagency.ie
contact: Teri Hayden

The Ann Curtis Agency
101 Collins Avenue West, Whitehall
Dublin 9, Republic of Ireland
tel: +353 (0)1 832 7708/831 9537
fax: +353 (0)1 831 9537
email: anncurtis@esatbiz.com
contact: Ann Curtis

Actors Ireland
Crescent Arts Centre
2-4 University Road
Belfast BT7 1NH, Northern Ireland
tel/fax: +44 (0)28 9024 8861
email: geraldine@actorsireland.com
web: www.actorsireland.com
contact: Geraldine O'Dwyer

Actors and Movers
13 Ballyfermot Drive
Dublin 10, Republic of Ireland
tel: +353 (0)1 625 9760
fax: +353 (0)1 625 9760
email: actorsandmovers@iol.ie
contact: Halina Froudist

Castaway Actors Agency
30/31 Wicklow Street, Dublin 2
Republic of Ireland
tel: +353 (0)1 671 9264
fax: +353 (0)1 671 9133
email: castaway@clubi.ie
web: www.irish-actors.com

Centre Stage Agency
7 Rutledge Terrace
off South Circular Road
Dublin 8, Republic of Ireland
tel: +353 (0)1 453 3599
fax: +353 (0)1 453 3599
email: geraldinecenterstage@eircom.net
contact: Geraldine Dunne

Dealers Agency
22 North Street Arcade
Belfast BT1 1PB, Northern Ireland
tel: +44 (0)28 9031 1075
fax: +44 (0)28 9023 4072
email: patrickduncan609@msn.com
web: www.dealersagency.co.uk
contact: Patrick Duncan

First Call Management
29/30 Dame Street, Dublin 2
Republic of Ireland
tel: +353 (0)1 679 8401
fax: +353 (0)1 679 8353
email: fcm@indigo.ie
contact: Maureen McGlynn

Front Line Actors Agency
Bayview House, 49 North Strand Road,
Dublin 3, Republic of Ireland
tel: +353 (0)1 836 4777/887 8556
fax: +353 (0)1 836 5252
email: frontlineactors@eircom.net
web: www.frontlineactors.org
contact: Bríd Ní Chumhaill

Hally Williams Agency
121 Grange Road, Rathfarnham
Dublin 14, Republic of Ireland
tel: +353 (0)1 493 3685
fax: +353 (0)1 493 3076
email: hallywilliams@eircom.net
contact: Yvette Hally, Ann Williams

IAM
Talent and Literary Agency
55 Shelbourne Road, Ballsbridge
Dublin 4, Republic of Ireland
tel: +353 (0)1 667 6455
fax: +353 (0)1 667 6474
contact: Lisa-Anne Porter

The Lisa Richards Agency
46 Upper Baggot Street
Dublin 4, Republic of Ireland
tel: +353 (0)1 660 3534
fax: +353 (0)1 660 3545
email: info@lisarichards.ie
web: www.lisarichards.ie
contact: Lisa Cook, Richard Cook

Lorraine Brennan Management (LBM)
Unit 22, Greenmount Industrial Estate
Harolds Cross, Dublin 6w
Republic of Ireland
tel: +353 (0)1 453 4355
fax: +353 (0)1 453 4412
email: lbm@clubi.ie
web: www.lbmactors.com
contact: Lorraine Brennan

ReActors Agency
1 Eden Quay, Dublin 1, Republic of Ireland
tel: +353 (0)1 878 6833
fax: +353 (0)1 878 3182
email: reactors@eircom.net
web: www.reactors.ie
contact: Úna Kavanagh

Stafford Management
41 Ardglass, Sandyford Road
Dundrum, Dublin 16, Republic of Ireland
tel: +353 (0)1 298 5944
fax: +353 (0)1 2981781
email: phyl@staffordm.com
web: www.staffordm.com
contact: Phyl Stafford

TN Enterprises
14 Beech Grove, Booterstown Avenue,
Blackrock, Co. Dublin, Republic of Ireland
tel: +353 (0)1 288 1537/(0)87 251 3485
fax: +353 (0)1 288 1541
email: info@tnenterprises.com
web: www.tnenterprises.com
contact: Theresa Nolan

Armourers:

Irish Arms Historical Preproductions
For contact information see Prop Hire

Theatrical Arms
Laurel Lodge, Stocking Lane
Rathfarnham, Dublin 16, Republic of Ireland
tel: +353 (0)1 493 0721/(0)87 258 4474
fax: +353 (0)1 493 0721
contact: John McKenna

Universal Arms
6 Rossmore Avenue, Templeogue
Dublin 6w, Republic of Ireland
tel: +353 (0)1 492 9391/(0)86 252 4270
fax: +353 (0)1 492 9391
email: joe_blackfox@msn.com

Arts Consultants/ Freelance Producers:

3Pcrew Ltd.
Clonmacken, Condell Road
Limerick, Republic of Ireland
tel: +353 (0)61 327770
fax: +353 (0)61 321602
email: info@3pcrew.ie
contact: John Gleeson

artBeat Management Services
81 Crestwood, Menlo Road
Galway, Republic of Ireland
tel/fax: +353 (0)91 779703
mobile: +353 (0)87 246 3399
email: artbeat@eircom.net
contact: Jane Daly

Patricia Baker
tel: +353 (0)87 830 8046
email: patricia@bakermob.com

Jan Branch
27 Pretoria Street, Belfast BT9 5AQ
Northern Ireland
tel/fax: +44 (0)28 9066 6995
email: jan_branch@branchlines.fsnet.co.uk

Rebecca Bartlett
59 Whitehall Road, Terenure
Dublin 12, Republic of Ireland
tel: +353 (0)1 455 5448/(0)87 220 8377
email: bartlettr@eircom.net

Anne Clarke
75 Bath Avenue, Dublin 4
Republic of Ireland
tel: +353 (0)1 667 4684/(0)87 649 3895
fax: +353 (0)1 668 2089
email: anneclarke@landmarkproductions.net

Susan Coughlan
37 Manor Place, Stoneybatter
Dublin 7, Republic of Ireland
tel: +353 (0)1 616 7095/(0)87 987 5180
fax: +353 (0)1 677 5688
email: susancoughlan@eircom.net

connect pr
50 Cloondara, Ballisodare
Co. Sligo, Republic of Ireland
tel: +353 (0)71 913 0484/(0)86 317 2161
fax: +353 (0)71 913 0484
email: connectpr@eircom.net
contact: Maeve McCormack

CultureWorks
19 Kirwan Street Cottages
Dublin 7, Republic of Ireland
tel: +353 (0)1 868 8108
email: sandyfitzgerald@eircom.net
contact: Sandy Fitzgerald

Phelim Donlon
50 New Park Road, Blackrock
Co. Dublin, Republic of Ireland
tel: +353 (0)1 289 5605/(0)87 930 9582
email: ptdonlon@iol.ie

Eugene Downes
11 Palmerston Grove, Milltown Road
Dublin 6, Republic of Ireland
tel: +353 (0)86 805 2215
email: downeseugene@eircom.net

Paul Fahy
Racecourse Road, Ballybrit
Galway, Republic of Ireland
tel: +353 (0)87 246 9971
email: pcfahy@iolfree.ie

Interactions
342 Mourne Road, Dublin 12
Republic of Ireland
tel/fax: +353 (0)1 465 0112
email: ideas@inter-actions.biz
web: www.inter-actions.biz
contact: Annette Clancy

Maureen Kennelly
9 The Spires, Dean St
Kilkenny, Republic of Ireland
tel: + 353 (0)56 775 1906/(0)86 829 1179
email: maureen.kennelly@eircom.net

Limelight Cultural
Event Management
Arts Project Management
49 Lissenfield, Lower Rathmines Road,
Dublin 6, Republic of Ireland
tel: +353 (0)1 497 9567
also
E6 Portora Wharf, Enniskillen
Co. Fermanagh BT74 7PW
Northern Ireland
contact: Aileen Connor
tel: +353 (0)87 253 0042
email: aileenc@iol.ie

Janice McAdam
213 Captain's Road
Crumlin, Dublin 12
tel: +353 (0)87 418 8650
email: janicemcadam@eircom.net

Fiach MacConghail
7 Lombard Street East
Dublin 2, Republic of Ireland
tel: +353 (0)1 670 4895
fax: +353 (0)1 670 3881
email: macconghail@eircom.net

Irma McLoughlin
tel: +353 (0)86 173 0235
email: irmamcloughlin@yahoo.com

Mary McPartlan
110a Ard na Coille, Lios Mor, Cappagh Road
Galway, Republic of Ireland
tel: + 353 (0)91 592700/(0)87 220 6629
fax: +353 (0)91 592723
email: marymcpartlan@eircom.net

Gráinne Millar
12 Granitefield Manor, Rochestown Avenue,
Dun Laoghaire, Co. Dublin
Republic of Ireland
tel: +353 (0)86 837 2586
email: grainne_millar@hotmail.com

Rupert Murray
*For contact information see Lighting
Designers*

Doireann Ní Bhriain
2 Palmerston Court, Palmerston Road
Dublin 6, Republic of Ireland
tel: +353 (0)1 496 0918/(0)87 2434814
fax: +353 (0)1 498 3200
email: dnib@eircom.net

Tony Ó Dálaigh
159 Sutton Park, Dublin 13
Republic of Ireland
tel: +353 (0)1 832 4040/(0)87 968 0152
email: tonyodalaigh@hotmail.com

Maura O'Keeffe
86 Rialto Court, Dublin 8, Republic of Ireland
tel: +353 (0)1 453 9179/(0)87 223 4201
fax: +353 (0)1 453 9719
email: mokeeffe24@eircom.net

Eileen O'Reilly
tel: +44 (0)141 637 1388/(0)87 960 3444
email: eileenoreillyuk@yahoo.co.uk

Maurice Power
1 Kevins Avenue, Strand Hill Road
Sligo, Republic of Ireland
tel/fax: +353 (0)71 916 9371
email: mauricpower@eircom.net

Nik Quaife
74 Dame Street, Dublin 2
Republic of Ireland
tel: +353 (0)1 679 8542/(0)87 799 7989
email: nquaife@eircom.net

Liam Rellis Arts Management
10 John's Hill, Waterford, Republic of Ireland
tel: +353 (0)51 854291/(0)86 602 1310
email: liamrellis@eircom.net
contact: Liam Rellis

Nick Reilly
2 Railway Terrace, Dublin Road
Drogheda, Co. Louth, Republic of Ireland
tel: +353 (0)86 829 0086
email: nickreilly@eircom.net

Donal Shiels
tel: +353 (0)87 259 7106
email: donalshiels@iol.ie

Ten42 Productions
Brittas South Lodge, Carrick on Suir
Co. Tipperary, Republic of Ireland
tel: +353 (0)87 797 3639
email: dteevan@eircom.net
web: www.twn42.com
contact: David Teevan

Richard Wakely
89 St Declans Road, Marino
Dublin 3, Republic of Ireland
tel/fax: +353 (0)1 833 2980
mobile +353 (0)87 667 2137
email: rwakely@eircom.net

Casting Directors:

Gillian Reynolds Casting
42 Simmons Court Castle
Dublin 4, Republic of Ireland
tel: +353 (0)1 212 0419
contact: Gillian Reynolds

Carmel O'Connor Casting
1 Serpentine Avenue, Ballsbridge
Dublin 4, Republic of Ireland
tel/fax: +353 (0)1 668 2450
email: coconnor@esatclear.ie
contact: Carmel O'Connor

Maureen Hughes Casting
33 St. Attracta Road, Cabra
Dublin 7, Republic of Ireland
tel: +353 (0)1 868 9889/(0)87 268 8273
fax: +353 (0)1 838 3583
email: maurz@indigo.ie
contact: Maureen Hughes

Denise Deasy Casting
10 Highfield Park, Dundrum
Dublin 14, Republic of Ireland
tel: +353 (0)1 298 2961/(0)86 257 1710
fax: +353 (0)1 298 2961
email: deasycasting@eircom.net
contact: Denise Deasy

Dorothy Mac Gabhann Casting
23 Castle Farm Woods, Shankill
Co. Dublin, Republic of Ireland
tel: +353 (0)1 211 5706/(0)86 375 1170
fax: +353 (0)1 211 5710

Rebecca Roper Casting
tel: +353 (0)402 30799
fax: +353 (0)402 30799
email: bbox@indigo.ie
contact: Rebecca Roper

Moiselle Casting
7 Corrig Avenue, Dun Laoghaire
Co. Dublin, Republic of Ireland
tel: +353 (0)1 280 2857

Composers:

Bell Helicopter
See also Sound Designers

Ivan Birthistle
See also Sound Designers

Paul Brennan
See also Sound Designers

Paul Boyd
100 Loopline Park
Belfast BT6 9DX, Northern Ireland
tel: +44 (0)28 9050 2235
email: info@paulboydmusic.co.uk
web: www.paulboydmusic.co.uk

Justin Carroll
See also Sound Designers

Jackie Conboy
See also Sound Designers

Vincent Doherty
See also Sound Designers

Roger Doyle
c/o Operating Theatre
web: www.rogerdoyle.com

Ciaran Eaton
See also Sound Designers

Pat Fitzpatrick
tel: +353 (0)87 278 1949
email: patrickfitz1@eicom.net

Laura Forrest-Hay
66 North Circle Road
Dublin 1, Republic of Ireland
tel: +353 (0)1 838 0561/(0)86 397 8556
email: lfl@gofree.indigo.ie

Roger Gregg
See also Sound Designers

Eoghan Horgan
See also Sound Designers

Brian Irvine
13 Bow Street, Donaghadee
Co. Down BT21 0HD, Northern Ireland
tel: +44 (0)28 9188 4660/(0)7789836392
email: brian.irvine@btinternet.com

Sam Jackson
See also Sound Designers

Trevor Knight
See also Sound Designers

Conor Linehan
tel: +353 (0)87 649 7761
email: linehanc@yahoo.co.uk

Rod McVey
See also Sound Designers

Neil Martin
42 Lansdowne Road
Belfast BT15 4AA, Northern Ireland
tel: +44 (0)7775 846663
email: nmmusic@ntlworld.com
web: www.neilmartinmusic.com

Natural 5th
Borris House, Borris, Co.Carlow
Republic of Ireland
tel: +353 (0)59 9771876
email: natural5th@eircom.net
contact: Denis Roche
See also Sound Designers

Cormac O'Connor
See also Sound Designers

Peter Sutton
See also Sound Designers

Andrew Synnott
tel: +353 (0)87 298 4245
email: andrewsynnott@eircom.net

Cathal Synnott
email: cathalsynnott@eircom.net
See also Sound Designers

J.J. Vernon
See also Sound Designers

Costume Designers:

Orla Bass
For contact information see Set Designers

Joan Bergin
52 Edenvale Road, Dublin 6
Republic of Ireland
tel: +353 (0)1 497 5895/(0)86 257 5091
also
Costume Mill
tel: +353 (0)1 874 8611
fax: +353 (0)1 874 0495

Carol Betera
152 Walsh Road, Dublin 9
Republic of Ireland
tel: +353 (0)1 837 8243/(0)87 419 9307
fax: +353 (0)1 837 8243
email: cbetera@iol.ie

Consolata Boyle
Killalane, Laragh, Co. Wicklow
Republic of Ireland
tel: +353 (0)404 45909/(0)86 850 9728

Michelle Butler
tel: +353 (0)86 271 7987

Suzanne Cave
Ardee, Adelaide Road, Glenageary
Co. Dublin, Republic of Ireland
tel: +353 (0)87 293 3749
email: suzcave@hotmail.com

Johanna Connor
For contact information see Set Designers

Liz Cullinane
86 Donnybrook Street
Belfast BT9 7DG, Northern Ireland
tel: +44 (0)28 9066 5853/(0)7976 267849

Fiona Cunningham
For contact information see Set Designers

Sinéad Cuthbert
2 Herbert Cottages, Ballsbridge
Dublin 4, Republic of Ireland
tel: +353 (0)87 989 0773
email: thecostumeworkshop@hotmail.com

Cliff Dolliver
For contact information see Set Designers

Moggie Douglas
For contact information see Set Designers

Monica Ennis
20 North Frederick Street
Dublin 1, Republic of Ireland
tel: +353 (0)87 242 8937

Catherine Fay
396 Clogher Road, Crumlin
Dublin 12, Republic of Ireland
tel: +353 (0)1 473 8422/(0)87 677 8630
email: catherinefay@eircom.net

Jacquie Fitzpatrick
tel: +353 (0)87 618 8019

Siobhan Ferrie
For contact information see Set Designers

Monica Frawley
For contact information see Set Designers

Sonia Haccius
For contact information see Set Designers

Joan Hickson
6 Hatchett's Tce, O'Mahoney Ave
Cork, Republic of Ireland
tel: +353 (0)87 939 1671
email: joanymay@hotmail.com

Alison Jayne Couture
For contact information see Costume Hire

Kathy Kavanagh
c/o Ace One Stop Party Shop
For contact information see Wigs and
Hairdressing
tel: +353 (0)1 457 0707
email: info@onestoppartyshop.com

Louise Kennedy
9 Ashgrove Avenue, Naas
Co. Kildare, Republic of Ireland
tel: +353 (0)86 829 4593
email: louise_kennedy_3@hotmail.com

Suzanne Keogh
tel: +353 (0)87 787 0480/
+44 (0)1708 707166
email: suekeo@hotmail.com

Sarah King
68 The Dunes, Portmarnock
Co. Dublin, Republic of Ireland
tel: +353 (0)87 603 6508
email: saraheking@eircom.net

Jacqueline Kobler
c/o Hally Williams Agency
For contact information see Acting Agencies

Lisa Lavery
tel: +44 (0)28 9029 9881/(0)7771 791465
email: lisa@clotheme.com
web: www.clotheme.com

Heather Long
10b Woodview Terrace, Braniel
Belfast BT5 7PE, Northern Ireland
tel: +44 (0)28 9022 4944/
+44 (0)7974 572194
email: heathert.long@ntlworld.com

Helen McCusker
7 Seafort Gardens, Sandymount
Dublin 4, Republic of Ireland
tel: +353 (0)87 814 0086

Nicola McCutcheon
2nd Floor, 10 Exchequer Street
Dublin 2, Republic of Ireland
tel: +353 (0)1 670 3191/(0)87 678 3751
email: sukiandnic@hotmail.com

Leonore McDonagh
6 Church Avenue South
Dublin 8, Republic of Ireland
tel: +353 (0)1 453 8599/(0)87 273 1162
email: leonore@esatclear.ie

Doreen McKenna
tel: +353 (0)87 606 4757
email: dors@eircom.net

Ferdia Murphy
For contact information see Set Designers

Pat Musgrave
164 Banbridge Road, Kinallen, Dromara,
Co. Down BT25 2NS, Northern Ireland
tel: +44 (0)28 9753 2881
email: pat_musgrave@hotmail.com

Eimer Ní Mhaoldomhnaigh
c/o Agent Lynda Mamy, PFD
tel: +44 (0)207 344 1046/
+353 (0)87 244 7674
email: eimerni@eircom.net

Paul O'Mahony
For contact information see Set Designers

Synan O'Mahony
c/o Hally Williams Agency
For contact information see Actors Agencies

Sherrie Scott
tel: +353 (0)71 985 2925/(0)7742 283825
email: flowingtide@hotmail.com

Bláithín Sheerin
For contact information see Set Designers

Louise Stewart
Hillcrest, 98 Upper Newtownards Road
Belfast BT4 3EN, Northern Ireland
tel: +44 (0)28 9058 9606/(0)7979 901301
fax: +44 (0)28 9058 9608
email: louisemstewart@hotmail.com

Kathy Strachan
30 Oldcourt Park, Bray
Co. Wicklow, Republic of Ireland
tel: +353 (0)1 274 5565/(0)87 269 2277

Marie Tierney
tel: +353 (0)87 252 4485
email: marietierney57@hotmail.com

Joe Vanek
For contact information see Set Designers

Whirligig
Mermaid Cottage, Hollow Road, Rossnowlagh,
Co. Donegal, Republic of Ireland
tel: +353 (0)71 985 2925/(0)86 151 9775
email: mandy_blinco@hotmail.com
contact: Mandy Blinco, Sherrie Scott

Sam Wynn
29 West Beach, Cobh, Co. Cork
Republic of Ireland
tel: +353 (0)86 813 7659
email: samwynn@esatclear.ie

Chisato Yoshimi
79 Mount Prospect Avenue
Clontarf, Dublin 3, Republic of Ireland
tel: +353 (0)1 833 0099/(0)87 221 8130
fax: +353 (0)1 833 0099

Annalisa Zagone
The Cottage, Ard na Laoi, Carrigrohane,
Co. Cork, Republic of Ireland
tel: +353 (0)87 779 9782
email: zagone@eircom.net

Costume Hire:

Alison Jayne Couture
(Made-to-Measure Costume)
3rd Floor, Marquis Building, 89-91 Adelaide
Street, Belfast BT2 8FE, Northern Ireland
tel: +44 (0)28 9032 5444
fax: +44 (0)28 9031 9428

Irish Arms Historical Reproductions
For contact information see Prop Hire

Lyric Theatre
55 Ridgeway Street, Stranmillis
Belfast BT9 5FB, Northern Ireland
tel: +44 (0)28 9038 5684
contact: Pat Musgrave

The Joke Box
Unit 357 the Square, Tallaght Dublin 24,
Republic of Ireland
tel/fax: +353 (0)1 459 0366
email: thejokebox@thejokebox.ie
also
The Joke Box, 10 Mainguard Street
Galway, Republic of Ireland
tel: +353 (0)91 566411

Thimblinas
27 Upper Abbeygate Street
Galway, Republic of Ireland
tel: +353 (0)91 568865
contact: Michelle Langan, Terri Dooley

NoMac Productions
Unit 1A, Tycor Business Centre, Tycor
Avenue, Waterford, Republic of Ireland
tel: +353 (0)51 379829/(0)87 285 3480
fax: +353 (0)51 379829
email: nomac2@oceanfree.net
contact: Blánaid MacCann

Costume Makers:

Liz Cullinane
For contact information see Costume Designers

Denis Darcy
65 Capel Street, Dublin 1, Republic of Ireland
tel: +353 (0)1 873 2256

Monica Ennis
For contact information see Costume Designers

Valerie Haugh
24 St Josephs Drive, Montenotte Park
Cork, Republic of Ireland
tel: +353 (0)87 237 5689
email: valeryhaugh@yahoo.co.uk

Ruth Hosty
1 Florence Street, Portobello
Dublin 8, Republic of Ireland
tel: +353 (0)1 475 5427

Irish Arms Historical Reproductions
For contact information see Prop Hire

Irish History Company
Northside Community Resource Centre
Forthill, Sligo, Republic of Ireland
tel: +353 (0)71 914 7616
email: info@irishhistoryco.com
contact: Kay Erb

Alison Jayne Couture
For contact information see Costume Designers

Heather Long
For contact information see Costume Designers

Lyndie MacIntyre
tel: +353 (0)87 285 8084/
+44 (0)141 883 4892

Doreen McKenna
For contact information see Costume Designers

Dance Floor Suppliers:

APDI
For contact information see Support Organisations

Cine Electric
For contact details see Technical Suppliers

Dialect/Voice Coaches:

Andrea Ainsworth (voice)
c/o The Abbey Theatre
tel: +353 (0)1 887 2293

Peter Ballance (both)
c/o Actors Ireland
For contact information see Actors Agencies/Agents

Derek Chapman
6 Rutledge Terrace, South Circular Road
Dublin 8, Republic of Ireland
tel: +353 (0)1 454 4950

Brendan Gunn MA PhD (dialect)
c/o The Agency
For contact information see Actors Agencies/Agents

Paul Keenan (voice/singing)
c/o The Samuel Beckett Centre, TCD
tel: +353 (0)1 608 1715
email: keenanp@tcd.ie

Patricia Logue (both)
tel: +44 (0)7973 702596
email: patricialogue@yahoo.co.uk

Jill McCullough (dialect)
89 Montague Mansions
London W1U 6LF, England
tel: +44 (0)7976 799739
email: dialectjillmcc@compuserve.com

Poll Moussoulides
tel: +353 (0)86 260 0035
email: pollm@indigo.ie
web: www.voicecoach.ie

Robert Price (both)
email: robertprice6969@hotmail.com

Cathal Quinn
c/o Gaiety School of Acting
For contact information, see Drama and Dance Training
tel: +353 (0)86 609 0974
email: cathaljquinn@hotmail.com

Helena Walsh (voice)
tel: +353 (0)86 854 8885
email: helenawalshvoice@yahoo.co.uk

Fabric Suppliers:

Fabric Select
181 Parnell Street
Dublin 1, Republic of Ireland
tel: +353 (0)1 878 6161
contact: Nancy Byrne, Liz Hennessy

TWI International
24 Mountjoy Square
Dublin 1, Republic of Ireland
tel: +353 (0)1 855 3777
fax: +353 (0)1 855 0049
email: twi@indigo.ie
web: www.fabricsireland.com
contact: Chris Synge, Mike Mooney

Murphy Sheehy & Co
14 Castle Market
Dublin 2, Republic of Ireland
tel: +353 (0)1 677 0316
email: info@murphysheehyfabrics.com
web: www.murphysheehyfabrics.com

Hickeys Fabrics
Henry Street, Dublin 1, Republic of Ireland
tel: +353 (0)1 873 0714
also
St Stephens Green
Dublin 2, Republic of Ireland
tel: +353 (0)1 478 4769

Fight Directors:

Paul Burke
17 Clonmacnoise Road, Crumlin
Dublin 12, Republic of Ireland
tel: +353 (0)87 203 4021
web: www.reelaction.com

Michael Poynor
For contact information see Freelance Directors

Freelance Choreographers:

Muirne Bloomer
tel: + 353 (0)86 324 2614
email: muirnebloomer@eircom.net

David Bolger
c/o CoisCéim Dance Theatre
For contact information see Subsidised Dance Companies

Adrienne Browne
tel: + 353 (0)1 286 1525/(0)86 393 2361
c/o New Balance Dance Company
For further contact information Partially Subsidised Dance Companies

Nick Bryson
17 Myrtle Hill Terrace, Tivoli
Cork, Republic of Ireland
tel: +353(0)86 157 1660
email: brysonnick@hotmail.com

Caimin Collins
68 Allen Park Road, Stillorgan
Co. Dublin, Republic of Ireland
tel: +353 (0)87 784 5111
email: caimincollins@hotmail.com
See also Freelance Directors

Niamh Condron
tel: +44 (0)7940 676 571
c/o This Torsion Dance Company
For contact information see Partially Subsidised Dance Companies

Robert Connor
c/o Dance Theatre of Ireland
For contact information see Subsidised Dance Companies

Finola Cronin
c/o Drama Studies Centre
UCD Blackrock Campus
Co. Dublin, Republic of Ireland
tel: +353 (0)1 716 8964
email: finola.cronin@ucd.ie

Natalie de Braam
Rathmore House, Fiddown
Co. Kilkenny, Republic of Ireland
tel: +353(0)86 818 0004/(0)51 643312
email: braam@eircom.net

Marguerite Donlon
Staatstheater Saarbruecken
Schillerplatz 1
66111 Saarbruecken, Germany
tel: +49 (0)681 309 2317
fax: +49 (0)681 309 2364
email: don.lon@snafu.de
web: www.donlon.de

Jenny Elliott
32 Station Road, Sydenham
Belfast BT4 1RF, Northern Ireland
tel: +44 (0)28 9065 3828
email: jenny@elliottj.fsworld.co.uk

Sarah Johnston
tel: +44 (0)28 9079 7809/(0)7074 434344
email: sarahjgtifly@aol.com

Debbie Kiernan
25 Lough Conn Road, Ballyfermot
Dublin 10, Republic of Ireland
tel: +353 (0)1 626 7126
email: kierno40@hotmail.com

Julie Lockett
tel: +353 (0)87 994 6768
email: julielockett@hotmail.com

Jenny McDonald
tel: +353 (0)87 967 3664

Ríonach Ní Néill
c/o APDI
tel: +49 (0)172 404 2832
email: prodance@iol.ie

Mary Nunan
Irish World Music Centre
University of Limerick
Limerick, Republic of Ireland
tel: +353 (0)61 213464/(0)87 668 9600
fax: +353 (0)61 202589
email: mary.nunan@ul.ie

Fearghus O'Conchuir
Corp Feasa Dance
4 Tennyson Road, Walthamstow
London E17 8PR, England
tel: +44 (0)7966 270212/(0)86 177 8156
email: fearghus.oconchuir@ntlworld.com

Cathy O'Kennedy
c/o Fluxus Dance
*For contact information see Subsidised
Dance Companies*

Rachel O'Riordan
Northern Ireland
tel: +44 (0)28 9096 4320/(0)7729 863543
email: r.welch@qub.ac.uk
See also Freelance Directors

Diane Richardson
tel: +353 (0) 87 667 8856
email: ditap@eircom.net
web: www.tapestry.ie

Liz Roche
c/o Rex Levitates
*For contact information see Subsidised
Dance Companies*

John Scott
c/o Irish Modern Dance Theatre
*For contact information see Subsidised
Dance Companies*

Judith Sibley
Chrysalis Dance Company, 28 Carraig Mor,
Lackagh, Co. Galway, Republic of Ireland
tel: +353 (0)87 797 0339
email: judithsibley@eircom.net

Morleigh Steinberg
c/o The Corn Exchange
*For contact information see Subsidised
Drama Companies*
tel: +353 (0)87 233 1273

Loretta Yurick
c/o Dance Theatre of Ireland
*For contact information see Subsidised
Dance Companies*

Freelance Directors:

Leticia Agudo
Flat 3, 16 Vesey Place, Dun Laoghaire,
Co. Dublin, Republic of Ireland
tel: +353 (0)1 230 2469/(0)87 288 5410
email: leticiaagudo@yahoo.co.uk

Alice Barry
Skerry Cross, Dromone, Oldcastle
Co. Meath, Republic of Ireland
tel: +353 (0)44 66550/(0)87 298 9784

Rebecca Bartlett
*For contact information see Arts
Consultants/Freelance Producers*

Natalie De Braam
*For contact information see Freelance
Choreographers*

Paul Brennan
6 New Avenue Wood, Shantalla
Galway, Republic of Ireland
tel: +353 (0)91 588913/(0)87 626 8897
email: apecf1@eircom.net

Patrick Burke
Basement 18, The Crescent, O'Connell
Avenue, Limerick, Republic of Ireland
tel: +353 (0)87 799 3087
email: impacttheatrecompany@eircom.net

Cabrini Cahill
Morette, Emo, Portlaoise
Co. Laois, Republic of Ireland
tel: +353 (0)87 821 0560
email: cabrini@eircom.net

Michael Caven
155 Inchicore Road, Dublin 8
Republic of Ireland
tel: +353 (0)1 453 3056
email: mcaven@gofree.indigo.ie

Veronica Coburn
c/o Barabbas... the company
*For contact information see Subsidised
Drama Companies*

Caimin Collins
*For contact information see Freelance
Choreographers*

John Comiskey
For contact information see Lighting Designers

Annabelle Comyn
tel: +353 (0)1 454 7683/(0)85 727 1073
email: anabellecomyn@aol.com

Thomas Conway
2 Blarney View, Gardiner's Hill
Cork, Republic of Ireland
tel: +353 (0)87 672 0149
email: tomconway66@hotmail.com

Tom Creed
2 Laurel Villas, Mardyke, Cork
Republic of Ireland
tel: +353 (0)87 633 3015
email: tomfromcork@hotmail.com

Andy Crook
tel: +353 (0)87 228 7608
tel: +353 (0)1 850 0903
email: crooka@eircom.net

Jim Culleton
c/o Fishamble
*For contact information see Subsidised
Drama Companies*

Martin Drury
3 Orwell Woods, Dartry
Dublin 6, Republic of Ireland
tel: +353 (0)1 496 5616
email: martindrury@eircom.net

Jimmy Fay
c/o Bedrock Theatre Company
*For contact information see Subsidised
Drama Companies*

Caroline FitzGerald
20 Kilbegnet Close, Dalkey
Co. Dublin, Republic of Ireland
tel: +353 (0)1 275 1916/(0)86 346 0430

Sarah FitzGibbon
152 Lally Road, Dublin 10
Republic of Ireland
tel: +353 (0)86 347 8841
email: fitzshankey@iolfree.ie

Donal Gallagher
c/o Asylum Productions, Triskel Arts
Centre, Cork, Republic of Ireland
tel: +353 (0)87 294 7270
email: donalsg@hotmail.com

Dan Gordon
email: dan@gordon3853.freeserve.co.uk

David Grant
4 Saint Helen's House, 155 High Street
Holywood, Co. Down BT18 9LG
Northern Ireland
tel: +44 (0)28 9042 8506
email: d.grant@qub.ac.uk

Max Hafler
The Anchorhold, Mount Ross, Headford,
Co. Galway, Republic of Ireland
tel: +353 (0)93 35957
email: maxhafler@iol.ie

Liam Halligan
c/o Quare Hawks Theatre Company
*For contact information see Subsidised
Drama Companies*

Judy Hegarty Lovett
10 Vieille Cote, Mericourt, France 78270
tel: +33 (0)1 34 79 36 74
fax: +33 (0)1 34 79 37 50
email: loverty@wanadoo.fr

David Horan
28 Maxwell Road, Rathgar
Dublin 6, Republic of Ireland
tel: +353 (0)87 629 9462
email: davidhoran@vodafone.ie

Peter Hussey
c/o Crooked House Theatre Company
*For contact information see Partially
Subsidised Drama Companies*

Raymond Keane
c/o Barabbas... the company
*For contact information see Subsidised
Drama Companies*

Oonagh Kearney
tel: +353 (0)87 965 2919
email: okearney@ireland.com

Alan Kinsella
1 Chester Road, Ranelagh
Dublin 6, Republic of Ireland
tel: +353 (0)1 491 3105
email: alanjk@eircom.net

Mark Lambert
110 Rathdown Park, Greystones
Co. Wicklow, Republic of Ireland
tel: +353 (0)1 287 3748
email: hedda@gofree.indigo.ie

Frank Laverty
66 North Circular Road, Dublin 7
Republic of Ireland
tel: +353 (0)1 838 0561/(0)86 852 8990
fax: +353 (0)1 838 0561
email: lfl@gofree.indigo.ie

Ronan Leahy
396 Clogher Road, Crumlin
Dublin 12, Republic of Ireland
tel: +353 (0)1 473 8422
email: ronanleahy@eircom.net

Tim Loane
tel: +44 (0)28 9027 8054
email: tim.loane@btconnect.com

Simon Magill
c/o Waterfront Hall
For contact information see Venues
tel: +44 (0)28 9033 4421
email: magills@waterfront.co.uk

Jo Mangan
c/o The Performance Corporation
*For contact information see Partially
Subsidised Drama Companies*

Tony McCleane-Fay
c/o The Granary Theatre
*For contact information see Partially
Subsidised Drama Companies*
tel: +353 (0)87 640 4187
email: t.mccleanefay@ucc.ie

John McKeown
tel: +353 (0)1 284 3023/(0)87 241 2293
email: johnjmck@eircom.net

Paul Meade
c/o Gúna Nua
*For contact information see Subsidised
Drama Companies*

Deirdre Molloy
20 Tyrconnell Grove, Thomas Davis Street West
Inchicore, Dublin 8, Republic of Ireland
email: molloyd@hotmail.com

Carol Moore
tel: +44(0)28 9070 4402/(0)7786 423131
email: carolmoore7@btopenworld.com

Conall Morrison
c/o The Abbey Theatre
*For contact information see Subsidised
Drama Companies*

Mikel Murfi
tel: +353 (0)1 287 0342/(0)86 601 7064

Bairbre Ní Chaoimh
c/o Calypso Productions
*For contact information see Subsidised
Drama Companies*
tel: +353 (0)87 954 5816

Jim Nolan
4 Andrew Street, Waterford, Republic of Ireland
tel: +353 (0)51 843 487
email: jamesjnolan@eircom.net

John O'Brien
11 The Avenue, Woodpark, Ballinteer
Dublin 16, Republic of Ireland
tel: +353 (0)86 817 7060
email: john21@eircom.net

Mark O'Brien
10 Glenmore Road, Dublin 7
Republic of Ireland
tel: +353 (0)1 869 0910
email: markpob@yahoo.com

Joe O'Byrne
C/o Peters Frazier & Dunlop
For contact information see Literary Agents

Sharon O'Doherty
c/o Actors and Movers
For contact information see Actors Agencies

Rachel O'Riordan
*For contact information see Freelance
Choreographers*

David Parnell
c/o Gúna Nua
*For contact information see Subsidised
Drama Companies*

Michael Poynor
The Old Barracks, 17 Duncrun Road
Bellarena, Limavady BT49 0JD
Northern Ireland
tel: +44 (0)28 7775 0240/(0)7721 503240
email: michaelpoynor@hotmail.com

Michael Scott
c/o SFX Theatre
For contact information see Venues

Zoë Seaton
c/o Big Telly Theatre Company
email: zoe@big-telly.com
*For contact information see Subsidised
Drama Companies*

Alan Stanford
c/o First Call Management
For contact information see Actors Agents

Karl Wallace
104 Kimberley Street, Belfast BT7 3DZ,
Northern Ireland
tel: +44 (0)28 9022 0836
email: karlwallace@yahoo.com
*See also Kabosh in Subsidised Drama
Companies*

Rachel West
7 Auburn Street, Broadstone
Dublin 7, Republic of Ireland
tel: +353 (0)23 47015
email: ianbel@eircom.net

Belinda Wild
Railway House, Desert, Enniskeane
Co. Cork, Republic of Ireland
tel: +353 (0)87 745 5098
email: rachelannawest@eircom.net

Lighting Designers:

ACK Productions
22 Alexandra Park, Holywood
Co. Down BT18 9ET, Northern Ireland
tel: +44 (0)28 9042 1513/(0)7802 642029
fax: +44 (0)28 9042 3084
email: info@ackproductions.co.uk
contact: Alastair Kerr

Nick Anton
Clonkeen, Portlaoise, Co. Laois
Republic of Ireland
tel: +353 (0)87 235 8067
fax: +353 (0)502 63357
email:nick@dunamaise.ie

Debbie Behan
tel: +353 (0)86 838 1997
email: debbiebehan@eircom.net

Blacklight
For contact information see Technical Suppliers

Paul Browne
The Pewter, Ballycashin, Butlerstown,
Waterford, Republic of Ireland
tel: +353 (0)86 873 7004
email: paulbrownelx@hotmail.com

Mick 'Psych' Byrne
17 Middle Street, Galway, Republic of Ireland
tel: +353 (0)87 639 0890
email: fireflytech@eircom.net

John Comiskey
17 Hawthorn Terrace, East Wall
Dublin 3, Republic of Ireland
tel: +353 (0)1 855 7323/(0)86 272 7180
email: johncomiskey@ireland.com

Aedín Cosgrove
c/o Pan Pan
tel: +353 (0)1 280 0544/(0)86 385 0696
email: aedin@panpantheatre.com
For contact information see Subsidised Drama Companies

John F. Cumiskey
email: jcumiske@hotmail.com

Davy Cunningham
c/o Performing Arts
tel: +44 (0)20 7255 1362
email: richard@performing-arts.co.uk
web: www.performing-arts.co.uk
contact: Richard Haigh

Jim Daly
24 Glencara, Ballybeg
Waterford, Republic of Ireland
tel: +353 (0)51 372715
email: jemser@oceanfree.net

Lee Davis
tel: +44 (0)7742 384566
email: leedavis11@hotmail.com

Paul Denby
Reagrove, Minane Bridge
Co. Cork, Republic of Ireland
tel: +353 (0)21 488 7300/(0)86 881 5055
fax: +353 (0)21 488 7901
email: paul@ctc.ie

Eamon Fox
19 The Old Dock, Little Ship Street
Dublin 8, Republic of Ireland
tel: +353 (0)87 236 7735
email: eamonfox@hotmail.com

Eamonn Fox
For contact information see Production Managers

Mark Galione
tel: +353 (0)86 261 1512
email: galione@eircom.net

John Gallagher
45 Cherrywood Grove, Newry
Co. Down BT34 1JJ, Northern Ireland
tel: +44 (0)7899 910881
email: john@gallagher.fsworld.co.uk

Kath Geraghty
c/o the Granary Theatre
For contact information see Venues
tel: +353 (0)87 997 9673
email: k.geraghty@ucc.ie

Frank Herraghty
Knock Road, Ballyhaunis
Co. Mayo, Republic of Ireland
tel: +353 (0)94 963 0538/(0)87 262 7306
email: foh2002@eircom.net

Gerry Jenkinson
tel: +44 (0)7905 512021
email: lx@gerryjenknison.co.uk
web: www.gerryjenkinson.co.uk

High Resolution Lighting
172 Merrion Road, Dublin 4
Republic of Ireland
tel: +353 (0)1 219 6345
fax: +353 (0)1 219 6346
email: peter@highreslighting.com
web: www.highreslighting.com

Paul Keogan
5 St James Terrace, Sandymount Road
Dublin 4, Republic of Ireland
tel: +353 (0)1 668 1153/(0)87 243 4352
fax: +353 (0)1 668 1153
email: keogs@indigo.ie

Nick McCall
Glasdrumman Mór, Drumkeeran
Co. Leitrim, Republic of Ireland
tel: +353 (0)71 964 8033/(0)87 229 8181
email: nmccall@ireland.com

Kevin McFadden
tel: +353 (0)87 771 4824
email: kevinmacfadden@eircom.net

James C. McFetridge
29 Dunlambert Gardens
Belfast BT15 3NN, Northern Ireland
tel: +44 (0)28 9028 7040/(0)7761 956877
email: james.mcfetridge@ntlworld.com

Sinead McKenna
tel: +353 (0)87 298 3852
fax: +353 (0)1 660 6773
email: sineadmakka@eircom.net

Rupert Murray
tel: +353 (0)1 497 4164/(0)87 237 5411
email: rupertm@eircom.net

Steve Neale
Skerry Cross, Dromone, Oldcastle
Co. Meath, Republic of Ireland
tel: +353 (0)44 66550/(0)87 618 7404

David O'Brien
University of Limerick Concert Hall
For contact information see Venues
tel: +353 (0)87 236 1728
email: davidobrien@vodafone.ie

Paul O'Neill
Little Brook, Newcastle, Co. Wicklow,
Republic of Ireland
tel: +353 (0)1 281 0969/(0)86 233 5357
fax: +353 (0)1 281 0979
email: paulolight@eircom.net

Michael Poynor
For contact information see Freelance Directors

Brian Rudden
For contact information see Sound Designers

Kevin Smith
2 Pinebrook Crescent, Artane
Dublin 5, Republic of Ireland
tel: +353 (0)1 831 3741/(0)87 288 9379
email: smithkj@eircom.net

Amy Smyth
c/o Down Arts Centre
*For contact information see Venues.
See also Set Design*
tel: +44 (0)7970 182947

Morleigh Steinberg
For contact information see Freelance Choreographers

Production House
For contact information see Technical Suppliers

Kevin Treacy
Apartment 50, Earlsfield Court, Francis
Street, Dublin 8, Republic of Ireland
tel: +353 (0)87 663 9737

Sinead Wallace
11 Parnell Road, Harold's Cross
Dublin 12, Republic of Ireland
tel: +353 (0)87 937 6981
email: neadwallace@eircom.net

Conleth White
tel: +353 (0)87 231 6464/
+44 (0)7775 521885
email: conleth1@eircom.net

Paul Winters
c/o Riverbank Arts Centre
tel: +353 (0)87 908 5452
email: paulws@eircom.net

Literary Agents:

The Agency
24 Pottery Lane, Holland Park
London W11 4LZ, England
tel: +44 (0)20 7727 1346
fax: +44 (0)20 7727 9037
email: info@theagency.co.uk
web: www.theagency.co.uk
contact: various agents

Alan Brodie Representation Ltd
(incorporating Michael Imison Playwrights)
211 Piccadilly, London W1J 9HF
tel: +44 (0)20 7917 2871
fax: +44 (0)20 7917 2872
email: info@alanbrodie.com
contact: Alan Brodie

Alexandra Cann Representation
12 Abingdon Road, London W8 6AF, England
tel: +44 (0)20 7938 4002
fax: +44 (0)20 7938 4228
email: enquiries@alexandracann.com
contact: Alexandra Cann

Berlin Associates
14 Floral Street, London WC2E 9DH, England
tel: +44 (0)20 7836 1112
fax: +44 (0)20 7632 5280
contact: various agents

Casarotto Ramsay & Associates Ltd
National House, 60-66 Wardour Street
London WIV 4ND, England
tel: +44 (0)20 7287 4450
fax: +44 (0)20 7287 9128
email: agents@casarotto.uk.com
contact: Jenne Casarotto, Mal Kenyon

Curtis Brown
Haymarket House, 28/29 Haymarket
London SW1Y 4SP, England
tel: +44 (0)20 7393 4400
fax: +44 (0)20 7393 4401
email: cb@curtisbrown.co.uk
contact: Nick Marston, Ben Hall

Hamilton Hodell Ltd
24 Hanway Street, London W1T 1UH
England
tel: +44 (0)20 7636 1221
fax: +44 (0)20 7636 1226
contact: Lorraine Hamilton, Christian Hodell

I.A.M. (Dublin) Ltd
For contact information see Acting Agencies
contact: Justin Moore-Lewy

I.C.M.
Oxford House, 76 Oxford Street
London W1D 1BS, England
tel: +44 (0)20 7636 6565
fax: +44 (0)20 7323 0101
contact: various agents

Judy Daish Associates Ltd
2 St Charles Place, London W10 6EG, England
tel: +44 (0)20 8964 8811
fax: +44 (0)20 8964 8966
contact: Judy Daish

The Lisa Richards Agency
For contact information see Actors Agencies
email: fogrady@eircom.net
contact: Faith O'Grady

Macnaughton Lord 2000 Ltd
19 Margravine Gardens,
London W6 8L, England
tel: +44 (0)20 8741 0606
fax: +44 (0)20 8741 7443
email: info@ml2000.org.uk
contact: Patricia Macnaughton, Gavin Plumley

Micheline Steinberg Associates
4th Floor, 104 Great Portland Street
London W1W 6PE, England
tel: +44 (0)20 7631 1310
fax: +44 (0)20 7631 1146
email: info@steinplays.com
contact: Micheline Steinberg, Ginny Sennett

The Rod Hall Agency
3 Charlotte Mews, London W1T 4DZ, England
tel: +44 (0)20 7637 0706
fax: +44 (0)20 7637 0807
email: office@rodhallagency.com
web: www.rodhallagency.com
contact: Charlotte Mann

Rosica Colin Ltd
1 Clareville Grove Mews
London SW7 5AH, England
tel: +44 (0)20 7370 1080
fax: +44 (0)20 7244 6441
contact: Joanna Marston

Samuel French Ltd
52 Fitzroy Street, Fitzrovia
London W1T 5JR, England
tel: +44 (0)20 7387 9373
fax: +44 (0)20 7387 2161
email: theatre@samuelfrench-london.co.uk
contact: various agents
irish agent: Drama League of Ireland
For contact information see Support Organisations

William Morris Agency (UK) Ltd
52-53 Poland Street, London W1F 7LX,
England
tel: +44 (0)20 7534 6800
fax: +44 (0)20 7534 6900
contact: Stephanie Cabot, Eugenie Furniss

Peters Frazier & Dunlop (PFD)
Drury House, 34-43 Russell Street
London WC2B 5HA, England
tel: +44 (0)20 7344 1000
fax: +44 (0)20 7836 9539
email: postmaster@pfd.co.uk
contact: various agents

Photographers:

John Baucher
1st Floor, Conway Mill, 5 Conway Street,
Belfast BT13, Northern Ireland
tel: +44 (0)7719 100371
email: johnbaucher@yahoo.com

Max Beer
The Playhouse, 5-7 Artillery Street
Derry BT48 6RG, Northern Ireland
tel: +44 (0)28 7126 8027/(0)86 858 9093
email: max@derryplayhouse.co.uk

Kip Carroll
4a Hagens Court, Lad Lane
Dublin 2, Republic of Ireland
tel: +353 (0)1 662 4748
email: kip@kipcarroll.com
web: www.kipcarroll.com

Dermot Donohue Studios
Port Road, Letterkenny
Co. Donegal, Republic of Ireland
tel: +353 (0)74 912 1125
fax: +353 (0)74 912 1078
email: info@donohuestudios.ie
web: www.donohuestudios.ie
contact: Dermot Donohue

Lesley Doyle
tel: +44 (0)7860 196268
email: Lesleydoyle@aol.com

F22 Photography
3 Morningside, Summerhill South
Cork, Republic of Ireland
tel: +353 (0)21 431 1500
fax: +353 (0)21 484 7517
email: f22photography@eircom.net
web: www.f22-razorsharp.com
contact: Janice O'Connell

Grid
Unit 15, Ormeau Business Park
Belfast BT7 2JA, Northern Ireland
tel: +44(0)28 9024 4234/(0)7802 570628
email: info@gridimage.com
web: www.gridimage.com
contact: George Roe, Nick Patterson

Chris Hill Photographic
17 Clarence Street
Belfast BT2 8DY, Northern Ireland
tel: +44 (0)28 9024 5038
fax: +44 (0)28 9023 1942
email: chrishillphotographic@btclick.com
web: www.scenicireland.com
contact: Chris Hill

Colm Hogan
tel: +353 (0)87 838 8526
email: colmho@hotmail.com
web: www.colmhogan.com

Annika Johansson
1 Chatham Row, Dublin 2
Republic of Ireland
tel: +353 (0)86 306 1586
email: annikajohans@hotmail.com

Ros Kavanagh
29-31 South William Street
Dublin 2, Republic of Ireland
tel: +353 (0)1 671 3689
email: ros@roskavanagh.com
web: www.roskavanagh.com

Tom Lawlor
34 Vernon Avenue, Clontarf
Dublin 3, Republic of Ireland
tel: +353 (0)1 833 1073
email: tomlawlorphoto@eircom.net

Paul McCarthy
Space 28, North Lotts
Dublin 1, Republic of Ireland
tel: +353 (0)1 878 6838/(0)86 821 1281
email: mrmccarthy@eircom.net

Shane McCarthy
4a Lad Lane, Dublin 2, Republic of Ireland
tel: +353 (0)1 676 0798/(0)87 252 6944
fax: +353 (0)1 676 0862
email: snap@eircom.net

Hugh McElveen
27 Temple Cottages, Dublin 7
Republic of Ireland
tel: +353 (0)87 416 9877
email: hughmcelveen@eircom.net

Kevin McFeely
16 Lioscian, Swords, Co. Dublin
Republic of Ireland
tel: +353 (0)1 890 1304/(0)87 246 0115
email: kevinmcfeely@eircom.net
web: www.kevinmcfeely.com

Jill McKeown
tel: +44 (0)7974 676660/
+44 (0)28 9029 3393
email: mckeownjill@hotmail.com/
jillmckeown@ntlworld.com

Adrian Melia FRPS
82 Hazelmere, Naas, Co. Kildare
Republic of Ireland
tel: +353 (0)45 879581/(0)86 241 3747
email: melia@indigo.ie

Peter Nash
7 Apollo Road, Portstewart BT55 7PX
Northern Ireland
tel: +44 (0)28 7083 2467
email: peter@peternashphotography.co.uk
web: www.peternashphotography.co.uk

Enda O'Brien
207 Strand Road, Sandymount
Dublin 4, Republic of Ireland
tel: +353 (0)87 232 2208
email: enda_beaker@hotmail.com

Vincent O'Byrne
The Rear, Regal House, Fitzwilliam Street,
Ringsend, Dublin 4, Republic of Ireland
tel: +353 (0)1 667 1065/668
5283/(0)87 233 4072
fax: +353 (0)1 668 5283
email: vincent@vincentobyrne.com
web: www.vincentobyrne.com

Gerry O'Carroll
52 Mayor's Walk, Waterford
Republic of Ireland
tel: +353(0)51 304050
email: gerryocarrollphotography@eircom.net
web: www.gerryocarroll.com

Mícheal Ó Súilleabháin
Knocknanes, Glenflesk
Co. Kerry, Republic of Ireland
tel: +353 (0)87 629 0556
email: mosuilleabhain@esatclear.ie

Mark O'Sullivan
tel: +353 (0)87 262 4540
email: osdphoto@eircom.net

Valerie O'Sullivan
New Street, Killarney, Republic of Ireland
tel: +353 (0)87 262 9375
email: valerieo@iol.ie

Provision
6 Cornmarket Street, Cork
Republic of Ireland
tel: +353 (0)21 427 2884
fax: +353 (0)21 427 1547
email: info@provision.ie
web: www.provision.ie

Pat Redmond
tel: +353 (0)87 260 0976
email: patrickredmond@dna.ie

Phil Smyth
15 Strangford Avenue
Belfast BT9 6PG, Northern Ireland
tel: +44 (0)28 9022 1922
mobile: +44 (0)7860 331819
email: phil@philsmyth.com
web: www.philsmyth.com

Derek Speirs
tel: +353 (0)1 855 8154/(0)87 258 7765
email: derekspeirs@eircom.net

Amelia Stein
4 Camden Market, Grantham Street
Dublin 8, Republic of Ireland
tel: +353 (0)1 475 1275

John Taggart
64 Ashgreen, Greystone Road
Co. Antrim BT41 1HL, Northern Ireland
tel: +44 (0)28 9446 5368/(0)7974 426747
email: johntaggart@utvinternet.com
web: www.johntaggartphotography.com

Michael Taylor
412 Beersbridge Road, Belfast BT5 5EB,
Northern Ireland
tel: +44 (0)28 9065 4450
email: michael@machtwo.co.uk

Physiotherapists:

Dublin Spine & Sports Physiotherapy
52 Heytesbury Street, Dublin 8
Republic of Ireland
tel: +353 (0)1 454 3335
fax: +353 (0)1 473 4226
email: heytphys@indigo.ie
contact: Eileen Murphy

IONA Physiotheraphy
10 Drumcondra Raod Upper
Dublin 9, Republic of Ireland
tel: +353 (0)1 797 9545
contact: Louise Keating

Poster Distributors:

Media Masters
c/o Everyman Palace Theatre
tel: +353 (0)86 825 6135

Irish Poster Advertising
Merchants Court, 24 Merchants Quay
Dublin 8, Republic of Ireland
tel: +353 (0)1 679 7700
fax: +353 (0)1 679 7495
contact: Anne Gara

Micromedia
7 Eustace Street, Temple Bar
Dublin 2, Republic of Ireland
tel: +353 (0)1 677 3834
fax: +353 (0)1 888 3600
email: erika@micromedia.ie
web: www.micromedia.ie
contact: Erika Fitzpatrick

MPI
138 Capel Street, Dublin 1, Republic of Ireland
tel: +353 (0)1 260 9040/(0)87 230 5713
fax: +353 (0)1 260 9042
email: mpibands@hotmail.com
contact: Martin Nolan

PR and Press:

Kate Bowe PR
50 South William Street
Dublin 2, Republic of Ireland
tel: +353 (0)1 671 3672
fax: +353 (0)1 677 3224
email: kate@katebowepr.ie
contact: Kate Bowe

Siobhan Colgan
tel: +353 (0)87 799 2330

connect pr
*For contact information see Arts
Consultants/Freelance Producers*

Doireann Gillan
tel: +353 (0) 86 171 7551
email: doireanngillan@yahoo.com

Paul Fahy
*For contact information see Arts
Consultants/Freelance Producers*

Gerry Lundberg PR
27 Dawson Street, Dublin 2
Republic of Ireland
tel: +353 (0)1 679 8476
fax: +353 (0)1 671 8296
email: glundpr@iol.ie

GM Publicity
Merchants Court, 24 Merchants Quay
Dublin 8, Republic of Ireland
tel: +353 (0)1 670 5692/(0)86 826 3040
email: gearoid@gmpublicity.com
contact: Gearóid McIntyre

Kearney Melia Communications
11 Marlboro Street, Cork
Republic of Ireland
tel: +353 (0)21 427 8580
fax: +353 (0)21 427 8581
email: kearneymelia@eircom.net
contact: Jean Kearney

Laura Kennedy
Public Relations Consultant
tel: +353 (0)21 435 0919/(0)86 172 3893
email: kennedypr@eircom.net

Cerstin Mudiwa
tel: +353 (0)87 659 6406
email: cerstin@vodafone.ie

Midnight Promotions
3 Lower Abbeygate Street
Galway, Republic of Ireland
tel: +353 (0)91 568674/(0)87 631 5574
fax: +353 (0)91 568554
email: info@midnightpromotions.net
web: www.midnightpromotions.net
contact: Catherine Laffey

Nik Quaife
For contact information see Arts
Consultants/Freelance Producers

Carmel White
34 Belgrave Square, Rathmines
Dublin 6, Republic of Ireland
tel: +353 (0)1 496 1494
fax: +353 (0)1 496 8388
email: carmelwhite@eircom.net

Production Managers:

Adrián Acosta
tel: +353 (0)87 993 3086
email: adrian_acosta76@hotmail.com

Marie Breen
10 Ontario Terrace, Portobello
Dublin 6, Republic of Ireland
tel: +353 (0)87 231 4507

Mike Burke
tel: +353 (0)87 231 3734
email: mikeburke22@hotmail.com

Paula Byrne
tel: + 353 (0)86 343 2051
email: paula@dandelionproductions.com

Martin Cahill
17 Cowper Downs, Rathmines
Dublin 6, Republic of Ireland
tel: +353 (0)86 880 4212

Bev Craig
3 Dunottar Park, Warren Road, Donaghadee,
Co. Down BT21 0PH, Northern Ireland
tel: +44 (0)28 9188 3826/(0)7761 181073
email: +deeb@deeb.fsnet.co.uk

Lee Davis
For contact information See Lighting Designers

Miriam Duffy
27 Sandymount Road
Dublin 4, Republic of Ireland
tel: +353 (0)1 660 3295/(0)87 248 6561
email: miriamduffy@eircom.net

Ronan FitzGibbon
tel: +353 (0)87 765 8541

Eamonn Fox
School Road, Carnmore West, Galway
Republic of Ireland
tel: +353 (0)86 242 4051
fax: +353 (0)91 788660
email: efox@eircom.net

Rob Furey
tel: +353 (0)87 249 5044
email: robfurey@hotmail.com

Brendan Galvin
15 Glincool Park, Maglin Road
Ballincollig, Co. Cork, Republic of Ireland
tel: +353 (0)87 247 5954
email: bgalvi2@attglobal.net

Liz Honan
98 Cannon Street, Waterford
Republic of Ireland
tel: +353 (0)86 873 8353

Des Kenny
tel: +353 (0)87 682 0322

Andy Keogh
tel: +353 (0)87 296 9463
email: andykeogh2000@hotmail.com

Tony Killeen
Boley Beg, Barna, Co. Galway
Republic of Ireland
tel: +353 (0)86 629 1792
email: tkilleen@eircom.net

Sheila Meaney
School Road, Carnmore West, Galway
Republic of Ireland
tel: +353 (0)87 274 8934
email: sheilameaney@eircom.net

Richard Meagher
tel: +353 (0)86 880 5418

Conor Mullan
6 Temple Park Avenue, Blackrock
Co. Dublin, Republic of Ireland
tel: +353 (0)87 624 3079

David 'Spud' Murphy
tel: +353 (0)87 259 4277
email: spud1@eircom.net
See also Technical Suppliers

Padraig O'Neill
17 Broadstone Avenue, Dublin 7
Republic of Ireland
tel: +353 (0)87 247 3450

Maurice Power
For contact information see Arts
Consultants/Freelance Producers

Joe Stockdale
tel: +353 (0) 86 389 2105
email: stockdalejoe@eircom.net

Marie Tierney
For contact information see Costume Designers

Prop Buyers:

Nicola Hughes
10 Lansdowne Square, Herbert Road
Dublin 4, Republic of Ireland
tel: +353 (0)87 695 1776

Prop Hire:

AM PM Hire Ltd
Broomlodge, Nun's Cross, Ashford
Co. Wicklow, Republic of Ireland
tel/fax: +353 (0)404 40404
contact: Karen Bennett

G & H Film and Television Services
182a Church Road, Holywood
Co. Down BT19 9RN, Northern Ireland
tel: +44 (0)28 9039 7808/(0)7880 711152
email: lisa@ghfilm.freeserve.co.uk
web: www.ghfilms.co.uk

Historic Interiors
Oberstown, Lusk, Co. Dublin
Republic of Ireland
tel: +353 (0)1 843 7174/(0)86 257 7232
fax: +353 (0)1 843 7174
email: killian@historicinteriors.net
contact: Killian McNulty

Irish Arms Historical Reproductions
Red House Farm, Claddagh, Ballyjamesduff
Co. Cavan, Republic of Ireland
tel: +353 (0)49 854 5856/(0)86 856 1931
fax: +353 (0)49 854 5856
email: info@irisharms.ie
web: www.irisharms.ie
contact: Lynne Williams, Boyd Rankin

Lyric Theatre
55 Ridgeway Street, Stranmillis
Belfast BT9 5FB, Northern Ireland
tel: +44 (0)28 9038 5681
contact: Anna Donovan

Marine Props
Irish National Sailing School
West Pier, Dun Laoghaire
Co. Dublin, Republic of Ireland
tel: +353 (0)1 284 4195/(0)86 258 4493
contact: Alistair Rumball, Arthur Rumball

Montague Heritage Services
Merrion Lodge
Gorey, Co. Wexford, Republic of Ireland
tel: +353 (0)55 80318/(0)86 823 0463
email: info@montague.ie
web: www.montague.ie
contact: Alan Montague

Theatrical Arms
For contact information see Armourers

Prop Makers:

Deirdre Byrne
Glassdrumman Mor, Drumkeeran
Co. Leitrim, Republic of Ireland
tel: +353 (0)87 284 5091
email: dedebyrne@ireland.com

Robert Clarke
tel: +353 (0)404 46385/(0)86 862 0263
email: bob_clarke@yahoo.com
web: www.the-moonbase.com

Vanessa Dawes
Ballynoonagh, Clonbur
Co. Galway, Republic of Ireland
tel: +353 (0)94 954 8884/(0)86 870 9077

Cliff Dolliver
For contact information see Set Designers

Anna Donovan
For contact information see Scenic Artists

Gabby Dowling
5 Henrietta Street, Dublin 1
Republic of Ireland
tel/fax: 01 872 3197

Melanie Downes
tel: +353 (0)87 667 2286

Miriam Duffy
*For contact information see Production
Managers*

Harry Harris
Bolger Farm, Cruttenclogh, Bilboa,
Co. Carlow, Republic of Ireland
tel: +353 (0)56 444 3078/(0)87 680 6313
fax: +353 (0)56 444 3078
email: harryharris@eircom.net

Mick Heffernan
For contact information see Set Construction

Genevieve Jon Designs
30 Rigg Road, Lockard Little
Enniskillen, Northern Ireland
tel: +44 (0) 28 6634 1399/ 0788 775 6090
email: genevievejondesigns@macunlimited.net

**Irish Arms Historical
Reproductions**
For contact information see Prop Hire

Jane Lee
Whiterock, Church Road Carrigaline
Cork, Republic of Ireland
tel: +353 (0)87 766 7456
email: janie113@hotmail.com

Eimer Murphy
35 Kenilworth Park, Harolds Cross
Dublin 6W, Republic of Ireland
tel: +353 (0)1 492 3616/(0)86 083 9202

Annelisa Zagone
For contact information see Costume Designers

Rehearsal Rooms:

Belvoir Players Rehearsal Studio
94 Belvoir Drive, Belfast BT8 7DT
Northern Ireland
tel: +44 (0)28 9064 9835/9049 1210
fax: +44 (0)28 9049 1213
email: webmaster@belvoirplayers.org
web: www.belvoirplayers.org
contact: Richard Mills MBE

Carman's Hall
Francis Street, Dublin 8, Republic of Ireland
tel: +353 (0)1 453 8648
fax: +353 (0)1 473 1409
contact: Sr. Laurentia, Owen Finlay

Crypt Arts Centre
For contact information see Venues

Dance Theatre of Ireland
*For contact information see Subsidised
Dance Companies*

Draíocht
For contact information see Venues

Dublin Central Mission Hall
9c Lower Abbey Street
Dublin 1, Republic of Ireland
tel: +353 (0)1 874 4668
contact: Graham Caswell

The Factory
35a Barrow Street, Dublin 4
Republic of Ireland
tel: +353 (0)1 668 4966
fax: +353 (0)1 668 4859
email: info@factorystudios.ie
web: www.factorystudios.ie
contact: Ken Allen

The Fit Up
Morette, Emo, Portlaoise
Co. Laois, Republic of Ireland
tel: +353 (0)87 821 0560
web: www.shakesthespeare.com
contact: Cabrini Cahill

Gaiety School of Acting, Dublin
*For contact information see Drama and
Dance Training*
contact: Andrew Lyster

The Helix, Dublin
For contact information see Venues
contact: Nick Reed

i space
c/o Impact Theatre Company, Limerick
*For contact information see Partially
Subsidised Drama Companies*
contact: Ann Blake

Leinster Cricket Club
Observatory Lane, Rathmines
Dublin 6, Republic of Ireland
tel: +353 (0)1 497 2428/497 4673
fax: +353 (0)1 497 4673
email: lccsports@eircom.net
contact: Linda McDonnell

Old Museum Arts Centre, Belfast
For contact information see Venues

Rough Magic, Dublin
*For contact information see Subsidised
Drama Companies*

SFX City Theatre, Dublin
For contact information see Venues

Southbank Playhouse
Belfast
tel: +44 (0)7780 695675
email: info@southbankplayhouse.com
web: www.southbankplayhouse.com
contact: Stephen Beggs

St Andrews Resource Centre
114-116 Pearse Street
Dublin 2, Republic of Ireland
tel: +353 (0)1 677 1930
fax: +353 (0)1 671 5734
email: kathryn.fox@standrews.ie
contact: Kathryn Fox

Spraoi, Waterford
For contact information see Irish Festivals
contact: T.V. Honan, Niamh O'Mahony

Sylvia Behan Dance Studio
30 Gardiner Place, Dublin 1
Republic of Ireland
tel: +353 (0)1 838 5255/(0)1 874 9536
contact: Sylvia Behan

**TEAM Educational Theatre
Company**
4 Marlborough Place, Dublin 1
Republic of Ireland
tel: +353 (0)1 878 6108/872 1192
fax: +353 (0)1 874 8989
email: team@eircom.net
web: www.teamtheatre.ie

The United Arts Club
3 Upper Fitzwilliam Street
Dublin 2, Republic of Ireland
tel: +353 (0)1 661 1411
email: office@dublinarts.com
contact: Margo Banks

Trinity Church
12C Lower Abbey Street
Dublin 1, Republic of Ireland
tel: +353 (0)1 831 6912
email: office@trinity.ie
contact: Margaret Dunne

Scenic Artists:

Liz Barker
596 Woodview Cottages, Rathfarnham,
Dublin 14, Republic of Ireland
tel: +353 (0)87 226 6212

Vincent Bell
110 The Strand, Donabate
Co Dublin, Republic of Ireland
tel: +353 (0)86 353 8007

Sandra Butler
207 Strand Rd, Dublin 4, Republic of Ireland
tel: +353 (0)87 346 5345

Bev Craig
*For contact information see Production
Managers*

Anna Donovan
40 Gibson Park Gardens
Belfast BT6 9GN, Northern Ireland
tel: +44 (0)7812 040784
email: anna.donovan2@ntlworld.com

Ciara Moore
tel: +353 (0)86 608 9130
email: ciara66@fastmail.fm

Edain O'Donnell
19 Millmount Avenue, Drumcondra
Dublin 9, Republic of Ireland
tel: +353 (0)1 857 0989/(0)87 285 9814
email: edain@eircom.net

Annalisa Zagone
For contact information see Costume Designers

Set Construction:

All Set Construction
Victoria Lodge, Victoria Road, Greystones
Co. Wicklow, Republic of Ireland
tel: +353 (0)86 250 7554
email: ednorton@ireland.com
contact: Ed Norton

Arena
Unit 9, Belview Industrial Estate
Finglas, Dublin 11, Republic of Ireland
tel: +353 (0)1 834 4121
fax: +353 (0)1 834 4161
email: info@arena-ireland.com
web: www.arena-ireland.com
contact: Michael Deegan

Jim Carson
63 Downpatrick Road, Crossgar
Co. Down BT30 9EH, Northern Ireland
tel/fax: +44 (0)28 4483 1670

Alan Clarke
tel: +353 (0)86 824 0435
email: lassel@gofree.indigo.ie

Kevin Courtney
tel: +353 (0)86 855 5843
email: kevincourtney@eircom.net

Ube Evans
3 Clarinda Park North, Dun Laoghaire
Co. Dublin, Republic of Ireland
tel: +353 (0)87 993 1210

Ronan FitzGibbon
*For contact information see Production
Managers*

Mick Heffernan
Bawnmoore, Macroom
Co. Cork, Republic of Ireland
tel: +353 (0)87 993 6219

Patrick Kelly and Janneke Sparrius
92 Broadford Drive, Ballinteer
Dublin 16, Republic of Ireland
tel: +353 (0)1 494 4377/(0)86 307 3178

Owen McCarthy
For contact information see Set Designers

Bryan McCorkell
The Workshop, 1 Causeway Villas, Island
Road, Ballycarry BT38 9HA, Northern Ireland
tel: +44 (0)28 9337 8096/(0)7718 871738
fax: +44 (0)28 9337 8096
email: bryan.mccorkell@lineone.net

Daniel O'Sullivan
Oughterard, Co. Galway, Republic of Ireland
tel: +353 (0)86 846 4940/(0)91 552829
email: dos61@hotmail.com

Theatre Production Services
Basement, 50 Synge Street
Dublin 8, Republic of Ireland
tel: +353 (0)87 260 4966/(0)87 244 4994
fax: +353 (0)1 855 1969
email: tpsltd@eircom.net
contacts: Pat Byrne, Paul Foley

Production House
For contact information see Technical Suppliers

Set Designers:

Robert Ballagh
tel: +353 (0)1 671 9075
email: ballaghb@eircom.net

Orla Bass
Ballanagh, Avoca, Co. Wicklow
Republic of Ireland
tel: +353 (0)87 644 0523
email: bassorla@hotmail.com

Carol Betera
*For contact information see Costume
Designers*

John Comiskey
*For contact information see Lighting
Designers*

Johanna Connor
Trees of the Earth, Bawnanockane
Ballydehob, West Cork, Republic of Ireland
tel: +353 (0)87 242 1496
email: jo@creaturesofserendipity.com

David Craig
tel: +44 (0)28 9188 3826/(0)7801 650545
email: deeb@deeb.fsnet.co.uk

Emma Cullen
Setanta, Castlebridge
Co. Wexford, Republic of Ireland
email: cullenemma@yahoo.co.uk

Fiona Cunningham
7 Loreto Terrace, Sidmonton Road
Bray, Co. Wicklow, Republic of Ireland
tel: +353 (0)1 276 8548/(0)87 989 2108
fax: +353 (0)1 276 8548
email: pov@eircom.net

Sabine Dargent
45 Longwood Avenue
Dublin 8, Republic of Ireland
tel: +353(0)87 776 8489
email: sabino@eircom.net

Cliff Dolliver
tel: +353 (0)87 614 3794
email: cliffdoliver@eircom.net

Moggie Douglas
Possextown, Enfield, Co. Meath
Republic of Ireland
tel: +353 (0)46 954 1655/(0)87 235 5783
email: moggiedouglas@eircom.net

Feargal Doyle
tel: +353 (0) 86 876 3676
email: feargaldoyle@ireland.com

Davy Dummigan
4 Glenview Terrace, Ballyhooley Road
Cork, Republic of Ireland
tel: +353 (0)21 450 1067/(0)87 906 4966
email: davy_dummigan@yahoo.co.uk

Alan Farquharson
38 Springhill Avenue, Blackrock
Co Dublin, Republic of Ireland
tel: +353 1 289 4912
mobile: +353 (0)87 240 7451
fax: +353 (0)875 240 7451
web: http://indigo.ie/~alanf

Siobhan Ferrie
53 Orchardville Cresent, Finaghy, Belfast
BT10 0JS, Northern Ireland
tel: +44 (0)7715 296666
email: siobhanferrie@hotmail.com

Monica Frawley
26 Primrose Street, The Broadstone,
Dublin 7, Republic of Ireland
tel: +353 (0)1 860 0872
email: monicafrawley@hotmail.com

Sonia Haccius
1 Crosthwaite Park West, Dun Laoghaire,
Co. Dublin, Republic of Ireland
tel: +353 (0)1 284 1365/(0)87 675 2457
fax: +353 (0)1 284 1365
email: shaccius@hotmail.com

Ben Hennessy
c/o Red Kettle Theatre Company
*For contact information see Subsidised
Drama Companies*

Maree Kearns
tel: +353 (0)86 827 7509
email: mareekearns@hotmail.com

Fiona Leech
tel: +353 (0)87 262 8860
email: jjvernon@eircom.net

Terry Loane
18 Cooldarragh Park
Belfast BT14 6TG, Northern Ireland
tel/fax: +44 (0)28 9028 4383
email: terryloane1@aol.com

Dolores Lyne
c/o Black Box Theatre, Dyke Road
Galway, Republic of Ireland
tel: +353 (0)91 556542/(0)87 263 8720
email: doloreslyne@eircom.net

Stuart Marshall
133 Deramore Avenue
Belfast BT7 3ET, Northern Ireland
tel: +44 (0)28 9022 9865
email: stumarsh@ntlworld.com
web: www.stagedesign.co.uk

Laurent Mellet
Laragh, Glendalough
Co. Wicklow, Republic of Ireland
tel: +353 (0)404 45717/(0)86 874 2111
email: laurent@fusio.net

Ferdia Murphy
47 Bremen Road, Irishtown
Dublin 4, Republic of Ireland
tel: +353 (0)1 660 7413/(0)87 610 3862
email: ferdiamurphy@eircom.net

Bairbre Murray
11 The Avenue, Woodpark, Ballinteer,
Dublin 16, Republic of Ireland
tel: +353 (0)87 298 6654
email: bairbrem@eircom.net

Owen McCarthy
33 Father Burke Road, The Claddagh
Galway, Republic of Ireland
tel: +353 (0)91 581217/(0)86 804 7133
email: owenmccarthy@eircom.net

Steve Neale
For contact information see Lighting Designers

Francis O'Connor
c/o Dennis Lyne
tel: +44 (0)20 7739 6200
email: dennis@dennislyne.com

Edain O'Donnell
For contact information see Scenic Artists

Sinead O'Hanlon
tel: +353 (0)86 358 5165
email: sineadoh@yahoo.com

Paul O'Mahony
Apt. 2, 34 Gardiner Place
Dublin 1, Republic of Ireland
tel: +353 (0)87 923 4697
email: mathuna1@yahoo.co.uk

Production House
*For contact information see Technical
Suppliers*

Bláithín Sheerin
4 Greenfield Place, Harolds Cross, Dublin 6
Republic of Ireland
tel/fax: +353 (0)1 497 9031

Amy Smyth
*For contact information see Lighting
Designers*

Kathy Strachan
For contact information see Costume Designers

Brien Vahey
Glasnamullen, Bray
Co. Wicklow, Republic of Ireland
tel: +353 (0)1 281 9807/(0)86 812 8742
email: bvahey@indigo.ie

Joe Vanek
c/o Simpson Fox Associates
tel: +44 (0)20 7434 9167
fax: +44 (0)20 7494 2887
contact: David Watson

Chisato Yoshimi
For contact information see Costume Designers

Set Storage:

Cliff Dolliver
For contact information see Set Designers

Mangan's
Milltown, Kilcock, Co. Meath
Republic of Ireland
tel: +353 (0)87 286 2082

Meadowfield Self Storage
Mount Seskin Road, Saggart
Co. Dublin, Republic of Ireland
tel: +353 1 452 6133/(0) 86 821 0184
contact: Brian Joyce

Trevor Price
2 Gleann Eorna, Ocean Wave
Salthill, Galway, Republic of Ireland
tel: +353 (0)87 256 9913
fax: +353 (0)91 589539
email: trevorpricetransport@hotmail.com

SGB Event Link
Newcourt Business Park
St. Margerets, Co. Dublin
Republic of Ireland
tel: +353 (0)1 834 0707/(0)86 257 0396
fax: +353 (0)1 856 7086
email: info@scafform.ie
web: www.sgb.co.uk
contact: Paul Griffin

TWIL Ltd
76 Sir John Rogerson's Quay
Dublin 1, Republic of Ireland
tel: +353 (0)1 677 0715/836 3188
fax: +353 (0)1 855 7045
email: admin@twil.ie
contact: Donal Prior

U Store It
Enterprise House, Upper Fair Hill
Cork, Republic of Ireland
tel: +353 (0)21 4300 366
email: tfoley@ustoreit.ie
contact: Trevor Foley

Watch This Space
9 The Anchorage, Bettystown
Co. Meath, Republic of Ireland
tel: +353 (0)41 982 3004/(0)86 813 5660
fax: +353 (0)41 982 3004
contact: Bertie McAlea

Sound Designers:

Audio Services
11 Brunswick Place
Dublin 2, Republic of Ireland
tel: +353 (0)1 677 6007
fax: +353 (0)1 677 0972
email: doreenaudioservices@eircom.net
contact: Terry Heron

Bell Helicopter
30 Whites Square, London SW4 7JL
England
tel: +44 (0)20 7627 8817
fax: +44 (0)20 7627 8817
email: b.copter@virgin.net
contact: Conor Kelly

Ivan Birthistle
9 Cannon Mews East, Beggars Bush
Dublin 4, Republic of Ireland
tel: +353 (0)1 660 6773/(0)87 669 9192
email: ibirth@hotmail.com

Blacklight
For contact information see Technical Suppliers

Paul Brennan
tel: +353 (0)7 768 2912
email: paulebrennan@eircom.net
See also Composers

Cormac Carroll
tel: +353 (0)1 833 6861/(0)87 222 5672
email: cormaccarroll@yahoo.com

Justin Carroll
8 Lisburn Street, Dublin 7, Republic of Ireland
tel: +353 (0)1 872 7461/(0)86 871 9377
email: justin@organicsmusic.com
web: www.organicsmusic.com
See also Composers

Jackie Conboy
See also Composers

Jackie Conboy
Real Music Management
tel: +353 (0)90 975 9950/(0)87 986 0455
email: jackieconboy@iol.ie

Dave Curran
c/o Red Kettle Theatre Company
For contact information see Subsidised Companies
tel: +353 (0)86 163 8620

Vincent Doherty
Flat 3, 378 Harolds Cross Road
Dublin 6W, Republic of Ireland
tel: +353 (0)87 937 4909
See also Composers

James Eadie
tel: +353 (0)87 980 2878
email: jimbo123@eircom.net

Ciaran Eaton
tel: +353 (0)87 994 6840
email: ciaraneaton@hotmail.com

Roger Gregg
91 Mount Drummond Square, Harolds
Cross, Dublin 6, Republic of Ireland
tel: +353 (0)1 497 3017
email: rogergregg@eircom.net
web: www.crazydogaudiotheatre.ie
See also Composers

Eoghan Horgan
tel: +353 (0)21 484 1344/(0)87 774 5636
email: pushingtheair@yahoo.com
See also Composers

Joe Hunt
73 Garavogue Villas, Sligo, Republic of Ireland
tel: +353 (0)87 930 8305
c/o Blue Raincoat Theatre Company

Sam Jackson
tel: +353 (0)1 497 0450/(0)87 235 2880
email: samjackson@eircom.net
See also Composers

Trevor Knight
54 Carnew Street, Stoneybatter
Dublin 7, Republic of Ireland
tel: +353 (0)1 868 2160
email: trevorknight@hotmail.com
See also Composers

Rod McVey
tel: +44 (0)7967 638233
email: rodmcvey@ntlworld.com
See also Composers

Michael McNulty
tel: +44 (0)7773 423407
email: mickelmoe@hotmail.com

Paul Marshall
8 Lord Warden's Parade, Bangor
Co. Down, Northern Ireland
tel: +44 (0)28 91 45 5737
email: paul@powerhaus.net
web: www.powerhaus.net

Natural Fifth
50 Synge Street, Dublin 8
Republic of Ireland
tel: +353 (0)1 475 5222
email: natural5@eircom.net
contact: Denis Roche
See also Composers

Cormac O'Connor
3 Windsor Place, St Lukes
Cork, Republic of Ireland
tel: +44 (0)7985 054 206/(0)87 692 8809
email: coc@waitrose.com
web: www.cormacoconnor.net
See also Composers

Production House
For contact information see Technical Suppliers

Brian Rudden
tel: +353 (0)86 087 2552

Soundscapes
45 The Hazels, Oakleigh Wood
Tulla Road, Ennis
Co. Clare, Republic of Ireland
tel: +353 (0)65 684 0255/(0)86 251 4341
email: purcellaudio@eircom.net
contact: Matt Purcell

Peter Sutton
Ardsallaghmór, Athlone Road
Roscommon Town, Republic of Ireland
tel: +353 (0)87 292 4872
See also Composers

Cathal Synnott
tel: +353 (0)87 202 7881
email: cathalsynnott@eircom.net
See also Composers

J.J. Vernon
tel: +353 (0)87 629 0022
email: info@jjvernon.com
web: www.jjvernon.com
See also Composers

Stage Managers:

Elaine Barnes
tel: +44 (0)7786 640335
email: elaine250@hotmail.com

Ailbhe Brennan
243 South Circular Road
Dublin 8, Republic of Ireland
tel: +353 (0)86 863 4131
email: alva.b@oceanfree.net

Anne Brodie
tel: +353 (0)87 249 9007
email: annebrodie@piggysurf.com,
annebrodie@vodafone.ie

Mike Burke
For contact information see Production Managers

Claire Burkitt
tel: +44 (0)7808 579780
email: claireburkitt@fsmail.net

Martin Cahill
For contact information see Production Managers

Margarita Corscadden
tel: +353 (0)87 982 2979

Niall Connolly
73 St Johns Wood, Clondalkin
Dublin 22, Republic of Ireland
tel: +353 (0)87 668 1195/
+44 (0)7881 414066
email: niallsm@eircom.net

Lisa-Marie Cooke
tel: +44 (0)7913 308890
email: lisa_mariecooke@hotmail.com

Mark Dornan
11 Brook Drive, Belfast BT11 9NW
Northern Ireland
tel: +44 (0)7887 941676
email: markcdornan@yahoo.com

Miriam Duffy
For contact information see Production Managers

Tara Furlong
tel: +353 (0)87 273 7633
email: tara0302@yahoo.com

Elizabeth Gerhardy
tel: +353 (0)86 394 7153
email: peppertea@planet-save.com

Miriam Harpur
11 Charleville Avenue, Dublin 3
Republic of Ireland
tel: +353 (0)87 271 2879
email: miharpur@indigo.ie

Nicola Hughes
For contact information see Prop Buyers

Audrey Cepeda
tel: +353 (0) 86 336 7922
email: audreyking23@yahoo.com

Anne Layde
tel: +353 (0)87 293 6802
email: alayde@eircom.net

Sarah Lynch
c/o Druid Theatre Company
For contact information see Subsidised Drama Companies

Laura McCabe
15 Cambourne Cresent, Newtownards
Belfast BT23 4WA, Northern Ireland
tel: +44 (0)28 9182 2954/(0)7817 376138
email: laurajmccabe_uk@yahoo.com

Pam McQueen
29 Stewart Hall, Ryders Row, Parnell
Street, Dublin 1, Republic of Ireland
tel: +353 (0)86 846 6623
email: pammcqueen@hotmail.com

Aisling Mooney
tel: +353 (0)86 826 5615
email: aislingmooney18@hotmail.com

Mags Mulvey
1 Windermere Cresent
Belfast BT8 6XY, Northern Ireland
tel: +44 (0)28 9028 8021/(0)7818 460717
email: magsmulvey@hotmail.com

Eimer Murphy
For contact information see Prop Makers

Casey Norton
20 Montpelier Court, Montpelier Hill,
Dublin 7, Republic of Ireland
tel: +353 (0)86 876 0520
email: casovski@hotmail.com

Fearga O'Doherty
tel: +353 (0)87 649 8383
email: fersher67@hotmail.com

Stephanie Ryan
tel: +353 (0)86 333 0353

Hannah Solley
tel: +353 (0)86 337 4164
email: hannahsolley@hotmail.com

Paula Tierney
20 Montpelier Court, Montpelier Hill
Dublin 7, Republic of Ireland

tel: +353 (0)87 244 5210
email: paulaian@gofree.indigo.ie

Marjolijn Venema
tel: +353 (0)86 886 8780
email: marjolijn@eircom.net

Technical Suppliers:

AMPEC
3 Roseville Avenue, Bangor
Co. Down BT19 1BZ, Northern Ireland
tel: +44 (0)28 9127 0221
email: ampec@btconnect.com
contact: John McDowell

Aquarius Sound and Lighting
Main Street, Leixlip, Co. Kildare
Republic of Ireland
tel: +353 (0)1 624 3382
fax: +353 (0)1 624 5711
email: sales@aquariussound.ie
web: www.aquariussound.ie
contact: Niall Connolly

Arena Lighting
For contact information see Set Builders

Audio Services
For contact information see Sound Designers

Audio International
14 Kenilworth Lane, Rathmines
Dublin 6, Republic of Ireland
tel: +353(0)1 496 4066/(0)87 255 8428
fax: +353(0)1 491 0345
email: info@audiointernational.net
web: www.audiointernational.net
contact: Pat O'Brien

AVA Systems
2 Witches Lane, Finisklin Business Park
Sligo, Republic of Ireland
tel: +353 (0)71 914 6300
fax: +353 (0)71 914 6333
email: info@ava.ie
web: www.ava.ie
contact: Odilon Hunt

Avcom Audio Visual
Communications Ltd, Unit B, Three Rock
Road, Sandyford Industrial Estate
Dublin 18, Republic of Ireland
tel: +353 (0)1 295 7213
fax: +353 (0)1 295 3783
email: avcom@avcom.ie
web: www.avcom.ie
contact: Paul Murphy

Blacklight
Unit 3a, Block 8, Ballybanebeg Industrial
Estate, Tuam Road, Galway, Republic of Ireland
tel/fax: +353 (0)91 771679
email: blacklightireland@eircom.net
web: www.blacklightltd.com
contact: David 'Spud' Murphy
See also Production Managers

Casey's Lighting
37 Lower John Street, Cork
Republic of Ireland
tel: +353(0)21 450 5881/(0)87 244 7878
fax: +353(0)21 450 5881
email: allight@eircom.net
contact: Ray Casey

Cine Electric
26 Corrig Road, Sandyford Industrial
Estate, Dublin 18, Republic of Ireland
tel: +353 (0)1 295 3999
fax: +353 (0)1 295 3799
email: sales@cine-electric.ie
contact: Dieter Hartfiel

Dublin Fringe Festival
For contact information, please see Irish Festivals

Eurolites Productions
Unit 3, John Keyes Business Park
Dublin Road, Portlaoise, Co. Laois
Republic of Ireland
tel/fax: +353 (0)502 46060
email: info@eurolites.biz
web: www.eurolites.biz
contact: Catherine Fisher

Frankie King
tel: +353 (0)87 259 9172
email: info@frankieking.com
web: www.frankieking.com

G&R Fire Retardant Services
Unit G8, Chapelizod Industrial Estate,
Dublin 20, Republic of Ireland
tel: +353 (0)1 623 4363/(0)86 854 2689
fax: +353 (0)1 623 4372
email: gandrfire@eircom.net
contact: Rachel Kelly

LX 2000: Stage Lighting Hire
19 Ashley Park, Meadowlands
Wexford, Republic of Ireland
tel/fax: +353 (0)53 45109
email: sreck@gofree.indigo.ie
contact: Seamus Reck

McKenna Distributors Sales Ltd
2 Aston Quay, Dublin 2
Republic of Ireland
tel: +353 (0)1 677 3132
fax: +353 (0)1 671 2070
contact: Frank Coll

Mongey Communications
Newhall, Naas, Co. Kildare
Republic of Ireland
tel: +353 (0)45 897450
fax: +353 (0)45 875791
email: mongcoms@indigo.ie
contact: David Mongey

Production House

Unit 5 Prince Regent Retail Park
Prince Regent Road
Belfast BT5 6QR, Northern Ireland
tel: +44 (0)28 9079 8999
fax: +44 (0)28 9079 8989
email: info@productionhouse.net
web: www.productionhouse.net
contact: Andrew Ferguson

Production Services Ireland

Unit 25, Lowes Industrial Estate
31 Ballynahinch Road, Carryduff
Belfast BT8 8EH, Northern Ireland
tel: +44 (0)28 9081 4858
fax: +44 (0)28 9081 4846
email: info@productionireland.com
web: www.productionireland.com
contact: Brian Reilly

Sensible Music Ireland

Unit 53 Parkwest Enterprise Centre, Nangor
Road, Dublin 12, Republic of Ireland
tel: +353 (0)1 620 8321/(0)86 8114593
email: info@sensiblemusic.ie
web: www.sensiblemusic.ie
contact: Greg (hire manager)

Solas Design
and Technical Supplies

57 Drum Road, Cookstown, Co. Tyrone
BT80 8QS, Northern Ireland
tel: +44 (0)28 8676 4059
fax: +44 (0)28 8676 4141
and
64 Wellington Park, Belfast BT9 6DP,
Northen Ireland
tel: +44 (0)28 9066 6654
and
7 Knockmitten Close, New Nangor Road,
Naas Road, Dublin 12, Republic of Ireland
tel: +353 (0)1 460 1660
email: roger@reasound.com
contact: Roger McMullan

Stage Lighting Centre

12 Brunswick Place
Dublin 2, Republic of Ireland
tel: +353 (0)1 677 3044
fax: +353 (0)1 677 3724
email: stagelighting@eircom.net
contact: Pat Walsh

Reay Thompson Limited

8 Lorne Street, Belfast BT9 7DU
Northern Ireland
tel: +44 (0)28 9066 4411
fax: +44 (0)28 9066 4831
email: reaythompson@hotmail.com
contact: Philip Marks

Session Hire

10 Upper Grand Canal Street
Dublin 4, Republic of Ireland
tel: +353 (0)1 660 6777
fax: +353 (0)1 660 7086
email: info@sessionhire.com
web: www.sessionhire.com
contact: Roy Kelly

Transport:

Act Now

14 Creighton Street, Dublin 2
Republic of Ireland
tel: +353 (0)87 246 7267/(0)87 260 0763
email: sherwin@indigo.ie
contact: Owen Sherwin

Simon Burke

119 Celtic Park Avenue, Whitehall Dublin
9, Republic of Ireland
tel: +353 (0)1 832 7755/(0)87 258 2585

J.J. Lowe Haulage Ltd

Ardmore Garage, Herbert Road, Bray,
Co. Wicklow, Republic of Ireland
tel: +353 (0)1 286 2181
fax: +353 (0)1 276 0240
email: jjlowehal@oceanfree.net
contact: Maria Wheeler

Jim O'Meara

Lissealan, Tramore, Co. Waterford
Republic of Ireland
tel: +353 (0)51 381400/(0)87 296 6789

Harry Power Transport

Gaulstown, Kilmacow, Waterford
Republic of Ireland
tel: +353 (0)87 272 3809
email: hartrans@eircom.net

Trevor Price

For contact information see Set Storage

Van-Go

20 St Declan's Road, Marino
Dublin 3, Republic of Ireland
tel: +353 (0)87 250 3210
email: tomvango@eircom.net
contact: Tom O'Brien

Watch This Space

For contact information see Set Storage

Wigs/Hairdressing:

Ace One Stop Party Shop

Clondalkin Town Centre, Watery Lane,
Clondalkin, Dublin 22, Republic of Ireland
tel: +353 (0)1 457 0707
fax: +353 (0)1 467 0970
email:info@aceonestoppartyshop.com
web: www.aceonestoppartyshop.com
contact: Kathy Kavanagh

Patsy Giles (make-up/ hair)

tel: +353 (0)1 839 3439/(0)86 2603808
email: lgiles@eircom.net

Lorraine McCrann (make-up)

tel: +353 (0)87 760 6341
email: lorraine@dublin.com

Val Sherlock

110 Baggot Street Lower, Dublin 2
Republic of Ireland
tel: +353 (0)1 676 4199/(0)87 252 8346
email: vals@eircom.net

WigWam

1st Floor, Powerscourt Townhouse Centre
Dublin 2, Republic of Ireland
tel: +353 (0)1 670 5998
also
Ground Floor Stephens Green
Republic of Ireland
tel: +353 (0)1 478 1290
email: sales@wigwam.ie
web: www.wigwam.ie
contact: Lynda Murphy

Eamonn Owens in Fishamble's production of Tadhg Stray Wandered In
by Michael Collins © Colm Hogan

notes